AMERICAN ILLUSTRATION SHOWCASE VOLUME 8

American Showcase, Inc.
New York

President and Publisher:
Ira Shapiro

Production Manager:
Fiona L'Estrange

Director of Marketing and New Projects:
Chris Curtis

Operations/Credit Manager:
Wendl Kornfeld

Distribution and Advertising Sales Manager:
Julia Morris

Book Sales Manager:
Chuck Novotny

Production Coordinator:
Kyla Kanz

New Projects Manager:
Beth Slone

Bookkeeper:
Cathy Arrigo

Operations Assistant/Mail Service:
Daria Dodds

Grey Pages:
Scott Holden

Production Assistant:
Aileen Rosen

Administrative Assistant:
Deborah Lovell

Sales Representatives:

New York:
**Julia Bahr, John Bergstrom, Deborah Darr,
Donna Levinstone, Barbara Preminger,
Wendy Saunders.**

Rocky Mountain:
Kate Hoffman

West Coast:
Bob Courtman, Ralph Redpath

Book Design and Mechanical Production:
Weeks & Toomey, Inc., NYC

Typesetting:
**Ultra Typographic Services, Inc., NYC
Automatech Graphics Corporation, NYC**

Color Separations, Printing and Binding:
Dai Nippon Printing Co. Ltd., Tokyo, Japan

U.S. Book Trade Distribution:
Robert Silver Associates
307 East 37th Street, New York, New York 10016
(212) 686-5630

Canadian Book Distribution:
Oxford University Press, Canada
70 Wynford Drive
Don Mills, Ontario M3C 1J9
(416) 441-2941

Published by
American Showcase, Inc.
724 Fifth Avenue, 10th Floor
New York, New York 10019
(212) 245-0981

CONTENTS

REPRESENTATIVES

ILLUSTRATION

VIEWPOINTS

GRAPHIC ARTS ORGANIZATIONS

GREY PAGES

Contents

INDEX

EVERY JOB IS DIFFERENT.
EVERY ARTIST IS DIFFERENT.
EVERY ART DIRECTOR IS DIFFERENT.
EVERY DEADLINE IS DIFFERENT.
EVERY ACCOUNT IS DIFFERENT.
EVERY BUDGET IS DIFFERENT.
EVERY DAY IS DIFFERENT.
WE UNDERSTAND.
AND THAT'S WHAT MAKES US DIFFERENT.

Bernstein & Andriulli, Inc. 60 East 42nd Street New York, N.Y. 10165 (212) 682-1490

Airstream/Pat Bailey

Airstream/Pam Wall

represented by Bernstein & Andriulli, Inc. 60 East 42nd Street New York, N.Y. 10165 (212) 682-1490

Tony Antonios

represented by Bernstein & Andriulli, Inc. 60 East 42nd Street New York, N.Y. 10165 (212) 682-1490

DOES YOUR BANK HAVE YOU BETWEEN A ROCK AND A HARD PLACE?

Get absolutely free checking at Palmetto Federal. Maybe your bank thinks it's too much trouble for you to switch your checking account. Maybe it thinks you'll just go on forever letting it weight you down with per check charges, monthly service fees, and more. They must think you enjoy letting hundreds of dollars lie around in your account just to qualify for "free" checking. They'll even slap a hefty service charge on you if your balance falls below the minimum even once.

Now, does that seem right to you? No. Not when checking is free at Palmetto Federal. No per check charges. No monthly service fees. No minimum balance to maintain after your initial $100 deposit. No changing the rules a few weeks after you've become a customer. Checking is free.

We'll buy back your current checks and pay you interest, too. You earn 5¼% interest in your Palmetto Federal checking account when your balance remains above $500. Add to that the $5 to $10 you could save each month in service charges and we'll pay you 3¢ apiece, for a limited time, for up to 200 of your current bank's checks. As you can see, your decision to open a Palmetto Federal checking account can make a substantial difference right from the start. Switching your account is as simple as writing a check for $100.00 or more on your current account, filling out the application we've enclosed, and bringing both of them to your nearest Palmetto Federal office. Then, when we send you your new checks, you'll discover you no longer have to worry with cancelled checks. Each check provides you with a duplicate, and we hold the originals for you!

So, take a load off. Fill out the application and bring your current checks to your nearest Palmetto Federal office. Then you can find out what it's like when the bank pays you for a change.

PALMETTO FEDERAL OF SOUTH CAROLINA

If you're over 55, ask us about the advantages of Prime Time Checking.

A QUICK COURSE ON COMPUTERS FOR EXECUTIVES WHO DON'T HAVE ALL DAY.

We're offering an executive seminar on the Burroughs B20 small business computer. In just three hours, you'll know virtually everything you'll need to know about our small business computer.

Find out what the B20 can do for your business. How it works. How easy it is to use. How it can share information among multiple workstations. And how we back it all up with full service support and telephone hotlines.

The B20 Seminar. It'll be short, informative and, like the B20, very productive.

Burroughs

A store for businesses afraid to buy a computer. And afraid not to.

If you're currently sandwiched between fears of having a computer and not having one, you aren't indecisive.

You've simply reached the point that drives small businesses to Datago.

We're an office systems store devoted to escorting the computerless into the computer age. But we don't take you a step in that direction until the "unknowns" are known beforehand. And the leading is done not just by salespeople, but trained consultants.

It's their job to do for small businesses what systems analysts have always done for large ones: to examine your business needs in detail and carefully match them to equipment by leading suppliers. Suppliers such as IBM, Wang and Compaq in computers, and Technicom and AT&T in telecommunications.

Then your equipment undergoes what amounts to a rigorous tryout: 24 hours of continuous operation in our store under the stern gaze of trained technicians—to make sure everything works the way it's intended.

Meanwhile, Datago training specialists perform another valuable service. They demystify the system, teaching your people to use it as they would any tool—to solve problems.

After all that, your system is ready. But even then we hand it over with more than just our best wishes and an instruction manual.

We back it with manufacturers' warranties, easily-arranged financing plans, a support hotline that places help a phone call away and optional on-site maintenance programs for repairs right on your premises. Sparing you the need to put your business on hold while a system is sent away to recuperate.

The reason for all this hand-holding is simple: It's perfectly natural to approach office technology with certain gnawing doubts.

There are plenty of stores all too eager to sell you a computer. We're the place where you exchange your doubts for one.

Datago
The safety net for small businesses leaping into the future.

Introducing the safety net for small businesses leaping into the future.

There's no shortage of stores out there urging you to take the plunge into an office system.

Now there's one that cares where you land.

We're the Datago Small Business Center—a store designed in the belief that in the brave new world of small business systems, it's better to be prudent than brave.

So before we recommend a computer or telecommunications system, we go through a process that most stores lack the patience or expertise to provide.

First, we sit you down with a trained Datago consultant who examines your business and its needs. The reason for this is obvious. If generally ignored. Since you buy an office system to solve problems, the office system you buy should be based on exactly what those problems are.

Next, we match those needs with systems we've already prepared for various types of small businesses—retailers, manufacturers, health-care professionals, and so on. Proven systems based on equipment from IBM, Wang, Compaq, Technicom and AT&T, companies whose products require no leap of faith to purchase.

Once the selection is made, we further custom-tailor it to fit your business. Then we undertake the gentle but crucial fine-tuning of your staff.

Our training programs teach you not just how to select and push buttons, but how to use your system the way you would any tool. To get work done. Quickly, simply and without bewilderment.

Finally, we test it for twenty-four hours of continuous use in our store. That way it arrives at your place of business ready for business—and accompanied by several reassuring certainties.

Such as manufacturers' warranties. A support hotline that places help a phone call away. Easily-arranged financing. And optional on-site maintenance plans for repairs right on your premises.

In short, Datago offers you something more important than just a wide selection of office systems.

A wise selection of office systems.

Datago

12

Garin Baker

represented by Bernstein & Andriulli, Inc. 60 East 42nd Street New York, N.Y. 10165 (212) 682-1490

Garie Blackwell

represented by Bernstein & Andriulli, Inc. 60 East 42nd Street New York, N.Y. 10165 (212) 682-1490

Melinda Bordelon

represented by Bernstein & Andriulli, Inc. 60 East 42nd Street New York, N.Y. 10165 (212) 682-1490

M. Bordelon

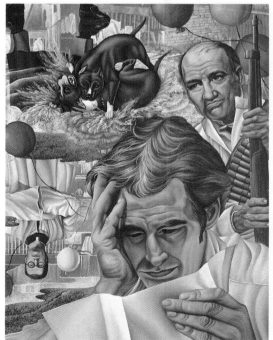

Everett Davidson

represented by Bernstein & Andriulli, Inc. 60 East 42nd Street New York, N.Y. 10165 (212) 682-1490

Cathy Deeter

represented by Bernstein & Andriulli, Inc. 60 East 42nd Street New York, N.Y. 10165 (212) 682-1490

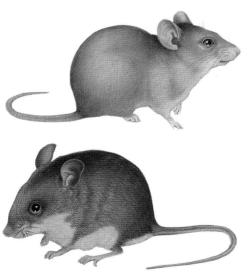

Ron Fleming/Graphic Associates

represented by Bernstein & Andriulli, Inc. 60 East 42nd Street New York, N.Y. 10165 (212) 682-1490

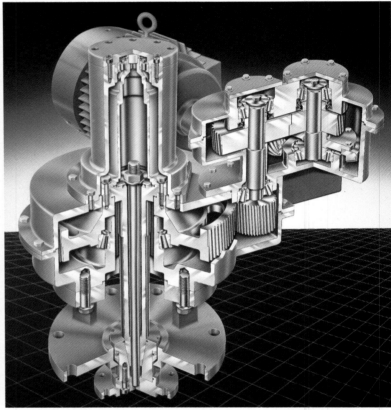

Clay Turner/Graphic Associates

represented by Bernstein & Andriulli, Inc. 60 East 42nd Street New York, N.Y. 10165 (212) 682-1490

Victor Gadino

represented by Bernstein & Andriulli, Inc. 60 East 42nd Street New York, N.Y. 10165 (212) 682-1490

Kid Kane

represented by Bernstein & Andriulli, Inc. 60 East 42nd Street New York, N.Y. 10165 (212) 682-1490

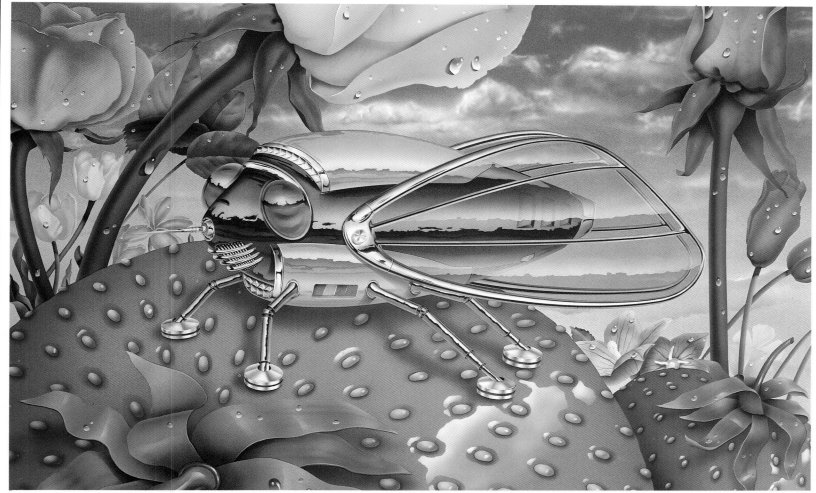

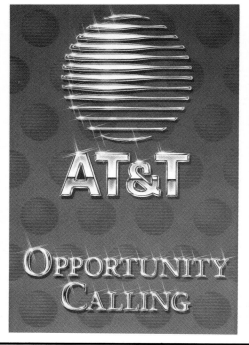

Griesbach/Martucci

represented by Bernstein & Andriulli, Inc. 60 East 42nd Street New York, N.Y. 10165 (212) 682-1490

Griesbach/Martucci

represented by Bernstein & Andriulli, Inc. 60 East 42nd Street New York, N.Y. 10165 (212) 682-1490

Mary Ann Lasher

represented by Bernstein & Andriulli, Inc. 60 East 42nd Street New York, N.Y. 10165 (212) 682-1490

Bette Levine

represented by Bernstein & Andriulli, Inc. 60 East 42nd Street New York, N.Y. 10165 (212) 682-1490

Marla Shega

represented by Bernstein & Andriulli, Inc. 60 East 42nd Street New York, N.Y. 10165 (212) 682-1490

Your Daily Bread

Ever see a pickle turn into bread? It's simple. Just set your sights on the refrigerated Bread 'n Butter pickle more people buy. Claussen.

Because unlike ordinary shelf pickles, they're never cooked. So that cold, crisp, conspicuously crunchy flavor is never cooked out. No wonder Claussen's the number one refrigerated pickle in America.

So why stock any old pickle when you can carry a real breadwinner?

claussen
#1 in refrigerated pickles.

STOP COPYING COST ROBBERY WITH INFORTEXT.®

We're Infortext, a computerized system that keeps your copiers on the right side of your financial planning.

No more feeling like your copiers are committing little white collar crimes. Right now, Infortext is working for hundreds of cost-conscious companies. Whether you have one copier or a hundred, Infortext can help you manage your copying costs, too.

Copying shouldn't hold up your organization.

Copiers and supplies cost money, but people and time cost even more money. Infortext can help you reduce all these expenses. Accurate recording of each copy transaction allows you to automatically charge each user department or client without running up costly accounting time. You can even evaluate the efficiency of your copy operation, get the right machines in the right places, reduce copying volume, and possibly eliminate some of your copiers.

Unmask hidden chargeback revenues.

Studies show that less than 50 percent of client and project copying charges are actually charged back. That is lost revenue for you. But, Infortext can automatically record, compile and analyze every transaction for proper billing. No more manual logs. You can give your client a verified accounting of his copy costs.

Get your copiers to go straight.

Give us a call and we'll show you how to reform your office copiers and get those copying costs back on the straight and narrow. Also, ask us what we can do to rehabilitate postage meter, word processor, shipping and messenger service costs, too!

Call Toll Free
800-323-6550
In Illinois call (312) 490-1155

Infortext® Systems Inc.
Get your copy costs under control.

27

Murray Tinkelman

represented by Bernstein & Andriulli, Inc. 60 East 42nd Street New York, N.Y. 10165 (212) 682-1490

Chuck Wilkinson

represented by Bernstein & Andriulli, Inc. 60 East 42nd Street New York, N.Y. 10165 (212) 682-1490

RUSSELL COBANE

RUSSELL COBANE

RUSSELL COBANE

RUSSELL COBANE

30

JOE LAPINSKI

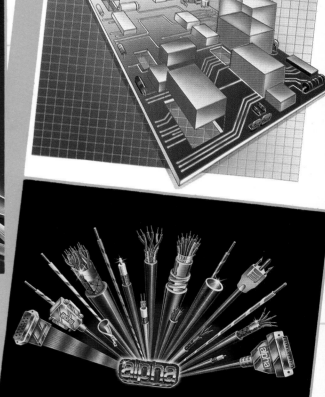

JIM HUNT

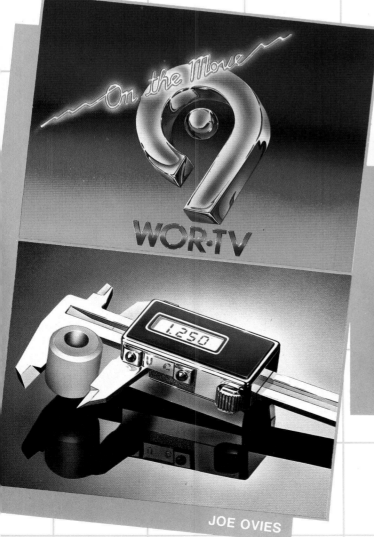

JOE OVIES

NIGHTHAWK STUDIO

E=MC²

ROGER LEYONMARK

ANNA DAVIDIAN

WILBUR BULLOCK

RON TOELKE

JACK CROMPTON

E·L·L·A

PHOTOGRAPHER'S & ARTIST'S REPRESENTATIVE

229 BERKELEY ST., BOSTON, MA·02116

(617) 266-3858

ROB CLINE

ANATOLY DVERIN

NORMAN ADAMS

BENTE ADLER

SUSAN DODGE

SCOTT GORDLEY

DAN SNEBERGER   GUY DEEL

WENDELL MINOR   DAVID COOK

EDWIN HERDER

EDWIN HERDER

EDWIN HERDER

EDWIN HERDER

EDWIN HERDER

Hankins+Tegenborg
Artist's Representatives
David Hankins Lars Tegenborg
60 E. 42nd Street
New York, N.Y. 10165
(212) 867-8092

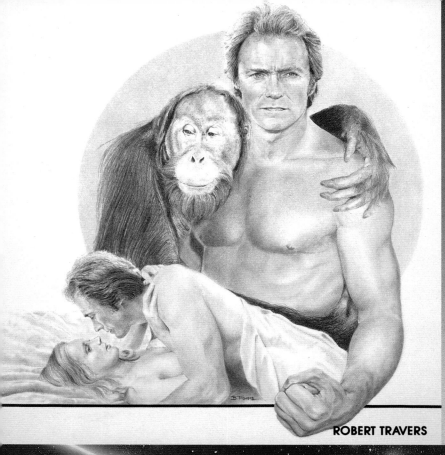

ROBERT TRAVERS

CHARLES MOLL

JOHN DISMUKES

ALETA JENKS

Foreign Imports

1980

1975

1970

MARIO STASOLLA

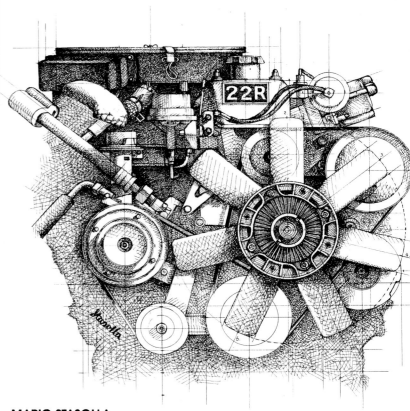

22R

MARIO STASOLLA

MIKE KANE

UNION PACIFIC

UNION PACIFIC

46

BANGOR AND AROOSTOOK

TRACKSIDE IN THE DIESEL AGE

DAVID GAADT

RALPH BRILLHART

RALPH BRILLHART

RALPH BRILLHART

RALPH BRILLHART

Hankins+Tegenborg
Artist's Representatives
David Hankins Lars Tegenborg
60 E. 42nd Street
New York, N.Y. 10165
(212) 867-8092

BILL SCHMIDT | **WALTER RANE**

DAN SNEBERGER | **ULDIS KLAVINS**

FRANK STEINER MICHAEL HERRING

JEFF WALKER DAVID GAADT

JEFF WALKER   JAMES GRIFFIN

VICTOR VALLA   GREG OLANOFF

ROBERT TRAVERS

ROBERT SABIN

FRANK STEINER   VICTOR VALLA

H-T

Hankins+Tegenborg
Artist's Representatives
David Hankins Lars Tegenborg
60 E. 42nd Street
New York, N.Y. 10165
(212)867-8092

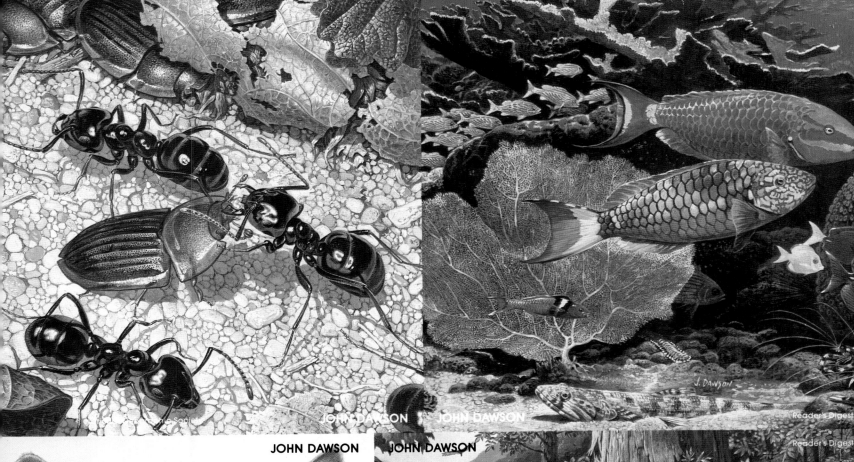

JOHN DAWSON

JOHN DAWSON

"Reproduced with permission of Star-Kist Foods, Inc., owner of the trademark and copyright 'Morris'."

Hankins+Tegenborg
Artist's Representatives
David Hankins Lars Tegenborg
60 E. 42nd Street
New York, N.Y. 10165
(212) 867-8092

New from
American Showcase!

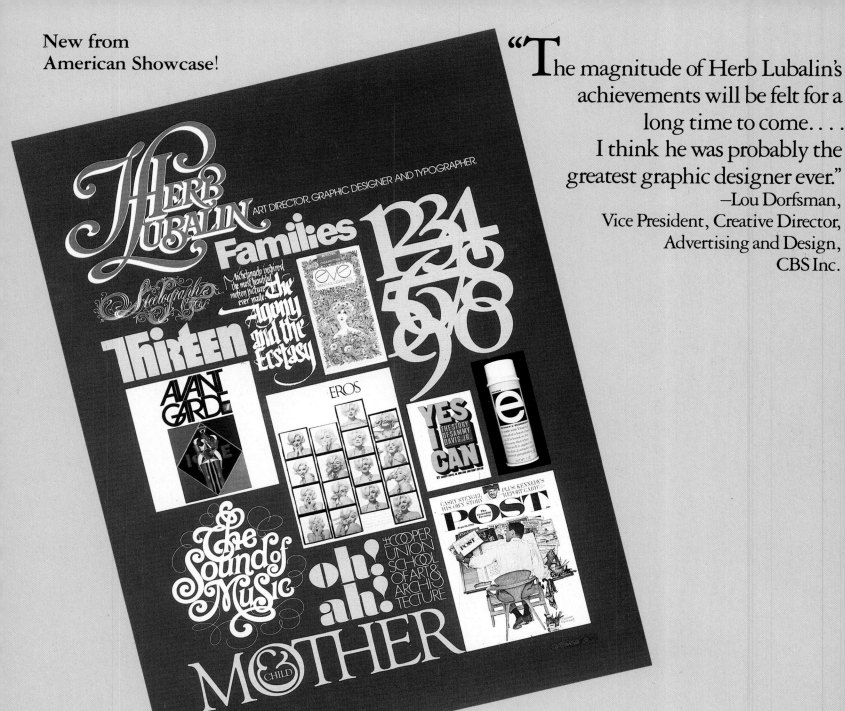

"The magnitude of Herb Lubalin's achievements will be felt for a long time to come.... I think he was probably the greatest graphic designer ever."
—Lou Dorfsman,
Vice President, Creative Director, Advertising and Design, CBS Inc.

Herb Lubalin is the definitive book about the typographic impresario and design master of our time. Illustrated with 360 extraordinary examples of Lubalin's award-winning work for editorial and book design, logos and letterheads, plus the best of *U&lc,* this handsome, 184-page, cloth-bound volume is more than just a record of one gentle man's expression through design. *Herb Lubalin* is also a record of a major chapter in the history of graphic design.

illustrations by **WILLIAM HARRISON**
represented by **BARNEY KANE & FRIENDS**
18 East 16 Street, N.Y.C. 10003
to see a complete portfolio
please call 212·206-0322

SUE ROTHER

BOB LAPSLEY

JACK DE GRAFFENRIED

LARRY WINBORG

PETER LLOYD

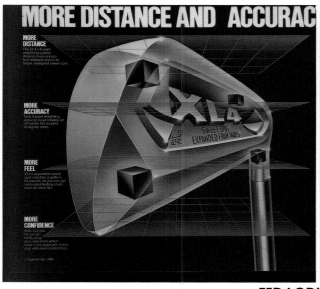

TED LODIGENSKY

RICH MAHON

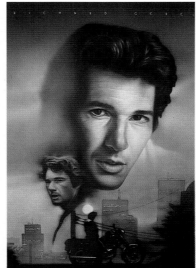

NATE GIORGIO

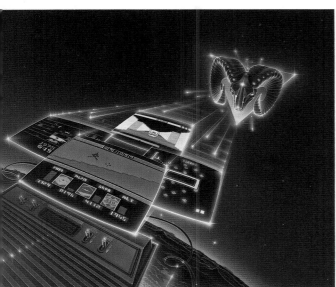

PETER LLOYD

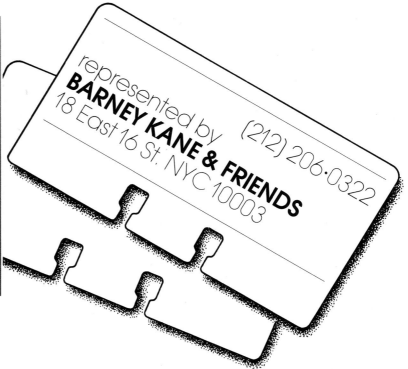

represented by (212) 206·0322
BARNEY KANE & FRIENDS
18 East 16 St. NYC 10003

JOSEPH DENARO

MARGARET BROWN

STEVEN KEYES

JESS NICHOLAS

GLEN TUNSTULL

LES MINTZ

REPRESENTS:

BERNARD BONHOMME ROBERT BURGER HOVIK DILAKIAN AMY HILL SUSANNAH KELLY
GEORGE MASI TINA MERCIE KIRSTEN SODERLIND DENNIS ZIEMIENSKI

(212) 925-0491
INCANDESCENT INK, INC.
111 WOOSTER STREET PH-C, NEW YORK, N.Y. 10012

BERNARD BONHOMME

HOVIK DILAKIAN

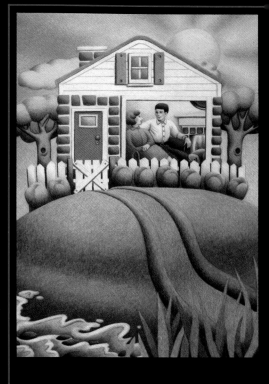

AMY HILL

SUSANNAH KELLY

GEORGE MASI

KIRSTEN SODERLIND

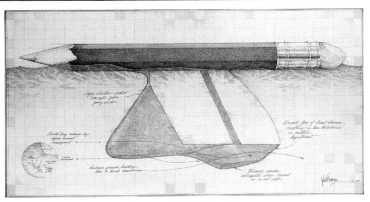

IT'S AMAZING HOW A
GOOD IDEA CAN BLOW EVERYTHING ELSE
OUT OF THE WATER.

JOHN BURGOYNE

CATHLEEN TOELKE

CATHLEEN TOELKE

JOHN BURGOYNE

CATHLEEN TOELKE

CHERYL ROBERTS

CHERYL ROBERTS

I'm Illustrious!

RAPHAEL BOGUSLAV

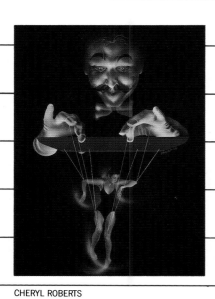

CATHLEEN TOELKE

BUNNY CARTER

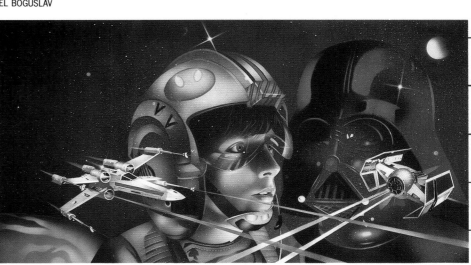

BUNNY CARTER

Arton Associates, Inc.

216 East 45th Street
New York, New York 10017
(212) 661-0850

Representatives: Barbara Rindner
Tony Gargagliano
Arthur Finer

Artists: **Paul Giovanopoulis**
Jacob Knight
Michelle Laporte

Dupe transparencies from art: Mann & Greene Color

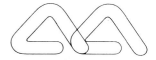

PAUL GIOVANOPOULIS

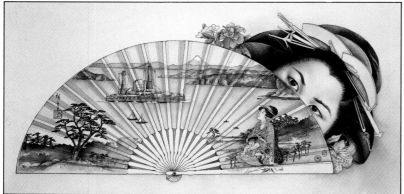

PAUL GIOVANOPOULIS

MICHELLE LAPORTE

JACOB KNIGHT

JACOB KNIGHT

MICHELLE LAPORTE

Anne Brody

Studio Six
55 Bethune Street
New York, New York 10014
(212) 242-1407

Represents:

Claude Martinot

Clients include:

Cunard Lines; Cunningham
& Walsh; The Bronx Zoo;
The Federal Reserve Bank of
New York; Harcourt Brace
Jovanovich; McGraw-Hill; Mothers
Today; Ogilvy & Mather; Scali,
McCabe, Sloves; Seventeen
Magazine; Ted Bates; Parents
Magazine; Ziff-Davis.

Member Graphic Artists Guild

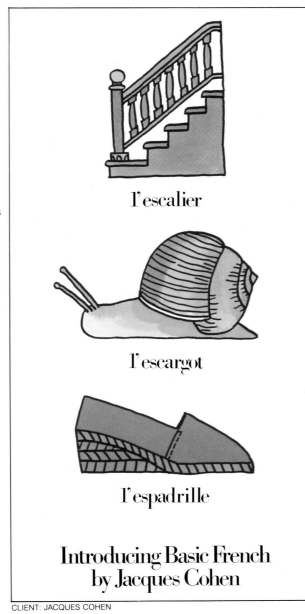

l'escalier

l'escargot

l'espadrille

**Introducing Basic French
by Jacques Cohen**

CLIENT: JACQUES COHEN

CLIENT: BRONX ZOO/HOUSE OF BIRDS

A N N E
B R O D Y

CLIENT: CUNARD LINES

Daniele Collignon

200 West 15th Street
New York, New York 10011
(212) 243-4209

Our clients include: Ziff-Davis, MGM, UA, Bloomingdale's, Arista Records, New American Library, R.C. Communications, Fairchild Publications, CBS Records, Revlon Inc., The New York Times, Playboy, Random House, Redbook,

Time-Life, Grey Direct, Ogilvy & Mather, Tracy-Locke/BBDO, U.S. Information Agency, Warner Music, RCA Records, Bantam Books, Audi, Upjohn, Uniroyal, L'egg's.

We also represent:

• Illustration: David Gambale, Mike Lester, Varlet-Martinelli Studio.
• Photography: Richard Hughes.

FRAN OELBAUM

MEL GREIFINGER

BOB AIESE

Daniele Collignon

200 West 15th Street
New York, New York 10011
(212) 243-4209

Our clients include: Ziff-Davis, MGM, UA, Bloomingdale's, Arista Records, New American Library, R.C. Communications, Fairchild Publications, CBS Records, Revlon Inc., The New York Times, Playboy, Random House, Redbook,

Time-Life, Grey Direct, Ogilvy & Mather, Tracy-Locke/BBDO, U.S. Information Agency, Warner Music, RCA Records, Bantam Books, Audi, Upjohn, Uniroyal, L'egg's.

We also represent:

• Illustration: David Gambale, Mike Lester, Varlet-Martinelli Studio.
• Photography: Richard Hughes.

MEL GREIFINGER

MEL GREIFINGER

BOB AIESE

BOB AIESE

57

THE MAN WHO WENT TO THE DOGS.

He was born and bred in Nebraska. His mother was a warm, loving woman, whose world revolved around her four children. His father was a wheat farmer; generous, red-blooded and full of strength. When he wasn't at school, or helping his father seed and harvest hundreds of acres of shimmering amber wheat, he sat in front of the television and was captivated by the commercials. Shortly, his mind turned toward the possibility of a career in advertising, and what it would be like to direct the thirty second pieces of film that flashed across the television tube, interrupting his family's favorite shows.

Instead of enrolling in the University of Nebraska, as his father and mother had wished, he said his tearful goodbyes, and headed for Hollywood, California. Within a week after his arrival, he secured a job as a messenger for a television commercial studio on Sunset Boulevard. Three years later, he had established himself as one of the most talented and sought-after television commercial directors on the West Coast. His legendary use of the camera to film everything from pie fillings to low octane gasoline soon spread to the East Coast, and he was summoned to Madison Avenue to film commercials for disposable diapers, designer jeans, and fast food chains. He took his beagle, Benny, with him.

Indeed, Benny had been part of his life for more than ten years. Before Benny, there had been Mac, a Scottish Collie, who had always been warm to the touch, and had a perpetual twinkle in his deep blue eyes. He loved dogs. There was no question about that.

One evening, he returned to his Park Avenue apartment after a hard day filming an extravaganza for a chicken soup commercial, and found himself barking his complaints at Benny. He railed at the many problems that actors and actresses were causing him. Admitted that he was growing impatient with the complications caused by wardrobe mistresses, makeup men, and set designers. Suggested that he was becoming short-tempered and irascible with actor's agents, whining starlets, and his camera crew.

He took a can of beer from the refrigerator, and motioned for Benny to follow him into the living room. And while he sat on his sofa, sipping his beer, his eyes turned from the glistening array of city lights visible through his window, to Benny. "Yes!" he exclaimed, as Benny reared back in surprise. "I'm going to specialize in filming dog commercials! Benny, think of the possibilities! There are hundreds of dog food commercials on television. And I'm going to be the director that is known as the expert. Yes, Benny, it's going to be pure joy. Working with dogs. What a delight."

Benny returned to the edge of the sofa, and curled-up on his special pillow, as the man continued: "Benny, it's going to be wonderful. We're going to be free at last. Look at it his way:

One: Afghan Hounds, Airdale Terriers, and Australian Cattle dogs, never have to worry about wardrobe. Therefore, the endless conversation about what kind of tie an actor should wear, or what sort of dress an actress should put on is avoided. Thank God.

Two: Beagles—such as yourself—Bloodhounds, and Boston Terriers don't have agents. Sure they have trainers. But no agents. Hence, I don't have to argue with guys who are trying to turn their client into an over-night star.

Three: Chihuahuas, Chow Chows, and Collies—like Mac—don't wet their diapers like all those bawling babies I have to film.

Four: Dachshunds, Dalmatians, and Doberman Pinschers can't talk. Therefore, they can't forget their lines, like most of the actors and actresses I work with.

Five: French Bulldogs, Fox Terriers, and Flat-Coated Retrievers, unlike kid actors, don't have mothers who take them to the studio, and hover around all day, making sure that their pride and joy is showing-off their acting talent.

Six: Great Danes, Greyhounds, and Groenendael's don't carry around pictures of themselves and thrust them at anybody who seems to be even half awake.

Seven: And get ready for this, Benny! Irish Setters, Irish Spaniels, and Irish Wolfhounds don't need a

continued on page 62

Creative Talent

Represented by:
Lauren Gelband
62 LeRoy Street
New York, New York 10014
(212) 243-7869

Representing:
Guy Smalley
Marshall Cetlin
Christine Ciesiel

GUY SMALLEY   BRISTOL MYERS   GUY SMALLEY   GUY SMALLEY   ASPCA

MARSHALL CETLIN
CITIBANK

MARSHALL CETLIN
WIND SURF MAGAZINE

Creative® TALENT

Represented By
Lauren Gelband
(212) 243-7869
62 LeRoy St.
N.Y.C., N.Y. 10014

CHRISTINE CIESIEL   CHRISTINE CIESIEL   J. WILEY & SONS   CHRISTINE CIESIEL COMMUNICATIONS OF THE ACM

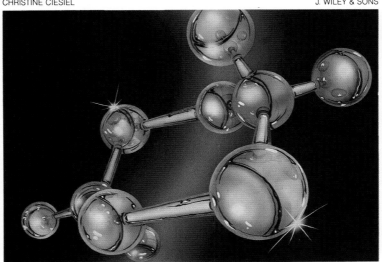

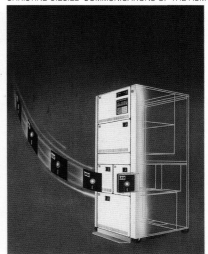

Barbara Gordon Associates

165 East 32nd Street
New York, New York 10016
(212) 686-3514

Barbara and Elliott Gordon

Barbara Gordon Associates works in all areas of the business, including advertising, paperbacks, movies, industrial, pharmaceutical, fashion, corporate, government, packaging, publishing and television.

Complete portfolios on all artists and photographers represented by the firm are available upon request.

SONJA LAMUT/NENAD JAKESEVIC

SONJA LAMUT/NENAD JAKESEVIC

JACKIE JASPER

JAS SZYGIEL

JIM DIETZ

60

Barbara Gordon
Associates

165 East 32nd Street
New York, New York 10016
(212) 686-3514

GLENN HARRINGTON

RON BARRY

ANDREW NITZBURG, PAPER SCULPTURE

JIM DIETZ

JACKIE JASPER

61

continued from page 58

manicure, or lipstick, or eye makeup. Therefore, we don't have to worry about makeup men running around a set waving a powderpuff, or screeching because someone's makeup or mascara is running.

Eight: Kerry Blue Terriers, Kelpies, and King Charles Spaniels never need a psychiatrist. That's a blessing, Benny. That means that I don't have to worry about an actor getting upset at something I said, and running off to his shrink in the middle of a scene.

Nine: Mastiffs, Manchester Terriers, and Miniature Pinschers don't demand a private limousine and chauffeur, a private dressing room, or caviar and champagne for lunch.

Ten: Poodles, Portuguese Cattle dogs, and Pugs never have love affairs that last more than ten minutes. So...we never have to worry about actors or actresses arriving at the set in the morning, dejected, depressed and despondent, because their lover did them wrong.

Eleven: St. Bernards, Schnauzers, and Staffordshire Bull Terriers, aren't like some celebrities who make commercials, and then end up on the front page of all the newspapers for one untidiness or another.

Twelve: And brace yourself for this one, Benny. Tibetan Terriers, Welsh Corgis, Welsh Springer Spaniels, Whippets, and Yorkshire Terriers don't try to act! Benny, what a joy! An agony, spared! What a wonderful future; filming dogs. I suppose it's what I wanted all along."

The man reached down and ran his warm hand along Benny's soft coat, and smiled. And two years later, he was the one commercial director most famous for filming dogs precisely as they should be filmed; with honesty, with love, and with care.

Vincent Daddiego
Senior Vice President
Associate Creative Director
Young&Rubicam
New York

Rob Kelly Represents

(303) 698-0073
(303) 733-9918

Ron Sauter
1032 South York Street
Denver, Colorado 80209

Pat Fujisaki
5917 South Kenton Way
Englewood, Colorado 80111

Clients include: Toyota, Hallmark Cards, Disney
Studios, Mattel Toys, Johns-Manville, Avco Financial,
U.S. Wildlife Service, Hilton Hotels

Tania Kimche

470 West 23rd Street
New York, New York 10011
(212) 242-6367

Representing:

Michael Hostovich

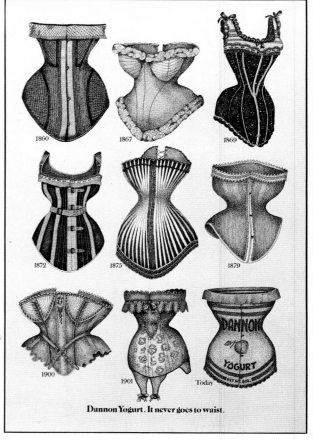

AMERICAN CYANAMIDE

Tania Kimche

470 West 23rd Street
New York, New York 10011
(212) 242-6367

Representing:

Rafaĺ Olbínski

DAEWOO CORP./J. WALTER THOMPSON USA

Tania Kimche

470 West 23rd Street
New York, New York 10011
(212) 242-6367

Representing:

M. Schottland

Tania Kimche

470 West 23rd Street
New York, New York 10011
(212) 242-6367

Representing:
E.T. Steadman

Bill and Maurine Klimt

15 West 72nd Street
New York, New York 10023
(212) 799-2231

Representing:

Jeffrey Adams
Stephen Gorman
Ken Joudrey
Frank Morris
and others

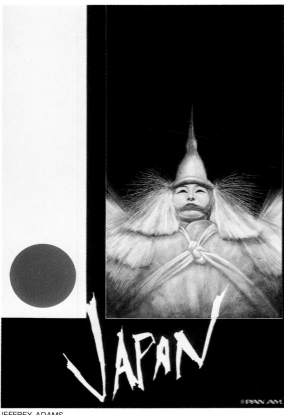

JEFFREY ADAMS

JEFFREY ADAMS

STEPHEN GORMAN

STEPHEN GORMAN

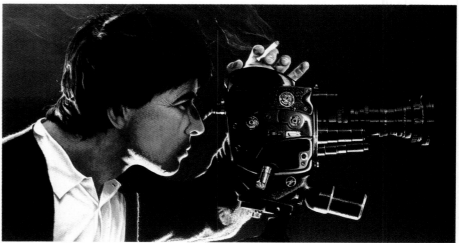

STEPHEN GORMAN

Bill and Maurine Klimt

15 West 72nd Street
New York, New York 10023
(212) 799-2231

Representing:
Jeffrey Adams
Stephen Gorman
Ken Joudrey
Frank Morris
and others

KLIMT

FRANK MORRIS

FRANK MORRIS

KEN JOUDREY

KEN JOUDREY

Deborah Lipman

Artists' Representative
506 Windsor Drive
Framingham, Massachusetts 01701
(617) 451-6528/877-8830

Representing:

Mark Fisher
Richard A. Goldberg
Carol LaCourse

Each artist works in both color and black & white, and in a variety of media. Their markets include advertising/promotion, corporate/collateral, as well as editorial and publishing.

Members Graphic Artists Guild

MARK FISHER

CAROL LACOURSE

RICHARD A. GOLDBERG

Deborah Lipman

Artists' Representative
506 Windsor Drive
Framingham, Massachusetts 01701
(617) 451-6528/877-8830

Artists' clients include:

Lotus Software
Data General Corp.
Digital Equipment Corp.
Prime Computer
Codex Corporation
New York Times

Cleveland Plain Dealer
Harvard Business Review
New England Business
Cahners Publishing Company
John Hancock Mutual Life Ins. Co.
New England Telephone
Fidelity Group

Codman Realty
INC/High Techonology
Sports Illustrated
S.D. Warren/Scott Paper
WGBH Educational Foundation
Children's Television Workshop
Ritz Carlton Hotel

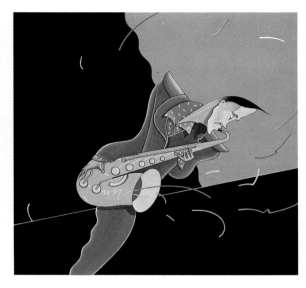

MARK FISHER

RICHARD A. GOLDBERG

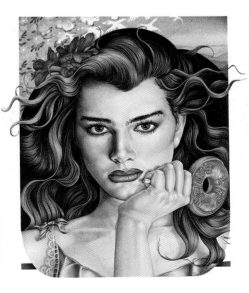

CAROL LACOURSE

71

Peter and George Lott

60 East 42nd Street
New York, New York 10165
(212) 687-4185

Represent:

David Halpern

Tony Cove

Juan C. Barberis

DAVID HALPERN

TONY COVE

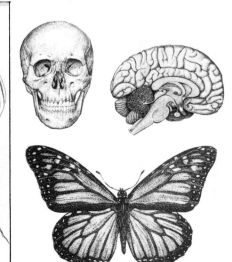

JUAN C. BARBERIS

Peter and George Lott

60 East 42nd Street
New York, New York 10165
(212) 687-4185

Represent:

Edward Kurtzman

McLean Represents Inc.

401 West Peachtree Street
Suite 1720
Atlanta, Georgia 30308
(404) 221-0798

Portfolios on all artists represented available upon request.

Represents:

Jack Jones

Clients Include: Anheuser-Busch, Brown & Williamson Tobacco, Miller Brewing, Gallo Wineries, York Steak House, Ace Books, R.J. Reynolds Tobacco, Datsun, Ballantine Books, Taylor California Cellars.

Steve Spetseris

Clients Include: Little General Stores, York Steak House, Anheuser-Busch, IBM, Analog Devices, Monroe, Hertz Rent-A-Car, Docutel, Blue-Cross.

Vicki Morgan
Associates

(212) 475-0440

Representing:
Brian Zick

Vicki Morgan
Associates
(212) 475-0440

Representing:
Richard Mantel

Richard is an illustrator and designer. He is a partner in the design firm of Mantel Koppel & Scher, Inc.

MAXWELL HOUSE MESSENGER

**And Now, the
Crème de la Decaf:
Yuban-D**

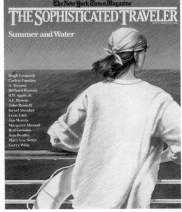

Vicki Morgan
Associates
(212) 475-0440

Representing:
Ray Cruz

Vicki Morgan
Associates

(212) 475-0440

Representing:

Emanuel
Schongut

Vicki Morgan
Associates

(212) 475-0440

Representing:

Wayne McLoughlin

I enjoy bringing a unique conceptual approach to technological and nature subjects.

Awards include: Playboy Magazine Editorial Award; Society of Illustrators Silver Medal.

Clients include: National Geographic Society Books; Woodshole Oceanographic Institute; Texaco; Citicorp; CBS; AT&T; Adidas; Time Magazine; Life Magazine; Ziff Davis.

I created and designed the dimensional construction "Space Ships" series for Little Brown Inc. and illustrated "Inside The Personal Computer" for Abbeville Press.

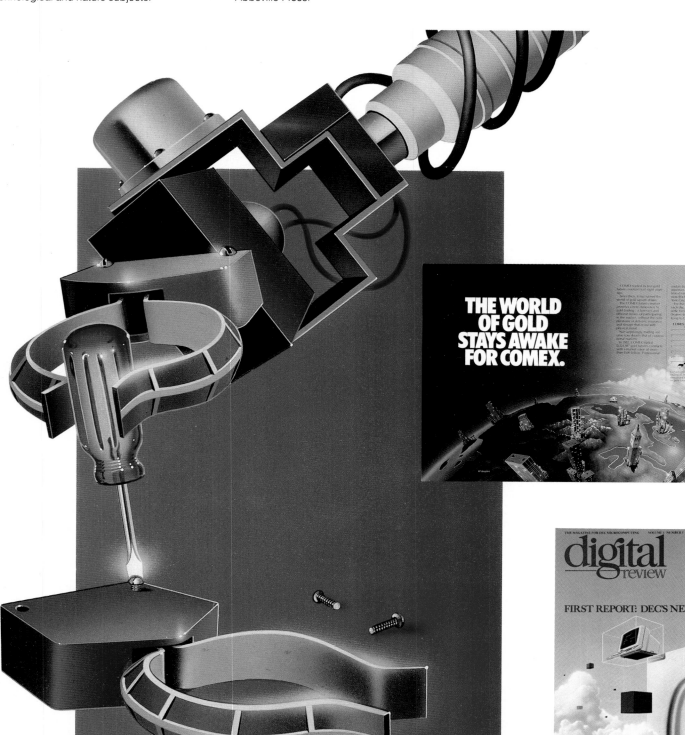

Vicki Morgan Associates

(212) 475-0440

Representing:

Tim Lewis

Member of Graphic Artists Guild
© 1984 Tim Lewis
all rights reserved

Illustrations:
From left to right, top to bottom:

1. CBS: Video Games That Stand Apart From The "PAC"

2. Forbes: How To Cut Legal Bills

3. Vanity Fair: Cover art for Summer issue (unpublished)

4. East/West Publications: Cover for Amtrak Express

5. Potlach: Cover for the Potlach Story

6. Vanity Fair: Proposed cover

212/475-0440
VICKI MORGAN
"Satisfies"
TELECOPIER IN OFFICE

Pamela R. Neail
Associates
233 East 82nd Street
New York, New York 10028
(212) 772-8444/8464

Represents:
Sean Daly

Pamela R. Neail Associates

233 East 82nd Street
New York, New York 10028
(212) 772-8444/8464

Represents:

Attila Hejja

Pamela R. Neail
Associates
233 East 82nd Street
New York, New York 10028
(212) 772-8444/772-8464

Represents:

Linda R. Richards
Clients: Toyota, Ford, Eastern Airlines, Molson Beer
& Ale, IBM, General Foods, NASA.

No Coast Graphics

Joe Malone
2544 15th Street
Denver, Colorado 80211
(303) 458-7086

Represents

Mike Steirnagle

4141 Pinnacle #132
El Paso, Texas 79902
(915) 533-9295

No Coast Graphics

Joe Malone
2544 15th Street
Denver, Colorado 80211
(303) 458-7086

Represents

Tom Nikosey
7417 Melrose Avenue
Los Angeles, California 90046
(213) 655-2184

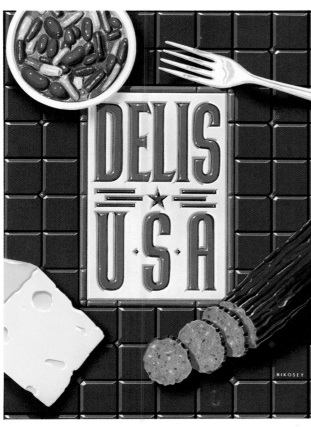

No Coast Graphics

Joe Malone
2544 15th Street
Denver, Colorado 80211
(303) 458-7086
Represents
John Cuneo

No Coast Graphics

Joe Malone
2544 15th Street
Denver, Colorado 80211
(303) 458-7086
Represents
Cindy Enright

Linda Oreman

Artists' Representative
15 Atkinson Street
Rochester, New York 14608
(716) 244-6956
(716) 232-1585

Representing:

Stephen Moscowitz

Roger DeMuth

Clients include:
Agway
Bausch & Lomb Inc.
Corning Glass
Doubleday Books
Eastman Kodak Company
Fisher-Price Toys
Fay's Drugstores
Holiday Inn
Mobil Chemical Company
Xerox Corporation

Additional examples of work available upon request.

Linda Oreman
ARTISTS' REPRESENTATIVE

ROGER DEMUTH

nourish and cultivate & in the fall harvest.

STEPHEN MOSCOWITZ

90

AD: Fabiano Canosa

The Penny & Stermer Group

A division of:
Barbara Penny Associates, Inc.
48 West 21st Street
New York, New York 10010
(212) 243-4412

Representing:

Bob Alcorn

1. AD: Robert Altemus
2. AD: Maryjane Fahey
3. AD: Joe Cupani/Judy Kolstad

1.

2.

3.

The Penny & Stermer Group

A division of:
Barbara Penny Associates, Inc.
48 West 21st Street
New York, New York 10010
(212) 243-4412

Representing:
Julian Graddon

1. AD: Charles Roth
2. AD: Tom Wichowski
3. AD: Michael Cancellieri/Mitch Achiron

1.

2.

3.

The Penny & Stermer Group

A division of:
Barbara Penny Associates, Inc.
48 West 21st Street
New York, New York 10010
(212) 243-4412

Representing:

Jane Clark

The Penny & Stermer Group

A division of:
Barbara Penny Associates, Inc.
48 West 21st Street
New York, New York 10010
(212) 243-4412

Representing:

Ron Becker

Paintings on exhibition at:
The James Hunt Barker Gallery
5 East 57th Street, New York City

Prints represented by:
The New York Graphics Guild

THE
PENNY &
STERMER
GROUP

The Penny & Stermer Group

A division of:
Barbara Penny Associates, Inc.
48 West 21st Street
New York, New York 10010
(212) 243-4412

Representing:

Gary Smith

The Penny & Stermer Group

A division of:
Barbara Penny Associates, Inc.
48 West 21st Street
New York, New York 10010
(212) 243-4412

Representing:

Deborah Bazzel

1. AD: William Snyder
2. AD: Brian Day
3. AD: Deborah Bazzel
4. AD: David Kaestle/Leslie Angle

2.

3.

1.

The Penny & Stermer Group

A division of:
Barbara Penny Associates, Inc.
48 West 21st Street
New York, New York 10010
(212) 243-4412

Representing:

Rich Grote

1. AD: Amy Fread
2. AD: Charlie Kornberger
3. AD: Toni Schowalter
4. AD: Lem Rauk

1.

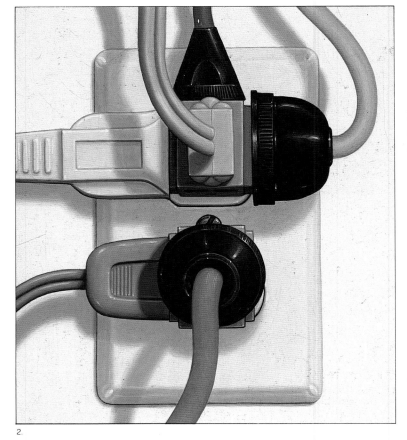

2.

3.

4.

The Penny & Stermer Group

A division of:
Barbara Penny Associates, Inc.
48 West 21st Street
New York, New York 10010
(212) 243-4412

Representing:

Michael Kanarek

AD: Charles Roth

Outrageous Opinions Welcome

We hope you've enjoyed reading the VIEWPOINTS in American Showcase Volume 8. This popular feature is designed to be enlightening as well as entertaining, providing unique insights and comments on the current state of advertising.

We'd like to take this opportunity to invite you to share your own thoughts, opinions and memories with thousands of your colleagues the world over. Please write for editorial guidelines:

Wendl Kornfeld
Operations Manager
American Showcase, Inc.
724 Fifth Avenue
10th Floor
New York, N.Y. 10019

Please include your name, title, company, address and phone number. We cannot, of course, guarantee inclusion of your article in our next edition; however, we will acknowledge and read each submission.

Thanks. We're looking forward to hearing from you. Hope to see you in VOLUME 9!

American Showcase, Inc.

Richard Salzman

Artist Representative
1352 Hornblend Street
San Diego, California 92109
(619) 272-8147
(213) 829-4429

Richard Salzman represents 15 of Southern California's finest Illustrators, Cartoonists, Photographers, Photo Retouchers and Visual Production Houses. We specialize in creating superlative works of art for advertisers, publishers and corporations.

Complete portfolios are available for all artists upon request. For further evidence of our complete range of creative services, please call for a free promotional poster.

Artists shown:

top row
DENISE HILTON PUTNAM

second row
JOYCE KITCHELL

third row
EVERETT PECK

bottom row
MANUEL GARCIA

Artists not shown:

JONATHAN WRIGHT
technical illustration

WALTER STUART
medical illustration

TERRY SMITH
whimsical illustration & cartoon maps

DAVID MOLLERING
people illustration

TONY BAKER
architectural illustration

BERNIE LANSKY
cartoonist

DIANNE O'QUINN BURKE
fantasy illustration

NONA REMOS
photo retouching & airbrush

JASON HARLEM
photography

GORDEN MENZIE
photography

IMAGERY THAT MOVES
visual production house

RICHARD · W · SALZMAN
ARTIST · REPRESENTATIVE

Fran Seigel

515 Madison Avenue
New York, New York 10022
(212) 486-9644

Representing:

Leslie Cabarga

Water you looking for? You want a picture of a fish, we'll give you a fish. Except when we digest that fish intellectually and spit it out onto the Bainbridge Coldpress you'll get an illustration that really swims! If you want a funny illustration, we say, "ha, ha, ha!" If you want it serious, we are not amused. Whatever it takes, we'll give you the kind of art you want to help your product splash in the marketplace!

Top Row: Paper Moon Graphics, Inc.; Time, Inc. (Fortune Magazine)

Middle: EMI America Records; Roche Laboratories/ Wm. Douglas McAdams; The Drakett Co./Kenyon & Eckhardt

Bottom: Ralston/Gerstman & Meyers; Madison Avenue Magazine; Radio Shack/Children's Computer Workshop

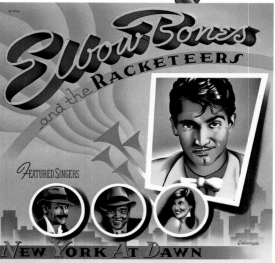

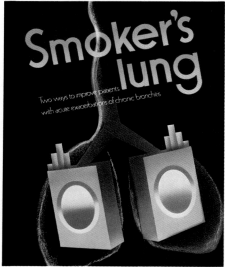

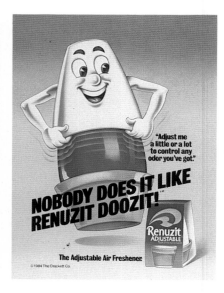

Fran Seigel

515 Madison Avenue
New York, New York 10022
(212) 486-9644

Representing:

Kinuko Y. Craft

A tailor-made unique visual image results from Kinuko
Craft's consideration of your client's specific needs.
Whether your message is fantastic or romantic,
historical or scientific, the concept will fit—complete
with painterly technique of the appropriate period
spanning primitive to contemporary styles.

KINUKO Y. CRAFT

CONTROL DATA CORP.

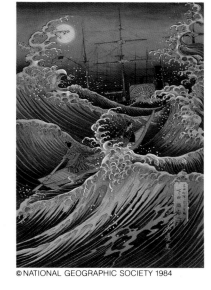

© NATIONAL GEOGRAPHIC SOCIETY 1984

TIME, INC.

TIME-LIFE BOOKS

NATIONAL LAMPOON

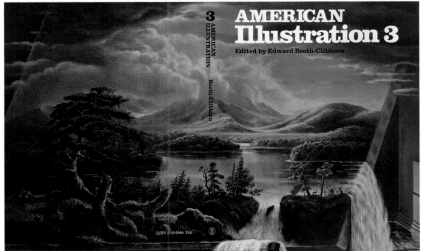

AMERICAN ILLUSTRATION, INC.

INFODATA SYSTEMS, INC.

103

Fran Seigel

515 Madison Avenue
New York, New York 10022
(212) 486-9644

Representing:

Peter Cross

Whether it's whimsical, surreal or a more subtle feeling that's wanted, Peter communicates your message with wit and clarity. Original concepts (or conceptual cooperation) a specialty. Clients include: ABC, Inc., AT&T, Carrier Corp., General Foods, IBM International, Sunshine, United Technologies Corp., Wall Street Journal, Avon Books, Crown Publishers, Penguin Books, Pocket Books, Reader's Digest, Redbook and Psychology Today.

Fran Seigel

515 Madison Avenue
New York, New York 10022
(212) 486-9644

Representing:

Earl Keleny

For referral to Chicago
representative call (608) 222-3194

Textures created by mixed media add expression to already strong concepts in Earl Keleny's stylized realism. Recognized by the Society of Illustrators both in New York and California, and featured in Art Direction Magazine, Earl has acquired a rapidly growing list of clients including those shown by visuals below as well as: AT&T, CBS Records, CBS Video, Gibson Guitars, Lanz of California, National Computer Systems, McGraw Hill, Madison Avenue, Playboy and PC Magazines.

EARL KELENY

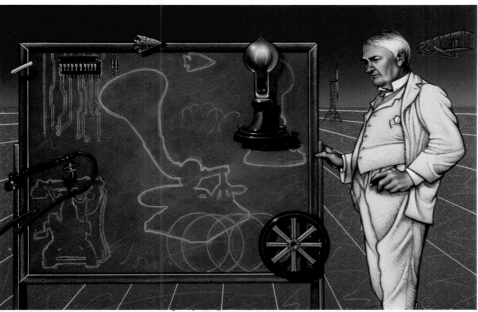

EPSON AMERICA INC.

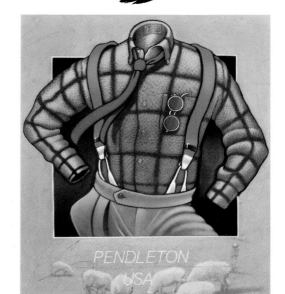

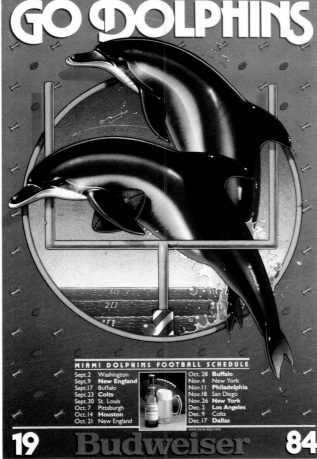

ANHEUSER-BUSCH

NORTHWESTERN MUTUAL LIFE INSURANCE

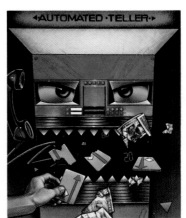

LOS ANGELES MAGAZINE

105

Joan Sigman

336 East 54th Street
New York, New York 10022
(212) 832-7980
(212) 421-0050

Represents:

Robert Goldstrom

471 Fifth Street
Brooklyn, New York 11215

1. Playboy "Search for the Golden Fleece"
2. Chicago Reader "Places of Power"
3. Quest "Igor Stravinsky"

1

2

3

John H. Howard

(212) 832-7980

1. N.Y. Times — "Beethoven"
2. Rolling Stone "Digital Discontent"
3. The Wine Spectator
4. N.Y. Times "International Banking"
5. CBS Disques "Musique Bimbo"

3

4

2

5

Susan Trimpe
Artist's Representative

2717 Western Avenue
Seattle, Washington 98121
(206) 382-1100

Represents:

Wendy Edelson
Stephen Peringer

Partial client list includes: Macmillan Publishing, Parents Magazine, American Library Association, Sunrise Publications, Tundra Books, Capital Records, Nike, McDonald's, Sea Galley, JanSport, Microsoft, Boeing, Roman Meal, Tree Top, Eddie Bauer.

Complete portfolios on all the artists and photographers represented by the firm sent upon request. Telecopier available.

WENDY EDELSON

STEPHEN PERINGER

Signed posters available...call.

INDEX REPRESENTATIVES

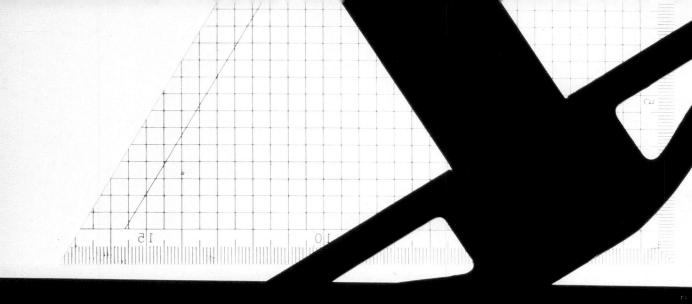

THE ATHLETE WINNER OF THE 1984 CLIO ILLUSTRATION AWARD

There's got to be a surprise there. And not just in a visual sense. It has to come out of the viewer, so that even he's surprised.

Not by what he sees so much but by what it makes him feel.

For me emotion is key, technique and craft almost secondary.

And trying to get it right can make you a little crazy.

BRUCE LESLIE WOLFE

REPRESENTED IN
SAN FRANCISCO/NORTHWEST
BY RON SWEET,
IN LOS ANGELES/SOUTHWEST
BY FRANCE ALINE,
IN CHICAGO/MIDWEST
BY JOEL HARLIB,
IN NEW YORK/EAST COAST
BY VICKIE MORGAN.

STUDIO ADDRESS:
206 EL CERRITO AVENUE
PIEDMONT, CALIFORNIA 94611
TELEPHONE 415 655-7871

EATON & IWEN, INC.
307 N. MICHIGAN AVE.
CHICAGO, ILLINOIS 60601
312-332-3256

EATON & IWEN, INC.
307 N. MICHIGAN AVE.
CHICAGO, ILLINOIS 60601
312-332-3256

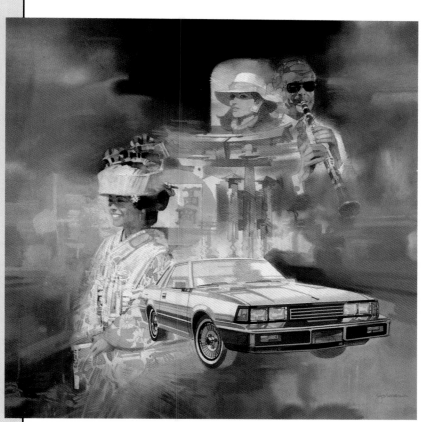

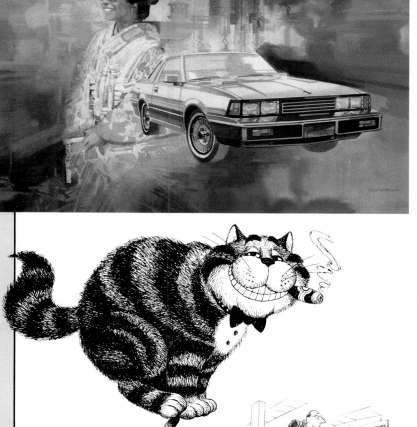

Tim Girvin Design, Inc.
911 Western
Suite 408
Seattle, Washington 98104
206 . 623 . 7918 / 7808

This office has consistently different approaches to design, illustration and the alphabet.

Tim Girvin has worked with architects and art directors, interior and graphic designers as well as client-direct to offer unique appraisals and solutions for design problems.

Tim Girvin Design has created for ABC, A&M, American Express, Bloomingdale's, Bullocks, CBS, Coors, Walt Disney Studios, Exxon, The Friends of Asian Art/Detroit Institute of the Arts, B.F. Goodrich, Hilton, Hoffmann LaRoche, IBM, Life Magazine, Louisiana Pacific, Rand McNally, Microsoft, Herman Miller, Nordstrom, Omni International Hotels, PBS, Pennzoil, Polaroid, The San Francisco Museum of Modern Art, Sheraton Hotels, Time/Life, Westin Hotels, Zales and many others. (Both client-direct and through affiliate agencies).

Additional relevant samples and transparencies will be sent immediately with a request and project description on your company letterhead.

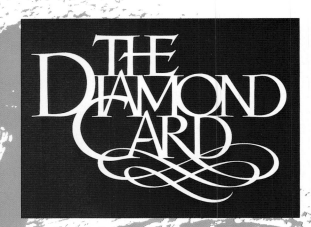

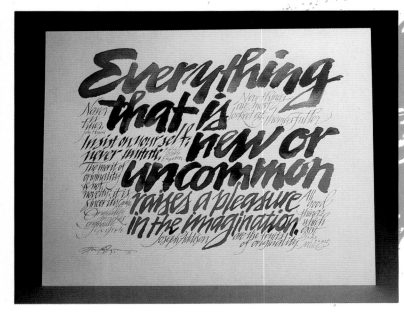

DENNIS MUKAI

LOS ANGELES
JOANNE HEDGE
213.874.1661

SAN FRANCISCO
MARY VANDAMME
415.433.1292

CHICAGO
JOEL HARLIB
312.329.1370

HOUSTON
DIANA DIORIO
713.266.9390

CLIENTS INCLUDE:

FOOTE, CONE
& BELDING/HONIG, INC.
MCCANN-ERICKSON, INC.
YOUNG & RUBICAM/
DENTSU, LOS ANGELES.

APPLE MAGAZINE
NBC
PAPER MOON GRAPHICS
PLAYBOY

Kathie Abrams

41 Union Square West
Room 1001
New York, New York 10003
(212) 741-1333

Humorous illustration for advertising, corporate, publishing and audio-visual clients, including:

American Express; American Health; American Symphony Orchestra; AT&T; Bose Audio; Burson-Marsteller; Columbia University; Dodd, Mead & Co.; Farrar, Straus & Giroux; Harper & Row; Hermes; Ibis Media; Marine Midland Bank; McGraw-Hill; Midco Pipe & Tube; Newsweek; Ogilvy & Mather; Random House; RFE Industries; Scholastic; Sports Illustrated; Frederick Warne; Ziff-Davis.

Illustrations:

1, 3. American Symphony Orchestra/Ogilvy & Mather
2. American Express/Ogilvy & Mather
4. Ronni Eisenberg & Associates
5. RFE Industries/Arnold Advertising Associates
6. Columbia University
7. Simon & Schuster
8. AT&T/Burson-Marsteller

Graphic Artists Guild member

Ace Studio

Katherine Ace
P.O. Box 332
Oregon House, California
(near Sacramento)
(916) 692-1816

Painting and pastels

Illustrations from left to right, top to bottom:

1. "Over the Rainbow" MGM Grand Reno Gallery
2. "California Poised"
3. Menu cover, Holiday Inn
4. "Illustrative Leonardo da Vinci"
5. "Oak Ridge Boys" Sahara Reno Gallery
6. "Wine, like art, is a process" Self promotion

Paul R. Alexander

37 Pine Mountain Road
Redding, Connecticut 06896
(203) 544-9293

Clients have included IBM,
Playboy, General Motors,
General Electric, Bethlehem
Steel, Republic Steel, ALCOA
Aluminum, Bank of New York,
Milton Bradley Co., Popular
Mechanics, Popular Science,
and extensive science fiction
work for most major paperback
publishers.

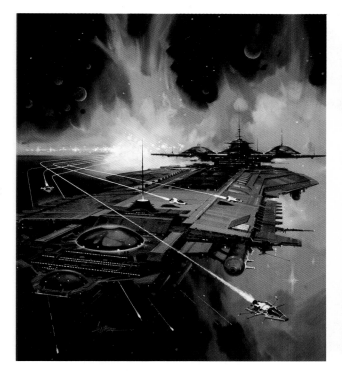

Annie Alleman

38 East 21st Street
New York, New York 10010
(212) 477-4185

Clients have included:
Manufacturers Hanover,
Bankers Trust, Chase
Manhattan Bank, Lincoln
Savings, The New York Times,
Ayerst Laboratories,
Harper & Row.

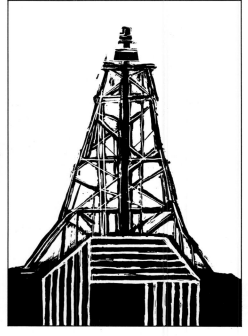

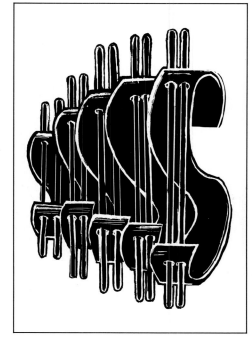

Vincent Amicosante

33 Route 5
Edgewater, New Jersey 07020
(201) 886-9354

Clients Include: Lyle Stuart, Scholastic, Ace Books,
Prentice Hall, Syndicate Magazines, Medical
Economics, High Times, Gallery, Atlantic City
Magazine

Member Graphic Artists Guild

Frank Ansley

1782 5th Street
Berkeley, California 94706
(415) 644-0585
(415) 527-1098

Clients:
FCB-Honig, J. Walter
Thompson, Doyle Dane
Bernbach, Young & Rubicam,
Atari, Shaklee Corp., Bank of
America Corporate
Communications, Consolidated
Capital Publishing Group,
Addison Wesley Publishers,
Pittman Learning Publishing,
Bass/Francis Productions.

Racquel Balin

Illustration and design

334 West 87th Street
New York, New York 10024
(212) 496-8358

Member Graphic Artists Guild

Barbara Banthien

Represented by:
Jan Collier
166 South Park
San Francisco, California 94107
(415) 552-4252

Clients have included:

Apple, Chevron, Christian Brothers, Consolidated Foods, Adolph Coors, Crown Zellerbach, Del Monte, Dole, Foremost, S&W, Safeway, Shaklee, Spice Islands, Sun Maid, Thom McAn, Henry Weinhard, Westin Hotels.

Ron Barrett

2112 Broadway
Room 402A
New York, New York 10023
(212) 874-1370

His list of clients reads like a Who's Who of
Multinational Blue Chip Conglomerates.

His motto: "I put a flap *on* your job,
I don't make one over it."

(1) CLIENT: SONY AUDIO AGENCY: AMMIRATI & PURIS ART DIRECTOR: BARBARA SCHUBECK

YOU'VE GOT 24 HOURS OF SPORTS, MUSIC AND NEWS.
BUT WHAT YOU NEED IS 24 HOURS OF AUDIENCE.

(2) AGENCY: DELLA FEMINA, TRAVISANO & PARTNERS ART DIRECTOR: MARK YUSTEIN

THE RIGHT CLOTHING WOULD MAKE YOU A BETTER SKIER.

(3) AGENCY: ALTSCHILLER, REITZFELD, SOLIN/NCK ART DIRECTOR: BOB REITZFELD

Roger Bergendorff, Inc.

17106 Sims Street, Suite A
Huntington Beach, California
92649
(714) 840-7665

Partial Client List:
Yamaha, CBS, Apple
Computers, Corning Glass,
Warner Bros., Orion Pictures,
Normark Skis, Paper Moon
Graphics, Mazda, O'Neill, AMF,
Doubleday, Izuzu, MCA
Records, Fairchild Industries,
Treesweet Products, TRW,
Armor All, National Park Service,
Caterpillar, Opto 22, Alitalia.

THE ONLY PRESCRIPTION SUNGLASSES THAT KNOW THE DIFFERENCE BETWEEN CLOUDY, PARTLY CLOUDY AND SUNNY.

Guy Billout

Represented by:

Judy Mattelson

88 Lexington Avenue 12G
New York, New York 10016
(212) 684-2974

Represented in Los Angeles by:
France Aline
(213) 383-0498

Top Left:
One of a series of five ads:
Client: JAL CARGO
Agency: Dentsu Young &
Rubicam

Top Right:
Advertising campaign for
CHINA SEAS:
Contract Designs—Textiles—
Wallcoverings

Bottom:
"The Lonely Person's Garden"
TWA Ambassador Magazine.

GRAPHIC ARTS ORGANIZATIONS

Arizona:

Phoenix Society of Visual Arts
P.O. Box 469
Phoenix, AZ 85001

California:

Advertising Club of Los Angeles
514 Shatto Pl., Rm. 328
Los Angeles, CA 90020
(213) 382-1228

Art Directors and Artists Club
2791 24th St.
Sacramento, CA 95818
(916) 731-8802

Book Club of California
312 Sutter St., Ste. 510
San Francisco, CA 94108
(415) 781-7532

Graphic Artists Guild of Los Angeles
849 S. Broadway
Los Angeles, CA 90014
(213) 622-0126

Institute of Business Designers
c/o Gensler & Associates
550 Kearney St.
San Francisco, CA 94108
(415) 433-3700

Los Angeles Advertising Women
5300 Laurel Canyon Blvd.
North Hollywood, CA 91607
(213) 762-4669

San Francisco Society of Communicating Arts
Fort Mason
Building A
San Francisco, CA 94123
(415) 474-3156

Society of Illustrators of Los Angeles
1258 N. Highland Ave.
Los Angeles, CA 90038
(213) 469-8465

Society of Motion Picture & TV Art Directors
14724 Ventura Blvd.
Sherman Oaks, CA
(818) 905-0599

Western Art Directors Club
P.O. Box 966
Palo Alto, CA 94302
(415) 321-4196

Women in Design
P.O. Box 2607
San Francisco, CA 94126
(415) 397-1748

Women's Graphic Center
The Woman's Building
1727 N. Spring St.
Los Angeles, CA 90012
(213) 222-2477

Colorado:

International Design Conference at Aspen
P.O. Box 664
Aspen, CO 81612
(303) 925-2257

Connecticut:

Connecticut Art Directors Club
P.O. Box 1974
New Haven, CT 06521

District of Columbia:

American Advertising Federation
1400 K St, Ste. 1000
Washington, DC 20005
(202) 898-0089

American Institute of Architects
1735 New York Avenue, N.W.
Washington, DC 20006
(202) 626-7300

Art Directors Club of Washington, DC
1523 22nd St., N.W.
Washington, DC 20037
(202) 293-3134

Federal Design Council
P.O. Box 7537
Washington, DC 20044

International Copyright Information Center, A.A.D.
1707 L Street, N.W
Washington, DC 20036

NEA: Design Arts Program
1100 Pennsylvania Ave., N.W.
Washington, DC 20506
(202) 682-5400

Georgia:

Atlanta Art Papers, Inc.
P.O. Box 77348
Atlanta, GA 30357
(404) 885-1273

Graphic Artists Guild
3158 Maple Drive, N.E., Ste. 46
Atlanta, GA 30305
(404) 262-8077

Illinois:

Institute of Business Designers
National
1155 Merchandise Mart
Chicago, IL 60654
(312) 467-1950

Society of Environmental Graphics Designers
228 N. LaSalle St., Ste. 1205
Chicago, IL 60601

STA
233 East Ontario St.
Chicago, IL 60611
(312) 787-2018

Women in Design
400 West Madison, Ste. 2400
Chicago, IL 60606
(312) 648-1874

Kansas:

Wichita Art Directors Club
P.O. Box 562
Wichita, KS 67202

Maryland:

Council of Communications Societies
P.O. Box 1074
Silver Springs, MD 20910

Massachusetts:

Art Directors Club of Boston
214 Beacon St.
Boston, MA 02116
(617) 536-8999

Center for Design of Industrial Schedules
50 Staniford St., Ste. 800
Boston, MA 02114
(617) 523-6048

Graphic Artists Guild
P.O. Box 1454 - GMF
Boston, MA 02205
(617) 451-5362

Michigan:

Creative Advertising Club of Detroit
c/o Rhoda Parkin
30400 Van Dyke
Warren, MI 48093

Minnesota:

Minnesota Graphic Designers Association
P.O. Box 24272
Minneapolis, MN 55424

Missouri:

Advertising Club of Greater St. Louis
410 Mansion House Center
St. Louis, MO 63102
(314) 231-4185

Advertising Club of Kansas City
1 Ward Parkway Center, Ste. 102
Kansas City, MO 64112
(816) 753-4088

New Jersey:

Point-of-Purchase Advertising Institute
2 Executive Dr.
Fort Lee, NJ 07024
(201) 585-8400

New York:

The Advertising Club of New York
Roosevelt Hotel, Rm. 310
New York, NY
(212) 697-0877

The Advertising Council, Inc.
825 Third Ave.
New York, NY 10022
(212) 758-0400

Advertising Typographers Association of America, Inc.
5 Penn Plaza, 12th Fl.
New York, NY 10001
(212) 594-0685

Advertising Women of New York Foundation, Inc.
153 E. 57th St.
New York, NY 10022
(212) 593-1950

American Association of Advertising Agencies
666 Third Ave.
New York, NY 10017
(212) 682-2500

American Booksellers Association, Inc.
122 E. 42nd St.
New York, NY 10168
(212) 867-9060

continued on page 144

Alice Brickner

4720 Grosvenor Avenue
Bronx, New York 10471
(212) 549-5909

Watercolor illustration for advertising, promotion, packaging, pharmaceutical and editorial use.

Clients include: American Airlines; AT&T; Robert A. Becker, Inc.; Boehringer Ingelheim, Ltd.; Book-of-the-Month Club, Inc.; Caswell-Massey Co. Ltd.; Chesebrough-Pond's, Inc.; Ciba-Geigy; Corning; Dancer-Fitzgerald-Sample, Inc.; Dolphin Productions; Games Magazine; Gross, Townsend, Frank; Fortune; Harcourt Brace Jovanovitch; IBM; KPR; Lavey/Wolff/Swift, Inc.; London Records; William Douglas McAdams; McGraw-Hill; Medical Economics; Merck & Co., Inc.; Nabisco; Nonesuch Records; Ogilvy & Mather; Sieber & McIntyre, Inc.; Smithkline Corp.; Sports Illustrated; Sudler & Hennessy; Vogue; John Wiley & Sons.

Work appeared in: Graphis Annuals, Society of Illustrators Exhibitions, NY Art Directors Club Exhibitions, AIGA Exhibitions, New Jersey Art Director's Club Exhibitions, Creativity Exhibitions and Print Magazine.

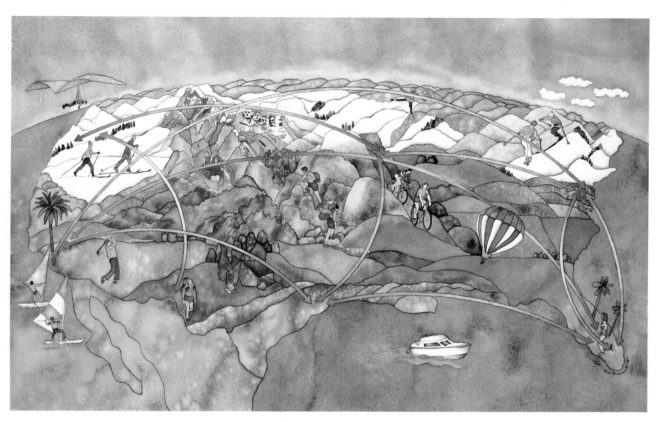

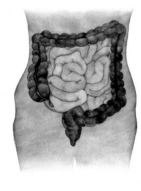

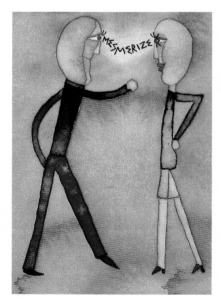

Lou Brooks

415 West 55th Street
New York, New York 10019
(212) 245-3632

Illustration, Design and Lettering

First page, clockwise from top:

Package art for "Donkey Kong" video game.
Cover for video game magazine.
Art promoting the New York Lottery.
Illustration about anger in teenagers.

Second page, clockwise from upper left:

Caricature of rock group, The Stray Cats.
Illustration about a man's fascination with prostitutes.
Ad for Cutex cosmetics.
Illustration about a baseball team called The Toledo Mud Hens.
Illustration about relationships between men and women.
Illustration for a science fiction story.

Telecopier in studio.

Member Graphic Artists Guild.

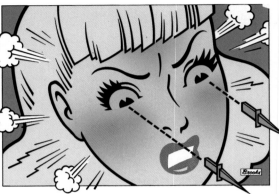

EROTIC RITES

A Parisian streetwalker triggered a lifelong obsession with sex-for-hire

THE MAN WHO LOVED PROSTITUTES

BY JEREMY COOPER

I am a screenwriter in my mid-30s. From 1968 to 1976 I had sex almost exclusively with prostitutes. My first time was in Paris. I was 19, sitting at a cafe, when I noticed that the woman across from me was not wearing panties. She was a redhead; her pubic hair was red, too. Suddenly I realized she was available. What I found so alluring was the lack of accessibility. She made no attempt to hide her availability. Nor did I have to feign any romantic interest in her. During high school I had always been socially clumsy. But I could almost smell the sexual allure of this woman.

We went to a hotel. Of course I was very nervous. The first thing she did was wash me. That has always been a tremendously erotic experience ever since—more so than almost anything else. But what amazed me and turned me off a little was that she also washed herself at the bidet in front of me. That was terribly intimidating and I lost my erection.

By the time we got to bed we had become quite taunting, saying, "Trop petit, trop petit." Her manner was rather impatient and her per-

ILLUSTRATION BY LOU BROOKS

Diana Bryan

200 East 16th Street, #1D
New York, New York 10003
(212) 475-7927

Clients include: Datsun, American Express, *Connoisseur Magazine, Business Week, Time Magazine, National Lampoon, The New York Times, Travel and Leisure, The Washington Post,* Time/Life Publications, *Glamour, Mademoiselle, Savvy, Sports Illustrated, Working Woman, Rolling Stone,* Workman Publications, The New Shakespeare Festival, The A.I.G.A.

Works Exhibited In: The Graphis Annual, Print Magazine, the Society of Illustrators Annual, Art Direction, Creativity '77, the New York Art Directors Club, the Society of Publication Designers, The A.I.G.A., the A.C.U.C.A.A. Graphics Competition, the Library of Congress.

Member Graphic Artists Guild

COMPUTER GRAPHIC ILLUSTRATIONS

Rows One and Two:
Created on Artronics/3M Paint System Courtesy of Studio Tech.

Row Three Left and Row Four Left:
Created on Artronics/3M Paint System.

Row Three Right and Row Four Right:
Created on Image System Courtesy of N.Y.I.T.

Yvonne Buchanan

411 14th Street
Brooklyn, New York 11215
(718) 965-3021

Clients include: AT&T; Ford Foundation; J.P. Martin
Associates; Cato-Johnson; N.W. Ayer; Specht, Gilbert
& Partners; Sachs & Rosen; Steve Phillips Design;
Hearst Publications; Fairchild Publications; Ziff-Davis;
Grey Communications; TV Guide; McGraw-Hill; Black
Enterprise; New York Times; Daily News; Village Voice.

133

Judith Cheng

88-57 195th Street
Hollis, New York 11423
(212) 465-5598

Clients include: Franklin Mint, Hamilton Mint, Simon & Schuster, Albert Whitman & Co., American Books, Atheneum, McGraw-Hill, Dutton, Sunrise Publishing, Reader's Digest, Scholastic, Western Publishing, Harper & Row, Ehn Graphics, Harcourt Brace Jovanovich, American Airlines, London Records.

Jim Cherry

Represented by:
Jean Yves Legrand
41 West 84th Street, #4
New York, New York 10024
(212) 724-5981

Clients include: ABC, CBS, NBC, Atlantic Records,
Volkswagon, HBO, MTV, Hearst, Nike, Springhill
Papers, Estée Lauder, Lois Sportswear, Gottex
Swimwear, Hertz, Arista Records, Rolling Stone,
Harper & Row, Condé Nast, Scholastic Press, Henson
Associates, and The New York Times.

135

Bob Conge

28 Harper Street
Rochester, New York 14607
(716) 473-0291

Illustration & Graphic Design

Clients include:
Bausch & Lomb; Circle Repertory Co.; Computer Consoles Inc.; Corning Glass; Eastman Kodak; Gannett Corp.; Mobil Chemical; R.I.T.; Sybron; Sykes; University of Rochester; Xerox.

Works exhibited in:
Illustrators 26; '83 "Andy Award" Annual; '83 CLIO Awards Annual; Creativity 83 and 84 Annuals; DESI 6

and 7 Annuals; New York Art Directors 62nd Annual; PRINT DESIGN Annual '83 and '84. Also in ADS Magazine #7 ('83) and #9 ('84); Art Direction Magazine Feb. '84; Graphic Design USA Feb. '84; PRINT Magazine July/Aug. '83 and '84.

• Slide portfolio of samples for your file sent upon request.

• Complete portfolio by appointment.

© 1984 Bob Conge

ALEXANDER GRAHAM BELL 1847–1922

Laura Cornell

118 East 93rd Street
New York, New York 10128
(212) 534-0596

Clients have included:
TRW, Price Waterhouse, The
Franklin Library, The New York
Times, New York Magazine,
Sports Illustrated, Seventeen,
Self Magazine, Redbook, Savvy,
Cuisine, Burson Marsteller,
Encyclopaedia Britannica,
Scholastic, Houghton Mifflin,
Dodd Mead, D.C. Heath.

Art credits, clockwise from top
left:

Windemere Press
Parents Magazine
Sports Illustrated

Member Graphic Artists Guild

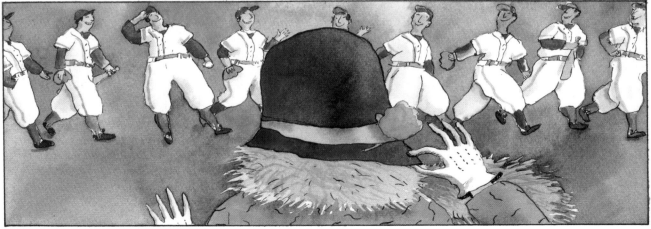

Dan Cosgrove

405 North Wabash
Chicago, Illinois 60611
(312) 527-0375

Illustration and Graphic Design

Clients Include: Busch Gardens, McDonald's, Shasta
Beverages, Seven-Up, Playboy, Time, S.C. Johnson,
Kellogg's, Sears, Anheuser-Busch, G.D. Searle,
United Airlines, Northern Telecom, Heileman Brewing
Company, Kraft Inc., Adolph Coors Company, and
Star-Kist Foods.

Member Graphic Artists Guild.

·COSGROVE·

John Craig

Route 2 Box 81
Soldiers Grove,
Wisconsin 54655.
(608) 872-2371

Telecopier Available.

Represented by: Carolyn Potts &
Associates
(312) 935-1701 or 664-9336

Collage

Clients include: *Advertising
Age;* Album Graphics Inc.;
American Way; A + ; Anheuser-
Busch; Chicago Ad Club;
Cracker Jack; *Cuisine;*
Encyclopedia Britannica;
Entrée; Films Inc.; Flavor House;
Follett Books; *Games;* Head &
Shoulders; *Horizon;* Mercury-
Phillips Records; *Moviegoer;*
*Minnesota Monthly; Northwest
Orient; Oui; PC World;*
Philadelphia; Playboy; Ruby
Street Cards; Scott, Foresman &
Co.; *Sesame Street;* Sieber
McIntyre; *Success;* 7-UP;
Sunshine; 13-30 Corporation;
TWA Ambassador; Warner Bros.
Records; Webb Co.; Williams
Pinball; World Book.

Member Graphic Artists Guild.

For additional samples in different
techniques, see American
Showcase #7, pgs. 94, 95.

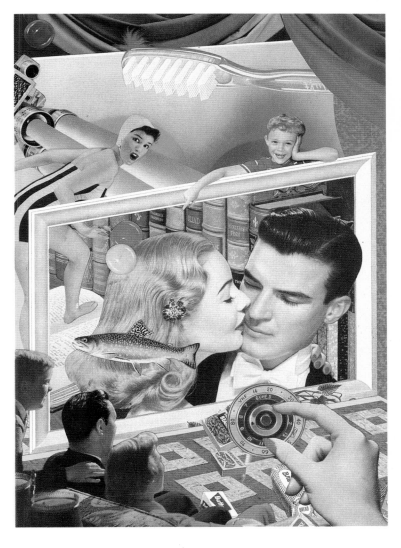

D.L. Cramer

Medical/Biological Illustration
10 Beechwood Drive
Wayne, New Jersey 07470
(201) 628-8793

MA, Johns Hopkins University
Ph.D., University of Chicago

Illustrations for: *Time, Sports Illustrated, Natural History, Runner, Science Digest, Med. Publishing,* Yearbook Medical Publishing Co., McGraw-Hill, S. Karger, Grolier, Wm. Douglas McAdams, CIBA, Hoffman-LaRoche, Searle & Co., Winthrop Labs, Pfizer, Health Learning Systems.

Teaching: Currently Director of the Human Gross Anatomy Labs at NYU School of Medicine.

Exhibitions: AIGA Show, Society of Illustrators Invitational, GAG Show.

Affiliations: American Association for the
Advancement of Science, New York
Academy of Sciences
Society of Illustrators, New York
Graphic Artists Guild

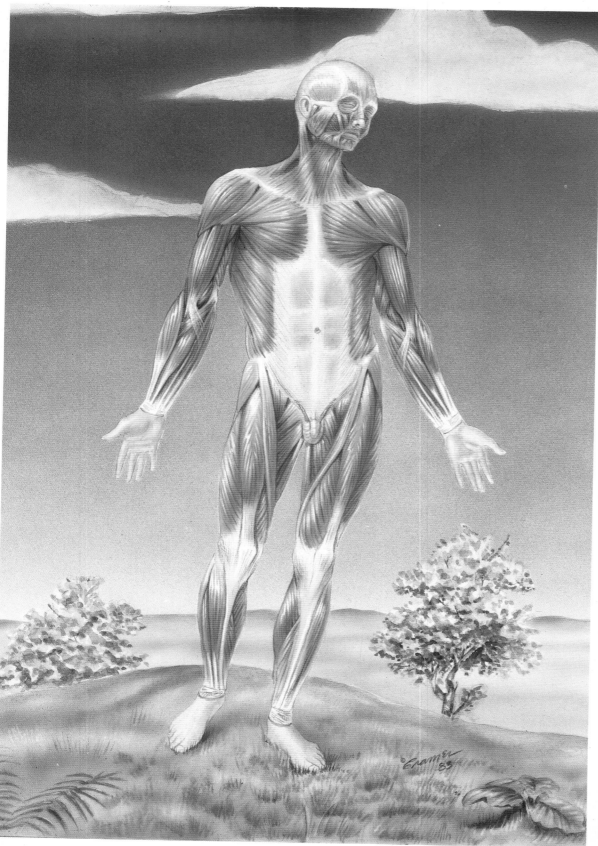

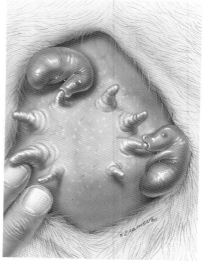

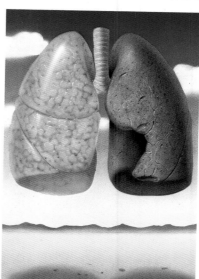

Robert Crawford

340 East 93rd Street, 9-I
New York, New York 10128
(212) 722-4964

Represented by Janice Crawford

Acrylic paintings

Clients:

AT&T
American Express
Avon Books
N.W. Ayer
Bantam Books
Boy Scouts of America
Business Week
Ciba-Geigy
Clorox
Fearon O'Leary
Gips & Balkind
Jamaica Tourist Board
Lowe's Hotels
NBC
National Lampoon
New American Library
Newsweek
New York Magazine
Northwestern Mutual Life
Pantheon Books
Paramount Pictures
Playboy
Polydor Records
Postgraduate Medicine
Psychology Today
Random House
Reader's Digest
Redbook
Rolling Stone
Sawdon & Bess
Triangle Publications
U.S. Army
Viking Penguin
Wellington & Messina
Wunderman, Ricotta & Kline
Xerox
Young & Rubicam

Bob Crofut

225 Peaceable Street
Ridgefield, Connecticut 06877
(203) 431-4304

Clients have included:
NBC; Outdoor Life; The Franklin Library; Seventeen;
Field & Stream; Guideposts; American Heritage;
Science 83; MGM; Avon Books; Signet; Prentice-Hall;
The Easton Press; Ballantine; Pocketbooks; Bristol
Babcock; Exxon Corporation; Reader's Digest; IBM;
Geer, DuBois; Minwax.

"Art flourishes where there is a sense of adventure."

—Alfred North Whitehead

Bob Crofut

225 Peaceable Street
Ridgefield, Connecticut 06877
(203) 431-4304

Books:
Society of Illustrators Annuals 21, 22, 23, 25 and 26
Art Directors Index Volume 10
American Showcase Volume 7, 8
A treasury of Outdoor Life
100 Years of American Illustration

Collections:
New Britain Museum of American Art
Permanent Museum of American Illustration—Society
of Illustrators.

Awards: Thirteen from The Society of Illustrators

Member:
American Portrait Society
Society of Illustrators

continued from page 128

**The Public Relations Society
of America, Inc.**
845 Third Ave.
New York, NY 10022
(212) 826-1750

American Council for the Arts
570 Seventh Ave.
New York, NY 10018
(212) 354-6655

The American Institute of Graphic Arts
1059 Third Ave.
New York, NY 10021
(212) 752-0813

American Society of Interior Designers
National Headquarters
1430 Broadway
New York, NY 10018
(212) 944-9220

New York Chapter
950 Third Ave.
New York, NY 10022
(212) 421-8765

**American Society of Magazine
Photographers**
205 Lexington Ave.
New York, NY 10016
(212) 889-9144

Art Directors Club of New York
488 Madison Ave.
New York, NY 10022
(212) 838-8140

Association of American Publishers, Inc.
1 Park Ave.
New York, NY 10016
(212) 689-8920

Center for Arts Information
625 Broadway
New York, NY 10012
(212) 677-7548

The Children's Book Council, Inc.
67 Irving Place
New York, NY 10003
(212) 254-2666

CLIO
336 E. 59th St.
New York, NY 10022
(212) 593-1900

Foundation for the Community of Artists
280 Broadway, Ste. 412
New York, NY 10007
(212) 227-3770

Graphic Artists Guild
30 E. 20th St., Rm 405
New York, NY 10003
(212) 777-7353

Guild of Book Workers
663 Fifth Ave.
New York, NY 10022
(212) 757-6454

Institute of Outdoor Advertising
342 Madison Ave.
New York, NY 10017
(212) 986-5920

**International Advertising
Association, Inc.**
475 Fifth Ave.
New York, NY 10017
(212) 684-1583

The One Club
251 E. 50th St.
New York, NY 10022
(212) 935-0121

**Printing Industries of Metropolitan
New York, Inc.**
5 Penn Plaza
New York, NY 10001
(212) 279-2100

Society of Illustrators
128 E. 63rd St.
New York, NY 10021
(212) 838-2560

**Society of Photographers and
Artists Representatives**
1123 Broadway
New York, NY 10010
(212) 924-6023

Society of Publication Designers
25 W. 43rd St., Ste. 711
New York, NY
(212) 354-8585

Television Bureau of Advertising
485 Lexington Ave.
New York, NY 10017
(212) 661-8440

Type Directors Club of New York
545 W. 45th St.
New York, NY 10036
(212) 245-6300

U.S. Trademark Association
6 E. 45th St.
New York, NY 10017
(212) 986-5880

Volunteer Lawyers for the Arts
1560 Broadway, Ste. 711
New York, NY 10036
(212) 575-1150

Women in the Arts
325 Spring St.
New York, NY 10013
(212) 691-0988

Women in Design
P.O. Box 5315
FDR Station
New York, NY 10022

Ohio:

Advertising Club of Cincinnati
385 West Main St.
Batavia, OH 45103
(513) 732-9422

**Cleveland Society of
Communicating Arts**
812 Huron Rd.
Cleveland, OH 44115
(216) 621-5139

**Columbus Society of
Communicating Arts**
c/o Salvato & Coe
2015 West Fifth Ave.
Columbus, OH 43221
(614) 488-3131

Design Collective
D.F. Cooke
55 West Long St.
Columbus, OH 43215
(614) 464-2883

Society of Communicating Arts
c/o Tailford Assoc.
1300 Indian Wood Circle
Maumee, OH 43537
(419) 891-0888

Pennsylvania:

Art Directors Club of Philadelphia
2017 Walnut St.
Philadelphia, PA 19103
(215) 569-3650

Tennessee:

**Engraved Stationery Manufacturers
Association**
c/o Printing Industries Association of the South
1000 17th Ave. South
Nashville, TN 37212
(615) 327-4444

Texas:

Advertising Artists of Fort Worth
3424 Falcon Dr.
Fort Worth, TX 76119

Art Directors Club of Houston
2135 Bissonet
Houston, TX 77005
(713) 523-1019

Dallas Society of Visual Communication
3530 High Mesa Dr.
Dallas, TX 75234
(214) 241-2017

Virginia:

Industrial Designers Society of America
6802 Poplar Pl., Ste. 303
McLean, VA 22101
(703) 556-0919

**Tidewater Society of
Communicating Arts**
P.O. Box 153
Norfolk, VA 23501

Washington:

Puget Sound Ad Federation
c/o Sylvia Fruichantie
Kraft Smith Advertising
200 1st West St.
Seattle, WA 98119
(206) 285-2222

Seattle Design Association
P.O. Box 1097
Main Office Station
Seattle, WA 98111
(206) 467-0518
(Formerly Seattle Women in Design)

Seattle Women in Advertising
219 First Avenue N., Ste. 300
Seattle, WA 98109
(206) 285-0919

Society of Professional Graphic Artists
c/o Steve Chin, Pres.
85 S. Washington Street, Ste. 204
Seattle, WA 98104

Wisconsin:

The Advertising Club
407 E. Michigan St.
Milwaukee, WI 53202
(414) 271-7351

Illustrators & Designers of Milwaukee
c/o Don Berg
207 E. Michigan
Milwaukee, WI 53202
(414) 276-7828

Tom Curry

Represented by:

Eileen Moss

333 East 49th Street
New York, New York 10017
(212) 980-8061

Partial Client list includes:
Apple Computer; American
Airlines; Steak & Ale
Restaurants; Exxon; Bozell &
Jacobs; Del Taco; Southwest
Airlines; Scali, McCabe &
Sloves; Dennard Creative;
Bloom Advertising; GSD & M
Advertising; Texas Monthly;
Newsweek; Chicago Magazine;
D Magazine; The Cleveland
Plain Dealer; The Dallas Times
Herald.

Dazzeland Studios

We create excitement!

Studio Hotline: (801) 355-8555

Los Angeles: Joanne Hedge (213) 874-1661

San Francisco: Mary VanDamme (415) 433-1292

Chicago: Joel Harlib (312) 329-1370

New York: Jerry Leff Associates, Inc. (212) 697-8525

Dallas: Liz McCann (214) 742-3138

Atlanta: The Williams Group (404) 873-2287

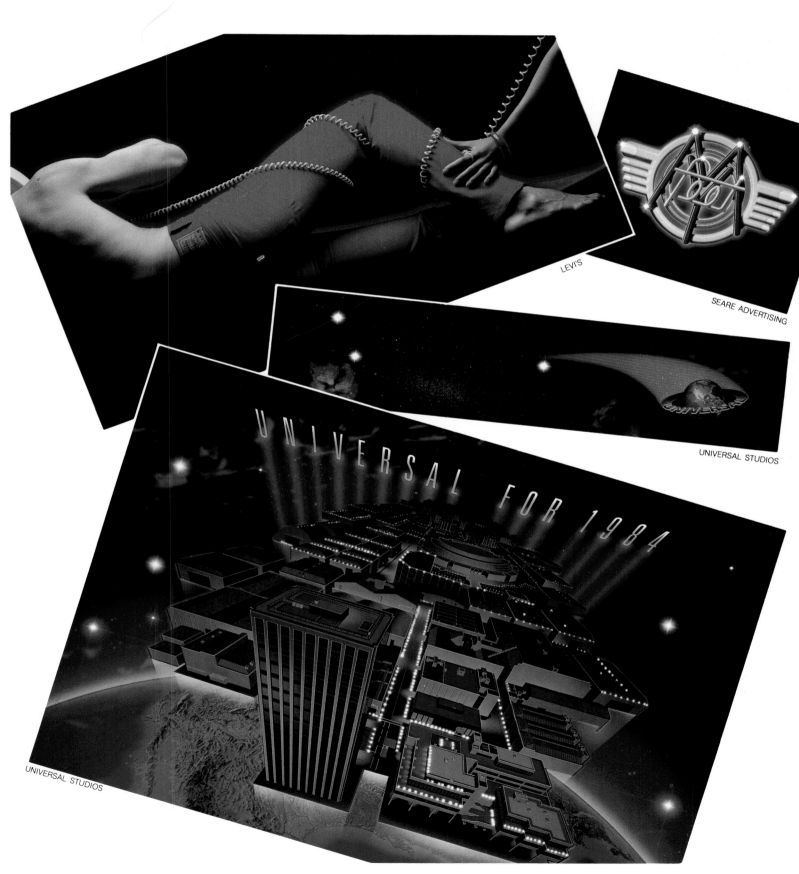

LEVI'S

SEARE ADVERTISING

UNIVERSAL STUDIOS

UNIVERSAL STUDIOS

Michael Dean

5512 Chaucer
Houston, Texas 77005
(713) 527-0295

Clients include: Shell, Exxon, Pennzoil, Pepsi, Pizza
Hut, Drilco, Texas Monthly, Houston City Magazine,
Outside Magazine, Astroworld, Waterworld,
Southwestern Bell, Houston Natural Gas, Goldlance,
First City Bank, U.S. Home, Gemcraft Homes,
Houston Gamblers, Republic Bank, ComputerCraft,
13-30 Corporation and Gulf Oil Corp.

Telecopier available.

Shell employees Claude Gray and Elmer Gaunt stand by their delivery truck in 1923. Solid rubber tires were still preferred.

Dennis Dittrich

42 West 72nd Street
New York, New York 10023
(212) 595-9773

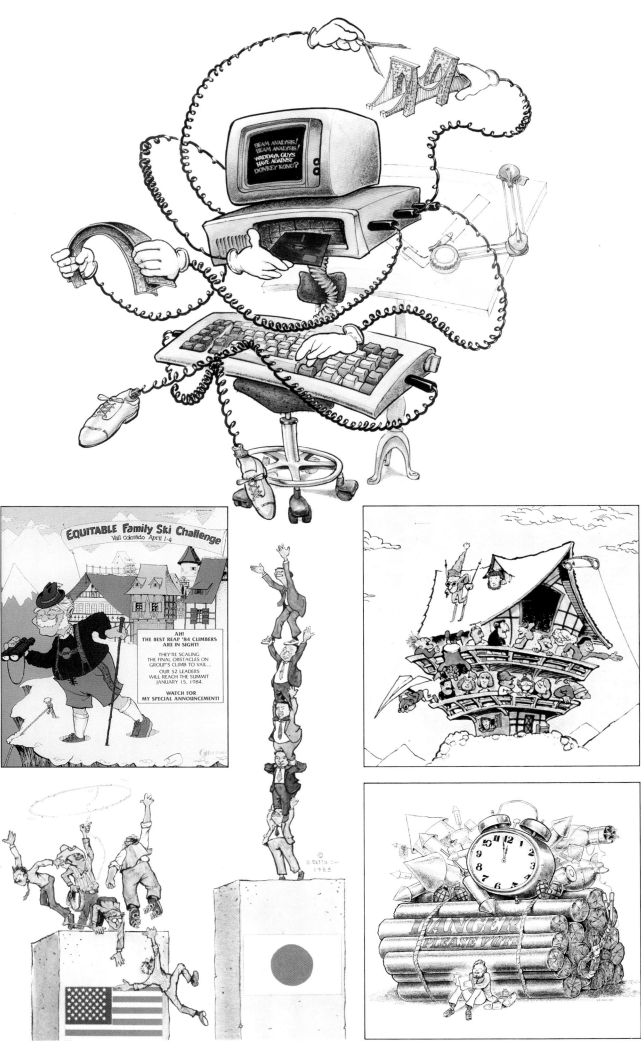

Glenn Dodds

392 Central Park West
New York, New York 10025
(212) 679-3630

Clients: Air Canada, NEC, Sony, New York Telephone, TIE Communications, Heinz, MCA, British Telecom International.

Agencies: Grey, McCaffrey and McCall, Warwick, McCann-Erickson, Waring & La Rosa, Rapp & Collins, Nadler & Larimer, William Esty, Dancer Fitzgerald Sample, Cavalieri & Kleier.

Magazines: Forbes, MD Magazine, Institutional Investor, American Heritage, Mechanics Illustrated.

Films/Animation: General Foods, Heinz.

Glenn Dodds

392 Central Park West
New York, New York 10025
(212) 679-3630

Clients: Air Canada, NEC, Sony, New York Telephone, TIE Communications, Heinz, MCA, British Telecom International.

Agencies: Grey, McCaffrey and McCall, Warwick, McCann-Erickson, Waring & La Rosa, Rapp & Collins, Nadler & Larimer, William Esty, Dancer Fitzgerald Sample, Cavalieri & Kleier.

Magazines: Forbes, MD Magazine, Institutional Investor, American Heritage, Mechanics Illustrated.

Films/Animation: General Foods, Heinz.

Doret/Smith Studios

12 East 14th Street
New York, New York 10003
(212) 929-1688

Michael Doret

Precision Illustration, Lettering and Design.

Represented in the Southwest by:
Liz McCann
(214) 742-3138

Represented in Europe by:
Margarethe Hubauer
49 40/486 003

Clockwise from top left:
Cover for TIME Magazine.
Logo for ice cream recipe contest.
Color-coded batteries designed
    for British Eveready Co.
Three lottery tickets designed for
    the Massachusetts State Lottery.
Lettering/illustration used as cover
    for trade magazine.

Member Graphic Artists' Guild

Doret/Smith Studios

12 East 14th Street
New York, New York 10003
(212) 206-9162

Laura Smith

Graphic Illustration

Clockwise from top left:
Double page spread for Ziff-Davis Publications
 comparing big cities.
Full page illustration for trade publication
 on "The Incentive Cruise."

Cover for Meetings & Conventions magazine.
Poster for the '84 Summer Games.
 See Showcase #7 for companion poster.*
Cover for Texas Monthly magazine.
Collaboration with Michael Doret on
 truck billboard advertising chili.

Member Graphic Artists' Guild.

* Available from ProCreations Publishing Co. 1-800-245-8779.

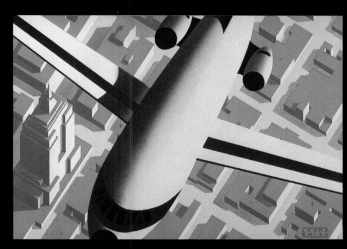

153

Lawrence W. Duke

Star Route Box 93
Woodside, California 94062
(415) 851-2705

Studio:
1258 Folsom Street
San Francisco, California 94103
(415) 861-0941

San Francisco representative:
Diane Sullivan
(415) 563-8884

Chicago representative:
Joel Harlib
(312) 329-1370

Seattle representative:
Pat Hackett
(206) 623-9459

"Trouble on the Trail"
was done for a Remington
Lock-Back knife poster.

David Fe Bland

670 West End Avenue
New York, New York 10025
(212) 580-9299

Clients include: J. Walter Thompson; Young & Rubicam; Ogilvy & Mather; Scali, McCabe, Sloves; Ted Bates; Grey; Dancer Fitzgerald Sample; N.W. Ayer; Benton & Bowles; Cato Johnson; Muir Cornelius Moore; Leber Katz; Nadler & Larimer; NBC; CBS; HBO; Exxon; Texaco; RCA; American Express; Burger King; Avis; TWA; New York Air; People Express; E.F. Hutton; Celanese; Avon Products; Lever Bros.; Bankers Trust; Macy's; Radio City Music Hall; McGraw-Hill; Houghton Mifflin; Pocket Books; Viking Press; Ziff-Davis; Macmillan Press; Harcourt Brace Jovanovich; Whitney Publications; Silver Burdett; McLean-Hunter; Business Week; New York Times; Readers Digest; McCalls; Condé-Nast; Harpers; Ladies' Home Journal; Europeo; Saturday Review; Institutional Investor; Scholastic Publications; and Children's Television Workshop.

Awards & Exhibitions:

Print Magazine 1984 Summer Annual
Art Direction Creativity 1984
Art Directors Annual, 1983
Feature Profile in Advertising Techniques, Summer 1981

Member Graphics Artist Guild

©David FeBland 1984

Who's who is going to Europe on the SS Norway.

Neil Feigeles

920 East 17th Street
Brooklyn, New York 11230
(718) 377-4418

A Partial List of Clients Include:
ABC Television
Ariel Press
Atheneum Publishers
High Society Magazine
Silhouette Romances
St. Martin's Press

Presented in:
ILLUSTRATORS 24
RSVP 8

Member Graphic Artists Guild

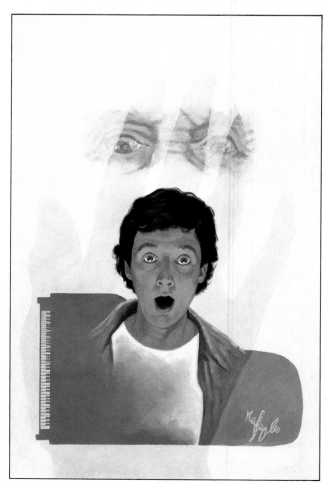

Jeff Feinen

Represented by:
Andy Badin and Associates
835 3rd Avenue   4th Floor
New York, New York 10022
(212) 986-8833

Clients include: Grey Advertising, Snow's Chowders,
Holly Farms, Wyler Foods, Robert Towers Advertising,
U.S. Open, Margeotes/Fertitta & Weiss, Godiva
Chocolates, Estée Lauder, Food & Wine Magazine,
Wyse Advertising, Smuckers, Ogilvy & Mather,
Chemlawn, Fisher-Price Toys, Goldome Savings Bank.
Member Graphic Artists Guild

Stanislaw Fernandes

Art & Design

(212) 533-2648

Sandra Filippucci

270 Park Avenue South
New York, New York 10010
(212) 477-8732

CLIENTS: High Tech Marketing
Magazine, Sports Illustrated,
Time Magazine, Oui Magazine,
Ciba-Geigy, Sports Medicine
Magazine, Dunn & Bradstreet
Magazine, Post-Graduate
Medicine Magazine, Video
Magazine, International
Robotics, New York Times,
Consumer Electronics, Satellite
Marketing Magazine, etc.

PUBLICATIONS: Society of
Illustrators Annual, Print's
Regional Annual, Graphis
Annual, Art Direction.

Judy Francis

110 West 96th Street
New York, New York 10025
(212) 866-7204

Illustration for fashion, beauty, merchandise and
"how-to"; printed matter and animatics.

Clients include: Good Housekeeping, Grey
Advertising, Newton Manufacturing Corp., DuPont,
Reborn Maternity, MacNamara Clapp & Klein, Ogilvy &
Mather, Ballantine Books, Beaumont-Bennett.

Winner 1984 DESI Award
Member Graphic Artists Guild
Member Society of Illustrators

Michael Garland

78 Columbia Avenue
Hartsdale, New York 10530
(914) 946-4536

Clients include:
J. Walter Thompson
AT&T
Hartford Insurance
IBM
General Electric
The United States Marines
Forbes Magazine
Ladies' Home Journal
Estée Lauder
Macmillan Press
Ziff-Davis
Muir Cornelius Moore
Frequent Flyer
Cosmopolitan
Parents Magazine
Putnam Publishing Group
Games Magazine
Avon
McGraw-Hill
Industry Week
Runner's World Magazine
Ashe LeDonne
Crown Publishers
Scribner/Atheneum Publishers
Fawcett Publications
Bantam Books
Ballantine Books
Random House
ABC
N.W. Ayer
NBC
Emergency Medicine Magazine
Woman's Day

Work exhibited in
Illustrators 23, 24, 25, 26
Communication Design Show
1983
The Original Art Show 1981,
1983

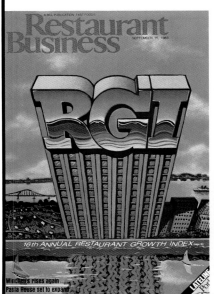

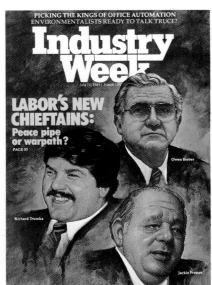

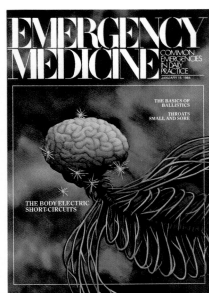

G. Allen Garns

3314 East El Moro
Mesa, Arizona 85204
(602) 830-7224

Clients: Universal Pictures, CBS Records,
Warner Records, Post/Newsweek Productions,
Continental Airlines, Diamonds Department Store,
Seventeen Magazine.

Awards Include: New York Art Directors Club,
Creativity 12, Society of Illustrators of L.A., Phoenix Art
Directors Club.

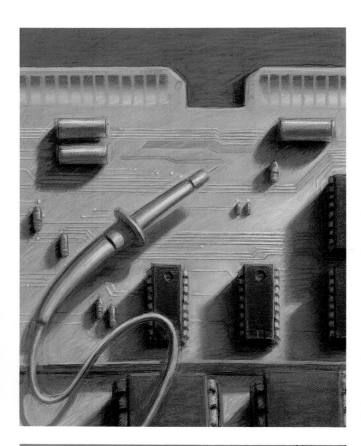

Robert Giusti

350 East 52nd Street
New York, New York 10022
(212) 752-0179
(203) 354-6539

Represented by:
Milton Newborn
135 East 54th Street
New York, New York 10022
(212) 421-0050

W.B. GRACE & CO.

CBS RECORDS

BARCLAY'S BANK

SCHOOL OF VISUAL ARTS

CBS RECORDS

GREY ADVERTISING

Randy Jay Glasbergen

34 South Main
Earlville, New York 13332
(315) 691-2424

Telecopier in studio.

Clients include: American Airlines, Ford Motors,
Hallmark Cards, Mead Johnson Pharmaceuticals,
New Woman, Reader's Digest, Wall St. Journal,
Cosmopolitan, Furniture Concepts International,
Ziff-Davis, Medical Economics, Changing Times.

Carter Goodrich

708 Broadway, 10th floor
New York, New York 10003
(212) 477-3015
(718) 499-8957

Mariah Graham Studio

670 West End Avenue
New York, New York 10025
(212) 580-8061

Fashion Illustrator

Clients have included: The New York Times; New York
Daily News; Vogue Magazine; London Times;
Women's Wear Daily; W's Magazine; Estée Lauder;
Elizabeth Arden; Revlon, Inc.; BBD&O Advertising
Agency; Doyle Dane Bernbach Inc.; Cosmopolitan
Magazine (New York and London); Avon Products, Inc.;
Budweiser; Cotton Inc.; Harpers Queen (London); and
Guy Leroche (Paris); Geers Gross Advertising, Inc.

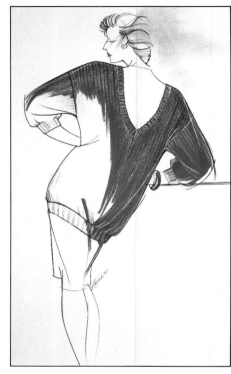

Susan Gray

2 West 12th Street
New York, New York 10011
(212) 787-5400/(212) 675-2243

Clients include:
McCann Erickson; Young & Rubicam;
J. Walter Thompson; D'Arcy, McManus, Masius;
Grey Advertising; Milton Glaser, Inc.; American Cancer
Society; Elizabeth Arden; Avon; Simon and Schuster;
Doubleday; Harcourt, Brace, Jovanovich; Barron's
Educational Series; Forbes; Fortune; Business Week;
Redbook; Ms.; Ladies Home Journal.

Member Graphic Artists Guild, Member Joint
Ethics Committee/Susan Gray ©1984

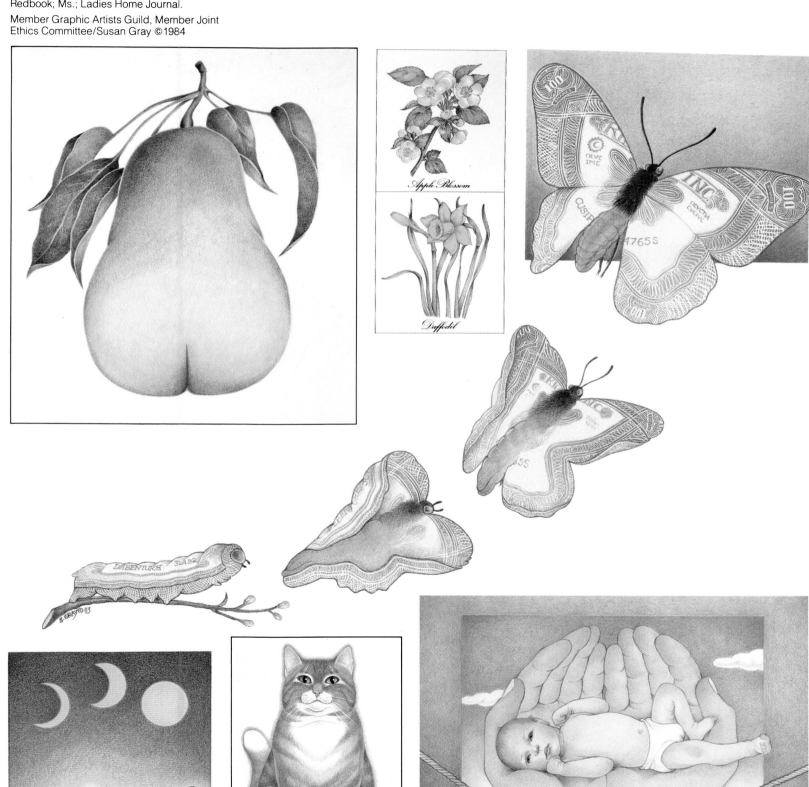

Apple Blossom

Daffodil

Don Grimes Design, Inc.

3514 Oak Grove
Dallas, Texas 75204
(214) 526-0040

When carefully conceived, properly designed and skillfully executed, a word can be worth a thousand pictures.

Here are a few choice words from the vocabulary of Don Grimes.

Deborah Ann Hall

105-28 65th Avenue
Studio 6B
Forest Hills, New York 11375
(212) 896-3152

American Broadcasting Company; National
Broadcasting Company; Home Box Office; TV Guide;
MGM/UA; Grey Advertising, Inc.; McCaffrey and
McCall, Inc.; Serino, Coyne & Nappi; Pearlman/
Rowe/Kolomatsky; Van Brunt Co.; Polydor Records;
WNEW-TV; Circle In The Square Theatre

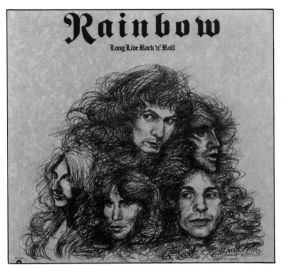

Joan Hall

155 Bank Street
Studio H954
New York, New York 10014
(212) 243-6059

Paris Representative:
Evelyne Menascé
(011) 227-2482

Two and Three Dimensional Collage Illustration

Clients include: IBM, Remy Martin, Estée Lauder, Warner Bros., International Paper Company, WPLJ, Hoechst Fibers Industries, RCA, The New York Times, Omni, Time, L'Express, Vogue, Gourmet, Popular Computing, Video Pro, New York, Seventeen, Redbook, McCalls, T.V. Guide, Psychology Today, Emergency Medicine, Book-of-the-Month Club, Warner Books, Avon Books, Random House, Simon & Schuster, Dell Publications.

Works Exhibited in: Print Magazine, Art Direction, The Society of Illustrators, The New York Art Directors Club, The Society of Publication Designers, The A.I.G.A., Graphis.

Instructor of "Collage & Assemblage" The School of Visual Arts, New York

Member Graphic Artists Guild.

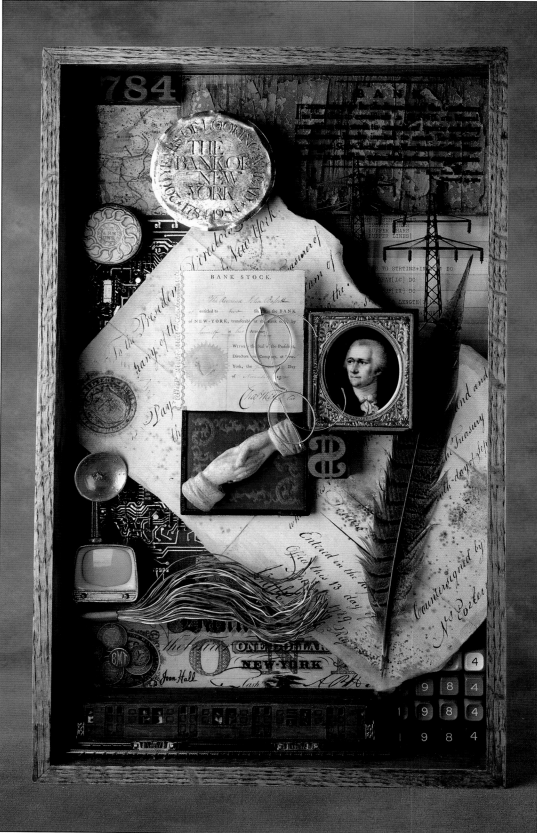

THE BANK OF NEW YORK: BICENTENNIAL

EMI/ODEON

ATLANTIC RECORDS

SELF PROMOTION

Gary Hallgren

6 West 37th Street
Fifth floor
New York, New York 10018
(212) 947-1054

COMIC ART ILLUSTRATION

Clients include: Popular Computing,* Forbes,* The
New York Times,* Ammirati & Puris, Time, National
Lampoon, New York Life, Family Weekly, DC Comics,
King Features, GQ, People, Bell Laboratories, Cuisine,
Mediamark, Geo, Rockshots.

*shown here

John Hamagami

7822 Croydon Avenue
Los Angeles, California 90045
(213) 641-1522

Representatives:

Los Angeles: Martha Productions (213) 204-1771

New York: American Artists (212) 682-2462

Chicago: Moshier & Maloney (312) 943-1668

San Francisco: Ron Sweet (415) 433-1222

Member Graphic Artists Guild

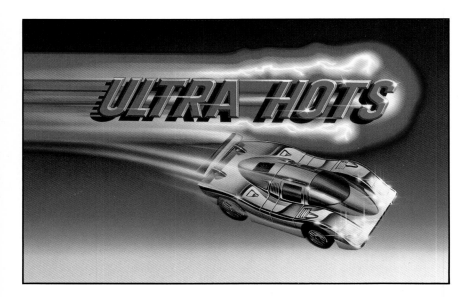

Joe and Kathy Heiner

850 North Grove Drive
Alpine, Utah 84003
(801) 756-6444

Representatives:
Vicki Morgan (New York—East Coast)
(212) 475-0440

Mary Vandamme (San Francisco)
(415) 433-1292

Ellen Knable (Los Angeles)
(213) 855-8855

All Other Areas Call Direct   Telecopier in Studio

Camera/Airbrush Combination
Versatility Unique to the style.

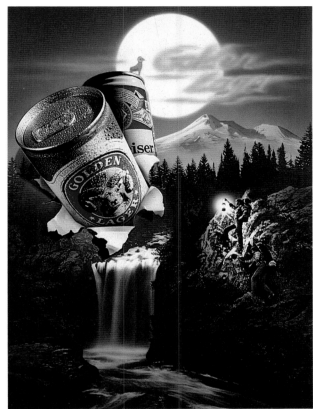

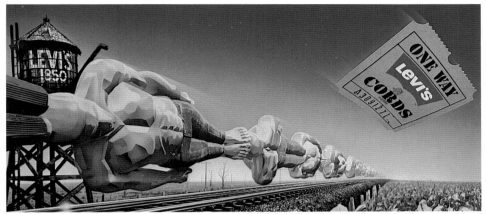

Karen Heller

300 West 108th Street
New York, New York 10025
(212) 866-5879

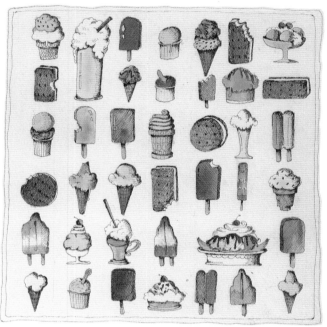

David Herbick
5 Montague Terrace
Brooklyn, New York 11201
(718) 852-6450

Lettering and design

Al Hering

Represented by:
Shelly Kopel & Associates
342 Madison Avenue
New York, New York 10017
(212) 986-3282

Partial list of Clients: IBM, GTE, Pepperidge Farms, Polaroid, Sunshine Cookies, Sony, Rye Town Hilton, Dannon, and Restaurant Associates.

Black and white portfolio available upon request.

Richard High Design

4500 Montrose Suite D
Houston, Texas 77006
(713) 521-2772

Richard High Design specializes in art direction, design and production of all graphic media involving custom letterforms and logotypes.

Our clients have included: Compaq Computers, Continental Airlines, Commercial Energy Systems, Dupont, Infocom Software, Jamail Limousines, River Oaks Bank, Russo Properties, Shell Oil Co, Simon & Schuster, Six Flags, Summit Software, USAA, Westbury Hospital and Ziff-Davis.

Our mini-portfolio of samples or slides are available upon request or refer to American Showcase 6 and 7. Call Richard High Design for unique approaches to advertising, design, packaging, and corporate identity.

Fred Hilliard

5425 Crystal Springs N.E.
Bainbridge Island, Washington 98110

Represented by:
Sam Brody
230 East 44th Street
Suite 2F
New York City 10017
(212) 758-0640

Upper left: "Soapy Smith" Seattle Repertory Theatre
Upper right: "Savages" Seattle Repertory Theatre
Lower left: Ally & Gargano
Lower right: "Cat Book"

Clients include: Ally & Gargano; D'Arcy-MacManus & Masius; The Richards Group; Wunderman, Ricotta & Kline; Ketchum Communications; Cole & Weber; Jones, Medinger, & Kindschi; John Deere Publications; D Magazine; Needham, Harper & Steers; Parents Magazine; SpringHouse Corp.; John Brown & Partners; Evans-Kraft; McCann-Erickson; Ehrig & Associates; Peat, Marwick, Mitchell & Co.; Faller, Klenk & Quinlan; Florida Trend Magazine; and Cosmos., Inc.

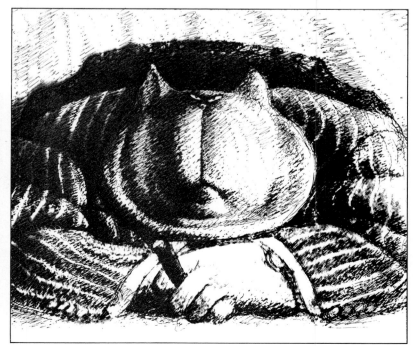

Christopher Hopkins

228 Main Street, Suite R
Venice, California 90921
(213) 392-9695

Represented by:
New York—American Artists
(212) 682-2462
Chicago—Joni Tuke
(312) 787-6826
San Francisco—
Cynde Broadhurst
(415) 382-1301

Kevin Hulsey

14755 Magnolia Boulevard
Sherman Oaks, California 91403
(818) 501-7105

Technical, Photo-real & Fashion illustration

Telecopier in studio

Los Angeles: Nancy Heimberg	(213) 933-8660
San Francisco: Vikki Hart	(415) 495-HART
Chicago: Gerald Siegal & Assoc.	(312) 661-1818
Atlanta: Wooden Reps.	(404) 892-6303

Image Electronic, Inc.

2030 Powers Ferry Road
Suite 226
Atlanta, Georgia 30339
(404) 951-9580

Represented by:

Wooden Reps
(404) 892-6303

i.e. computer-aided
design/illustration
a/v • print • video

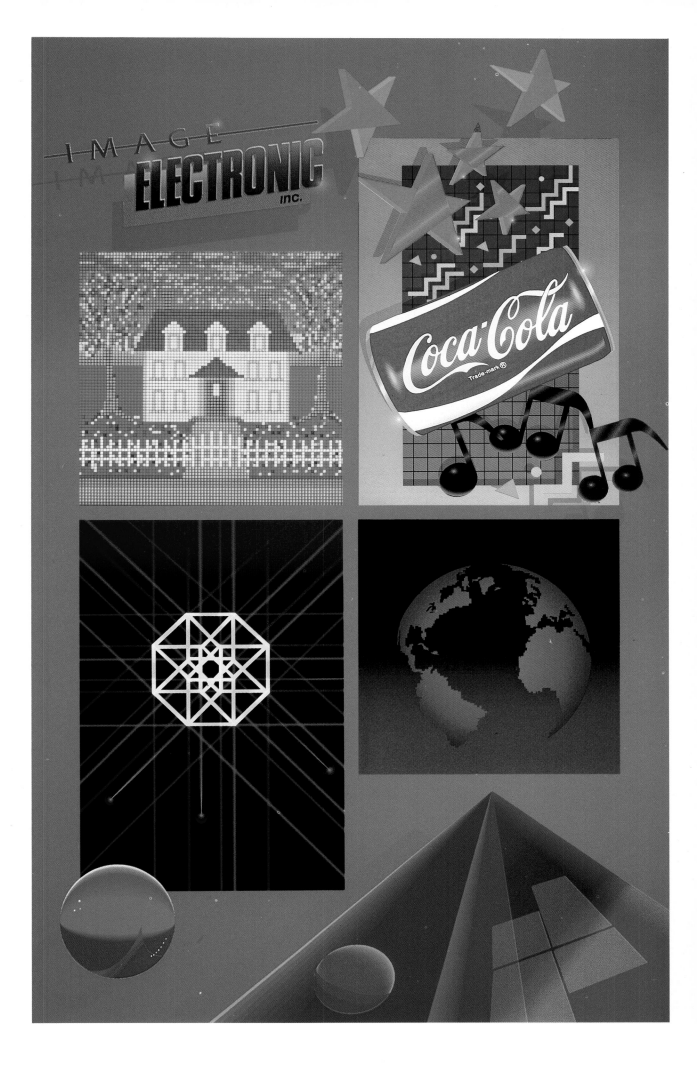

Izume Inoue

311 East 12th Street
New York, New York 10003
(212) 473-1614

Member Graphic Artists Guild

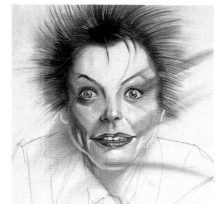

Trevor Irvin
330 Southerland Terrace
Atlanta, Georgia 30307
(404) 377-4754

Represented by:
Gail Centini
333 Adams Street
Decatur, Georgia 30030
(404) 377-8383

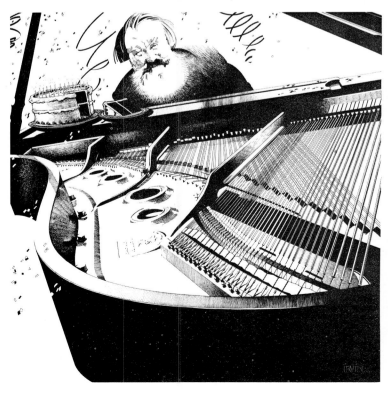

J·H Illustration

3832 Langley Road
Charlotte, North Carolina 28215
(704) 568-8137

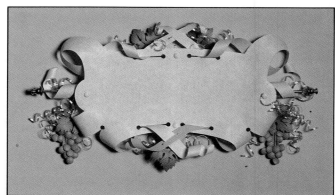

Seth Jaben

New York City
(212) 260-7859

Clients include:

Time Inc.
IBM
New York Times
Peat-Marwick Inc.
McGraw-Hill
Muir Cornelius Moore
Psychology Today
Scholastic Publishers
Dish Is It Tile
Adweek
Rodale Press
New York Magazine
Webb Company
Penthouse
Playboy
Science Digest
E.G. Smith
13-30 Corporation

Doug Jamieson

42-20 69th Street
Woodside, New York 11377
(718) 565-6034

Clients include: *The New York Times, Psychology Today, Fortune, Business Week, Seventeen, Science Digest, Family Circle, Travel & Leisure, Co-Ed, Family Health, Institutional Investors, Financial World, The Daily News, Village Voice.*

Accounts include: Warner Communications; Atheneum; Bantam; Simon & Schuster; Ziff-Davis; Scholastic; MacMillan; Doubleday; Harper & Row; McGraw-Hill; Western Publishing; C.T.W.; Young & Rubicam; Benton & Bowles; Chalik & Dryer; Daniel & Charles; Homer & Durham; Lord, Geller, Fererico, Einstein, Inc.

Jay

15119 Woodlawn Avenue
Dolton, Illinois 60419
(312) 849-5676

Represented by:
Chicago: Sell Inc. (312) 565-2701
Dallas: Barbara Boster (214) 373-4284
Member: Artist Guild of Chicago

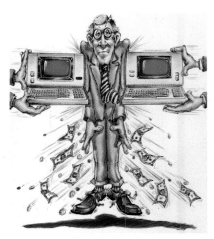

VISUAL

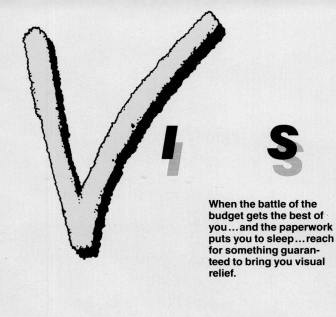

When the battle of the budget gets the best of you…and the paperwork puts you to sleep…reach for something guaranteed to bring you visual relief.

▶ Reach for *Fame 2* by Brad Benedict. With an introduction by Bette Midler and close to 400 wildly imaginative, full-color celebrity portraits, it's a delightful romp through the glittering arena of fame—as seen through the eyes of almost 100 of the world's most successful artists.

▶ Or take a trip beyond hip in *Megastar,* a giant, 11″ × 14″, full-color paperback. Featuring 70 fabulous superstar portraits by *Interview* cover artist Richard Bernstein. And an introduction by Paloma Picasso. Plus a wicked text by fashion columnist André Leon Talley.

Brought to you from the publishers of *American Showcase.*

Your eyes will love you for it!

RELIEF

Kathy Jeffers

106 East 19th Street, 12th Floor
New York, New York 10003
(212) 475-1756

3-dimensional illustration, models, props, and prototypes.

Clients include:
Doyle Dane Bernbach
J. Walter Thompson
IBM
Elizabeth Arden
Avon Products
Fortune Magazine

Esquire Magazine
Ziff-Davis
Medical Economics Co.

Photo credits (clockwise from top left):

Todd Watts
Eric Streiff
Irv Bahrt
Walter Wick
Rick Barrick
Walter Wick

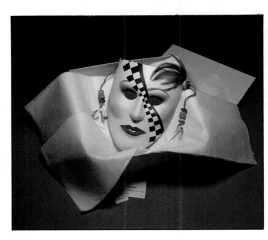

B. E. Johnson

366 Oxford Street
Rochester, New York 14607
(716) 461-4240

Los Angeles:
Robert Jones
10889 Wilshire Boulevard
Los Angeles, California 90024
(213) 208-5093

Technical and Astronomical Art, Optical and
Mechanical Effects, Industrial Design.

© 1984 B.E. Johnson

"It is a fine thread that contains the volatile balance
between accuracy, clarity and creativity. The art of a
fine illustrator, is his ability to strain these connections
without breaking the thread."

Member: Graphic Artists Guild, Society of Illustrators

Images from top:

CBS Sports
AD Marie-Christine Lawrence

Private Collection

IBM Corporation
Jones Medinger Kindschi
AD Wynn Medinger

Ztel Communications Network
Blouin & Co. AD Peter Perry

Spread: Moog, Inc.
AD B.E. Johnson

Technology
and the Art to understand it,

Nature
and the Art to appreciate it,

The Unknown
and the Art to experience it.

Concept One
Gizmo

DESIGNERS
ILLUSTRATORS
CONSTRUCTORS

Doug Johnson

45 East 19 Street
New York, New York 10003
(212) 260-1880

Member Graphic Artists Guild

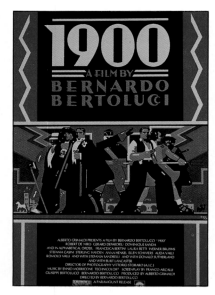

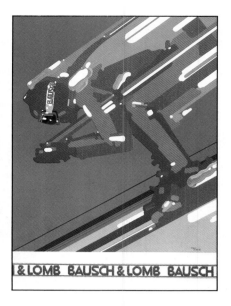

Kristin Johnson

902 Broadway
New York, New York 10010
(212) 477-4033

Member Graphic Artists Guild

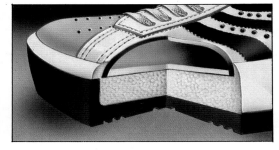

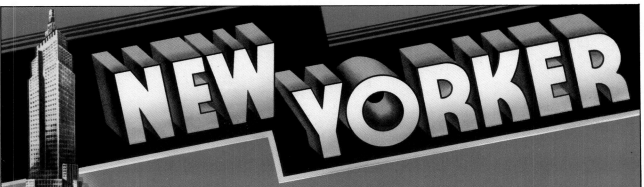

Rick Johnson

Represented by:
Moshier & Maloney
535 North Michigan Avenue
Suite 1416
Chicago, Illinois 60611
(312) 943-1668

Partial Client List:
AT&T
Arthur Andersen & Co.
Allied Van Lines
American Broadcasting Co.
Panasonic
Bell & Howell
US Gypsum Company
United Airlines
G.D. Searle
Abbott Labs
Solo Cup

ARTHUR ANDERSEN & CO.

ARTHUR ANDERSEN & CO.

ARTHUR ANDERSEN & CO.

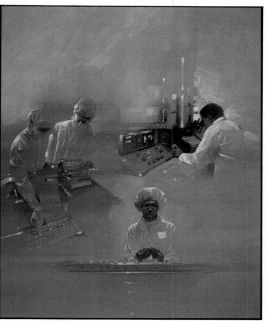

ARTHUR ANDERSEN & CO.

Les Katz

New York City
(718) 284-4779

To our out-of-town clients, please note our new area code.

Represented by: Sharon Drexler

Like a well-designed product, where the form becomes beautiful because the function is so well served, an illustration can completely satisfy the client's selling requirements and still be exciting and creative.

1. PCJr. Magazine
2. Trout & Ries Advertising
3. Engineering News Record Magazine
4. Adolph Coors Company
5. Marsteller Advertising
6. Foote Cone & Belding Advertising
7. Good Housekeeping Magazine

Gregg
Bernard
Keeling

659 Boulevard Way
Oakland, California 94610
(415) 444-8688

Represented on the
West Coast by:
Ron Sweet
(415) 433-1222
and in the Midwest by:
Joel Harlib
(312) 329-1370

Specializing in food and still-life
for packaging and advertising.
Working mainly in oil on canvas
I've painted pictures for Italian
Swiss Colony wine, Chiffon
margarine, Dole (Fruit'n Juice
Bars), Twentieth Century Fox
(video game promotion), Atari
(video game package), P.E.
O'Hair (bath fixtures), Del
Monte Foods

Other clients include:
Gemco, IBM, The Franklin
Money Fund, The Bank of
California, Broderbund

DESIGN BY SIDJAKOV BERMAN & GOMEZ/©1983 WELCH FOOD FOODS, INC.

Karen Kluglein

Watercolor Paintings

Represented by:

Judy Mattelson

88 Lexington Avenue 12G
New York, New York 10016
(212) 684-2974

Member Graphic Artists Guild

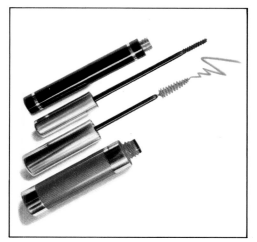

Terry Kovalcik

15½ Van Houten Street, Apt. 307
Paterson, New Jersey 07501
(212) 620-7772 (work)/(201) 345-2155

Clients include: Scholastic Magazines, McGraw-Hill,
Harcourt Brace Jovanovich, Reader's Digest,
Parents Magazine, Graduating Engineer, Consumer
Electronics, Video Business, Audio Times, Institutional
Investors, Medical Economics, Electronic Learning,
The New York Times, New Jersey First National Bank,
Howard Savings, WNEW-FM, Vernon Valley Great
Gorge Ski Corp., Aspen Ski Corp., Chas. P. Young,
Fine Art Studio, Iberia Airlines, Well-Bred Loaf, Inc.,
USAIR.

Member Graphic Artists Guild.

©1984 Terry Kovalcik

Shannon Kriegshauser

Represented by:
Ceci Bartels & Associates
111 Jefferson Road
St. Louis, Missouri 63119
(314) 961-1670

Studio: (309) 565-7110

Telecopier: (314) 781-4350

Ketti Kupper

6527 Lakewood Boulevard
Dallas, Texas 75214
(214) 824-3435

Advertising and editorial illustrations of distinctive styles.

Clients include: Nestle Group—Frankfurt; Kitchens of Sarah Lee; Hunt-Wesson Foods; Clorox Co.; Nautilus Fitness Centers; NBC and CBS Affiliates; Texas Instruments Inc.; AMI-American Medical International, Inc.; Health Care.

John Langdon

106 South Marion Avenue
Wenonah, New Jersey 08090
(609) 468-7868

John Langdon designs words and letters for
every imaginable use, in a remarkable variety
of styles, with unusual attention to detail
from concept through finish.

His work has been featured in *U&lc* and
Omni Magazines.

For more samples see page 134 of American
Showcase, Volume 7. A mini-portfolio will be
mailed upon request.

A list of clients includes the following:

ABC-TV
Bali Park Place Casino
Claridge Hotel and Casino
Cycle Guide Publications
Gino's Restaurants
Nursing Magazine
Pennsylvania Lottery
Philadelphia Inquirer
Philadelphia Magazine
Playboy Enterprises
Realities Magazine
Resorts International
Sands Hotel and Casino
Tastykake

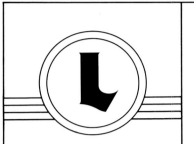

SCHI ZOPHREN IC

compülsive

INFERiORITY

GRANDIOSE DELUSIONS

introvert

MANIC DEPRESSIVE

James A. Lebbad

220 5th Avenue, Room 1707
New York, New York 10001
(212) 679-2234

Typography and Design

Clients include: Arista Records; Berkley Publishing Group; Bloomingdales; CBS Publications; Grey Advertising; Home Box Office; McCaffrey & McCall; NBC; Ogilvy & Mather; Wunderman, Ricotta & Kline; Young & Rubicam.

Clockwise from Upper Right: Logo for HBO, Party Invitation, On-Air Logo for Cinemax, Logo for CBS Electronics Video Game, Logo treatment for Christmas Box, Title treatment for ABC Movie, On-Air Logo for HBO

Member Graphic Artists Guild.

Jared D. Lee

2942 Hamilton Road
Lebanon, Ohio 45036
(513) 932-2154

Telecopier Service.

Animation Reel Available.

Partial client list: Young &
Rubicam; BBDO; J. Walter
Thompson; Needham, Harper &
Steers; Ogilvy & Mather; Frankel
& Co.; D'Arcy-MacManus &
Masius; Sports Illustrated;
Woman's World; Woman's Day;
Reader's Digest; Scholastic
Publications.

Member Graphic Artists Guild.

1. Humphrey Browning
   Macdougall
2. Datamation Magazine
3. Buzzard Advertising
4. Courtesy of Sports Illustrated
   © Time, Inc., 1983

1.

2.

3.

4.

Mike Lester, Illustration

1001 Eulalia Road
Atlanta, Georgia 30319
(404) 233-3093

In Atlanta
Represented by:
Sarah Roe
(404) 872-2335

In New York
Represented by:
Daniele Collignon
(212) 243-4209

Robert S. Levy

(212) 986-8833

Represented by:
Ann & Andy Badin
835 Third Avenue
New York, New York 10022

Clients: DDB, O&M, B&B,
Marsteller, IBM, GTE, Digital
Equipment Corporation,
Armstrong.

Chris Lewis

Represented by:
Wooden Reps
503 Ansley Villa Drive
Atlanta, Georgia 30324
Telephone: (404) 892-6303
Studio: (404) 876-0288

American Express
Bozell & Jacobs, Inc.
Cargill, Wilson & Acree
Contel
Cooper Copeland Inc.
D'Arcy-Macmanus & Masius, Inc.
Georgia-Pacific
Henderson Advertising
Jartran Inc.
Krystal Co.
Liller Neal
Ogilvy & Mather
Peachtree Center
Shoney's Inc.
Six Flags
Southern Company
Texize

H. B. Lewis

708 Broadway
New York, New York 10003
(212) 477-3015
(718) 875-2762

Member Graphic Artists Guild

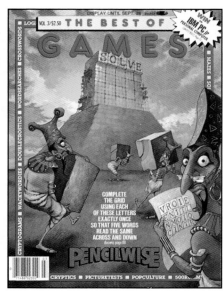

Ron Lieberman

109 West 28th Street
New York, New York 10001
(212) 947-0653

Illustrator & Designer

Representation:
In New York:
SUSAN GOMBERG
(212) 473-8747

In Chicago:
VINCENT KAMIN & ASSOCS.
(312) 787-8834

Clients include: Eastern Airlines, Children's Computer Workshop, Volkswagen, Air France, Legg's, Chemical Bank, New York Times, New West, New York, Esquire, Geo, Ziff-Davis, Ballantine Books, Random House, Harmony Books, Lily Tomlin, Peter Allen/Dee Anthony Org., Arista & Warner Bros. Records.

Member Graphic Artists Guild

Little Apple Art

Marshall & Richie Moseley
409 Sixth Avenue
Brooklyn, New York 11215
(718) 499-7045

Illustration, graphic design and lettering.

The studio of Marshall and Richie Moseley provides services to advertising agencies, corporations and publishers. Clients have included: Polaroid; National Airlines; American Airlines; Coca-Cola; Parker Brothers; International Paper; Sheraton International; Continental Insurance; Ralston Purina; Holiday Inn; Thomas Cook; General Foods; NBC; CBS Records; Proctor & Gamble; Maxwell House; Dun & Bradstreet; Colgate-Palmolive; GAB; Hearst Corporation; LILCO; Independence Savings Bank; Union Savings Bank; Random House; Dell; Ballantine; Harper & Row; *Parents* Magazine; *Changing Times; The New York Times; Scholastic* Publications; Book-of-the-Month Club; Children's Television Workshop; Doyle Dane Bernbach; N.W. Ayer; BBDO; Scali, McCabe, Sloves; Cunningham & Walsh; McCann-Erickson; Compton Advertising; Ted Bates; William Esty; Ogilvy & Mather; Dancer Fitzgerald Sample; Hutchins/Y&R; Doremus; and others.

Additional samples available on request.

Member Graphic Artists Guild.

Al Lorenz

(203) 226-7674

Represented by: Carol Bancroft & Friends
185 Goodhill Road
Weston, Connecticut 06883

Clients include
Arlen Realty; Barton & Gillette; Batten, Barton, Durstine & Osborne, Inc.; Benton & Bowles, Inc.; Charles F. Noyes; Compton Advertising; Doremus & Company; Doyle Dane Bernbach; Edward Larabee Barnes; Elton Design; Gips & Balkind; J. Walter Thompson; John Carl Warnecke; Johnson-Burgee; Kenyon & Eckhardt; Loucks/Atelier; Marcel Breuer Associates; Ogilvy & Mather; Olympia & York, Perkins & Will; Scali, McCabe, Sloves, Inc.; Skidmore, Owings & Merrill; Ted Bates Advertising; Wells, Rich, Green, Inc.; Williamson, Picket, Gross, Inc.; Young & Rubicam.

Awards:
1982 Society of Illustrators
Certificate of Merit
1983 Society of Illustrators
Certificate of Merit

1983 AIGA: Certificate of
Excellence—Communication Graphics
1983 Silver Award: Advertising Club of
Fairfield County
1983 Communication Arts Magazine:
Award of Excellence

Author of
Illustrating Architecture, Fall 1984
Van Nostrand Reinhold Company, Inc.

Professor School of Architecture
Pratt Institute
Brooklyn, New York

NYNEX CORPORATION

Rick Lovell, Inc.

745 Kirk Road
Decatur, Georgia 30030
(404) 371-0681

Represented by:
The Williams Group
1106 West Peachtree Street
Suite 201
Atlanta, Georgia 30309
(404) 873-2287

In New York,
Contact Tricia Weber
(212) 460-5690

Telecopier Available

Member Graphic Artists Guild

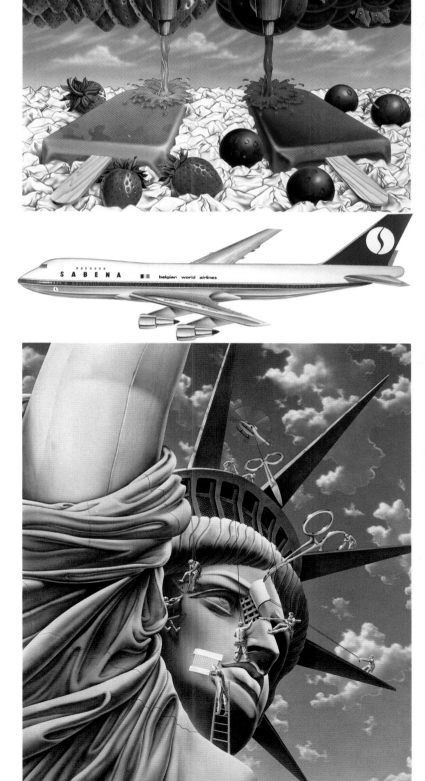

Dennis Luzak

Represented by:

New York:
Loretta Luzak
Box 342
Redding Ridge,
Connecticut 06876
(203) 938-3158

Chicago:
Moshier & Maloney
535 Michigan Avenue
Chicago, Illinois 60611
(312) 943-1668

Clients:
Time, Inc.
Ford Motor Company
Chrysler Corporation
General Motors Corporation
NBC
CBS
ABC
Burroughs Wellcome Corp.
McCall's Magazine
Ladies' Home Journal
Good Housekeeping Magazine
Redbook
Playboy
Sports Illustrated
Fortune Magazine
Forbes
Yankee Magazine
Changing Times
Random House
Reader's Digest Corporation
Simon & Schuster
New American Library
National Geographic Society
Franklin Mint
Xerox Corporation
Eli Lilly Corporation
Outboard Marine Corporation
International Paper Corporation
Consolidated Paper Corp.
Universal City Studios
Columbia Pictures Industries
Paramount Pictures Corporation
Time-Life Records
Warner Communications
Institutional Investor
Randolph Computer Corp.
General Electric
Air Canada
Borden Company
Lederle Pharmaceutical
Manufacturers Hanover Trust
First National Bank of Chicago
First National Bank of Boston
McGraw-Hill Publishers
Renault Corporation
RCA
United States Postal Service
MBI
Beechnut
Ayerst Pharmaceutical
Westwood Pharmaceutical
Ciba-Geigy
AmTrak
Schweppes
Colgate-Palmolive
Coca-Cola
Levi Strauss
Foote, Cone & Belding
DuPont Corporation
McCaffrey and McCall
Dancer Fitzgerald Sample
William Douglas McAdams
Grey Advertising
GGK/NY

Member:
Society of Illustrators
Graphic Artists Guild

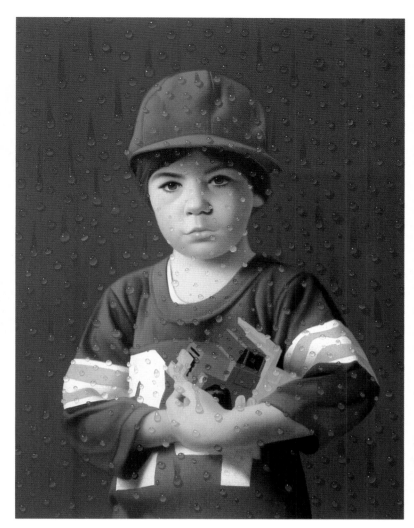

Benton Mahan

P.O. Box 66
Chesterville, Ohio 43317
(419) 768-2204

Portfolio of slides upon request.
Partial client list: Yankee
Magazine, McGraw-Hill,
Doubleday Publishing,
Children's Television Workshop,
Merrill Publishing, J. Walter
Thompson, Ohio Magazine,
Living Single Magazine,
Benjamin Franklin Society,
Silver-Burdett Publishing, ITT,
Borden Inc., Sheraton-Hilton,
General Electric, Peabody
Galion and others.

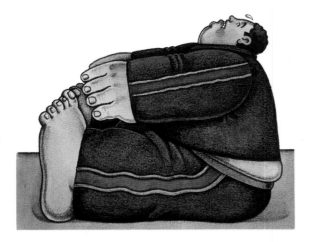

Margaret & Frank & Friends, Inc.
Margaret Cusack

Design and Fabric Art
124 Hoyt Street
Brooklyn, New York 11217
(718) 237-0145

Margaret Cusack has been creating fabric illustrations and props since 1972. Now, hand-stitched samplers and soft sculpture as well, are an important part of her award-winning portfolio. Fortunately, this work doesn't cost any more than more conventional illustration styles. Nor does it take longer to produce. Given normal time, pencil sketches and a fabric paste-up of the work are shown before the final sewing begins. A 4" × 5" transparency of the artwork is included in the one fee.

Having worked as an art director and graphic designer herself, Cusack is aware that extra-tight deadlines are often the norm. Most assignments are completed within two weeks, although there have been one-week and even overnight deadlines.

Clients include: Peek Freans, Singer, Perrier, Texaco, Mobil, Thai Airlines, Shenandoah Musical, Altman's, Bloomingdale's, Chivas Regal, The New York Times, HBJ, RCA, Ortho, Ciba-Geigy.

ASSOCIATED BISCUITS

DRUG TOPICS MAGAZINE

PORTFOLIO PIECE

"THE CHRISTMAS CAROL SAMPLER"

MEETINGS & CONVENTIONS MAGAZINE

David Marks

750 Clemont Drive, NE
Atlanta, Georgia 30306
(404) 872-1824

Graphic design, logos and
logotype design, calligraphy
and fine hand lettering.

Represented by:
Gail Centini
333 Adams Street
Decatur, Georgia 30030
(404) 377-8383

Simple Amusements

Calligraphic Symphonies

The Boca Experience

Pacesetters

häng..

Flemings

Barbara Maslen

226 East 29th Street
New York, New York 10016
(212) 686-6559

Clients: New York Times, New
York Magazine, Burlington,
Condé Nast, Estée Lauder,
Frances Denney, McGraw-Hill,
Simon & Schuster, Redbook,
Savvy, Seventeen, Ziff-Davis,
WWD.

Member Graphic Artists Guild

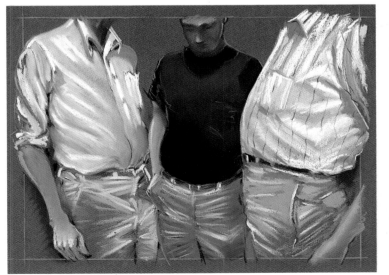

David McKelvey
Illustrator

2702 Frontier Court
Atlanta, Georgia 30341
(404) 457-3615

Represented by: The Williams Group
Contact Phillip Williams or Richard Coveny
(404) 873-2287

In New York Contact Tricia Weber
(212) 460-5690

Telecopier Available

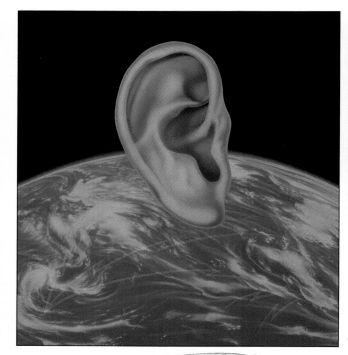

Randall McKissick

PO Box 21811
Columbia, South Carolina 29221
(803) 798-3688

Clients include:
American Express, Boy Scouts of America, Coca-Cola, Doubleday & Co., Georgia-Pacific, Marathon Oil Co., McDonald's, RJ Reynolds, Sprite, Universal Pictures, Wrangler.

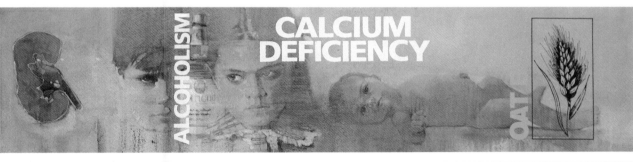

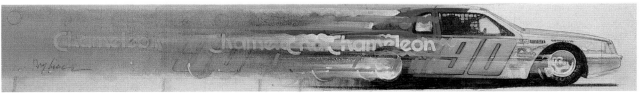

Roy Meade

Meade Creative
240 Tenth Street
Toledo, Ohio 43624
(419) 244-9074

Designer/Graphic Communications
Illustrator

Patrick
Merrell

48 West 20th Street
New York, New York 10011
(212) 620-7777

Illustration, Design and
Lettering

Clients include: Xerox,
Macmillan Publishing,
Westinghouse, Popular
Science, Burger King, Venture
Magazine, Marvel, Ketchum
New York, Parachute Press,
Scholastic, DC Comics.

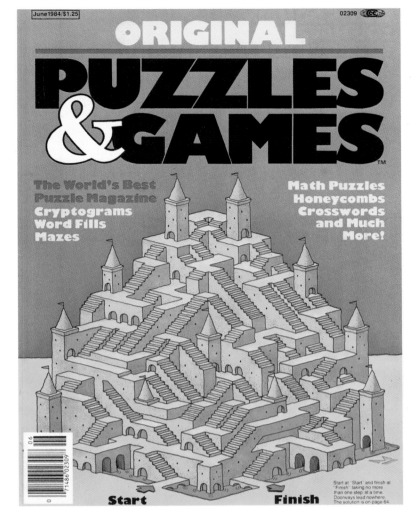

Gary Meyer

227 West Channel Road
Santa Monica, California 90402
(213) 454-2174

Member of the Society of
Illustrators and the Society of
Illustrators of Los Angeles.

Awards:

Illustration West 22:
Best of Show
Best of Category
Special Judges Award

Illustration West 21:
Two Special Judges awards

Illustration West 19:
Best of Category

Twelfth Annual Key Arts Awards:
First Place

Tima X, Color Illustration:
First Place
Third Place

Tima 11, Color Illustration:
First Place

North American Sculpture
  Exhibition, 1983:
The Beyond Bronze Award

North American Sculpture
  Exhibition, 1981:
Art Castings of Colorado Award

Clients:
Universal Studios; Columbia
Pictures; Twentieth Century Fox;
Paramount Studios; Levi's;
Tomy Toys; Hughes Helicopters;
Litton Ship Systems; Garrett
Corporation; Popular
Mechanics; Apple Computers;
Blitz Weinhard; Western
Microtechnology; Visicorp;
MGM; CBS Records; A&M
Records; Lionhart Productions;
Ogilvy & Mather; Seiniger
Advertising; Jeff Bacon
Design Inc.; Foote, Cone &
Belding/Honig; Salisbury
Communications; Warner Bros.;
Wells, Rich, Green; Steinhilber
Deutsch & Gard.

David Montiel

115 West 16th Street #211
New York, New York 10011
(212) 989-7426

Illustrations:

From left to right, top to bottom

1. Advertising poster: Kennex Corp.
2. Fortune Magazine: IBM's "peanut" computer.
3. Congdon & Weed; "Shad Sentell, Love Lust & Louisiana Oil"
4. Random House: "You Know Me Al"
5. Random House: "Lying Low"

Other Clients include:
Jonson Pedersen Hinrichs & Shakery; Geer, DuBois Inc.; Playboy, Time; Ciba-Geigy Pharmaceuticals.

Manuel Morales

P.O. Box 1763
Bloomfield, New Jersey 07003
(201) 429-0848

WANTED

Clients interested in a creative, unique and very reliable Illustrator specializing in visual communication.

Look for me in the Budweiser commercial titled "Painter." I am the one painting the van.

Clients: Budweiser; D'Arcy-MacManus & Masius, Inc.; Pocket Books; Mysterious Press; Tor Books; Iron Horse Products; Art Direction Magazine.

Member Graphic Artists Guild.

Jacqui Morgan

315 East 58th Street
New York, New York 10022
(212) 421-0766

Watercolor

Represented in Germany by:
Mayer-Norten Group
089/986230

Clients include: AT&T, Avon,
N.W. Ayer, American Home
Products, Booz Allen &
Hamilton, Burlington Mills,
Busch Gardens, Champion
Paper, Eastern Airlines, Franklin
Watts, General Foods, Hilton
International, Holland
America, IBM, ITC, Irving Trust,
Macmillan, NBC, New York
Times, Pfiser, Playboy, Prentice-
Hall, Procter & Gamble, RCA,
Sansui, Van Nostrand Reinhold.

Works exhibited in: Arras
Gallery, Linden Gallery, NYC.,
Florida, Smithsonian Institute,
Washington D.C., London,
Munich, Tokyo, Warsaw.
Also seen in: Graphis, Print
Magazine, Gebrauchs Graphik,
Society of Illustrator's Annuals,
Society of Publication Designers
& Art Director's Annuals.

Listed in *Who's Who in Graphic
Art*. Winner of VI Warsaw Int'l
Poster Biennale.
Author of *Watercolor for
Illustration* to be published
shortly by Van Nostrand
Reinhold.

Member Graphic
Artists Guild.

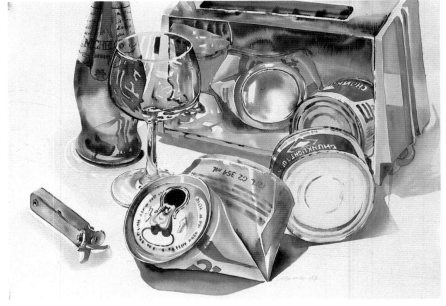

Barry Morgen

337 West 87th Street
New York, New York 10024
(212) 595-6835

Clients Include:
N.W. Ayer; Anagraphics; Creative Freelancers; American Express; Warner Communications, Inc.; *Reader's Digest;* Exxon; Xerox; Hummelwerk; Time-Life, Inc.; Mobile Masterpiece Theatre; CBS Records; RCA Selectavision; Popular Library; New American Library; Berkeley; Ballantine Books; Filmways; HBO; *Showtime Entertainment;* Columbia Pictures, Inc.;

PBS-TV; CBS-TV; ABC-TV; NBC-TV; Viacom; Solters-Roskin; BBD&O; Bolling Peterson Advertising; Fisher-Price; Ogilvy & Mather.

Member Graphic Artists Guild.

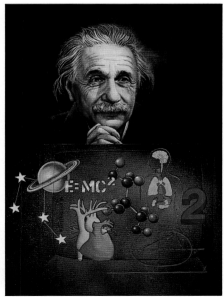

David Myers

228 Bleecker Street
New York, New York 10014
(212) 989-5260

Lettering, Airbrush, Illustration,
and Graphic Effects

Clients have included:
Benton & Bowles
Dancer Fitzgerald Sample
Diener/Hauser/Bates
Doyle Dane Bernbach
Jarman, Spitzer & Felix
Kurtz & Tarlow
McCaffrey and McCall
Ogilvy & Mather
J. Walter Thompson
Trout & Ries
Wunderman, Ricotta & Kline
Young & Rubicam
ABC
NBC
CBS
WKTU
Macy's
Levi-Strauss
Western Union
AT&T
General Foods
American Express
Twentieth Century-Fox
Stroh's
New York Magazine
Rolling Stone
Ziff-Davis
Simon & Schuster
Harper & Row
Ballantine
Dell
Avon
McGraw-Hill
Harcourt Brace Jovanovich
Random House
Macmillan
Reader's Digest
Holt, Rinehart & Winston

Member Graphic Artists Guild

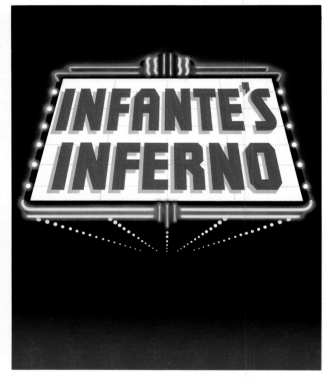

228

Marina Neyman-Levikova

Represented by Anita Grien
155 East 38th Street
New York, New York 10016
(212) 697-6170

Illustration & Design
TV Commercials, Film & Music Video: Production &
Costume Designer

Clients include: Ogilvy & Mather, McCaffrey & McCall,
Wells Rich Greene, Young & Rubicam, ABC,
CBS/Epic Records, Arista Records, Sergio Valente,

Personal Computing, Omni Magazine, Cosmopolitan,
L'Oreal, Revlon.

Film credits include:
DISC (Mosfilm Studio, Moscow)
MAYAKOVSKY LAUGHS (Mosfilm Studio, Moscow)
LIQUID SKY (Z Films, New York City)

MORTON MYLES FOR THE WARRENS   550 SEVENTH AVENUE, NEW YORK, 10018   212/391-8700

229

Jim Parkinson
6170 Broadway Terrace
Oakland, California 94618
(415) 547-3100

Represented by:
Kathy Braun
(415) 543-7377

Thomas Payne

11 Colonial Avenue
Albany, New York 12203
(518) 482-1756

Member Graphic Artists Guild

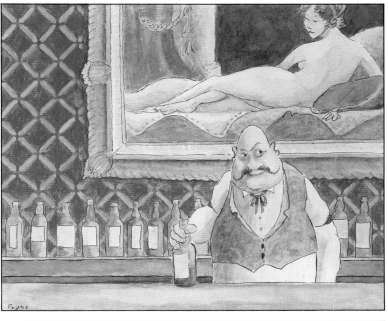

Daniel Pelavin
45 Carmine Street
New York, New York 10014
(212) 929-2706

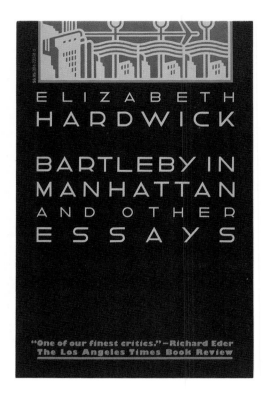

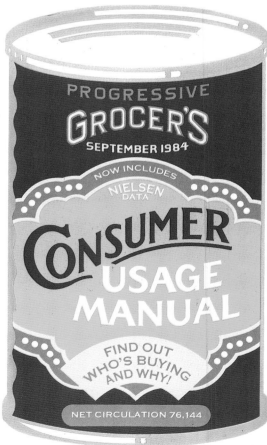

Winslow
Pinney Pels

Represented by:

Julia
DellaCroce

120 West 81st Street
New York, New York 10024
(212) 580-1321

1. CORIOLANUS
   Client: Exxon, The Morgan
   Bank, Metropolitan Life for
   Channel 13 PBS. Agency:
   McCaffrey and McCall.
   AD: Peggy Pettus

2. THE CRUCIBLE
   Client: The Empire State
   Institute for the Performing
   Arts.

3. PASTA BY BEARD
   Client: Gannett

4. BEATRIX POTTER
   Client: Mobil for Channel 13
   PBS. Agency: Gips + Balkind,
   AD: Pam Smith

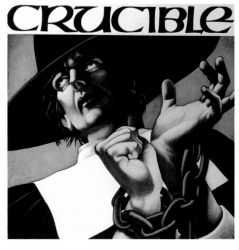

Scott Pollack

Represented by:

Eileen Moss

333 East 49th Street
New York, New York 10017
(212) 980-8061

Partial Client List:

Ally & Gargano; Backer &
Spielvogel; Doyle Dane
Bernbach; Rumrill-Hoyt; William
Douglas McAdams; Sudler &
Hennessey; E.B. Wilson; Mingo-
Jones; Peat Marwick Mitchell &
Co.; Larson, Bateman &
McAllister; Working Mother; Ski;
Barron's; The Wall Street
Journal; Outdoor Life; 13-30
Corporation; Fairchild
Publications.

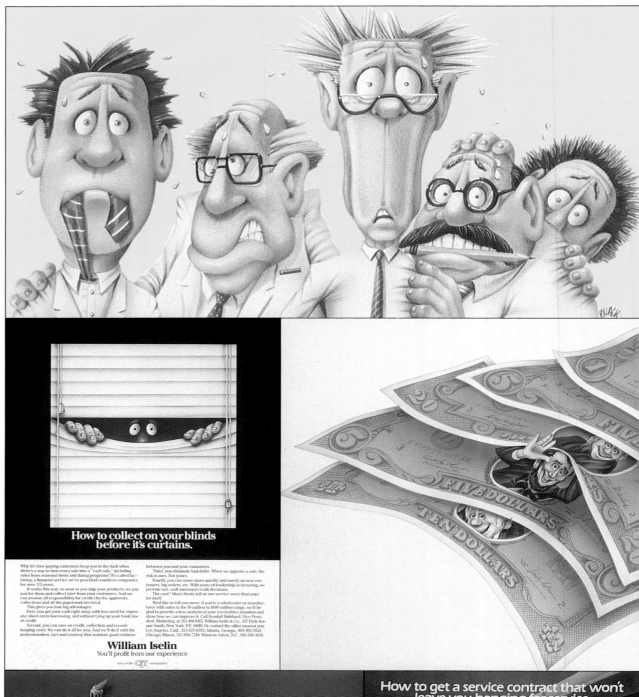

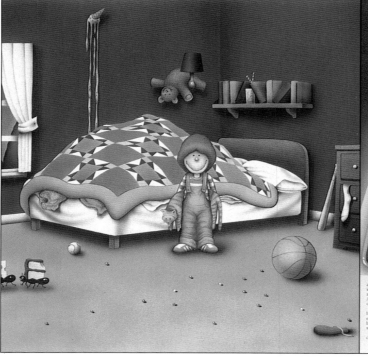

Bill Purdom

780 Madison Avenue
New York, New York 10021
(212) 988-4566

Member Society of Illustrators

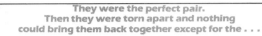
They were the perfect pair.
Then they were torn apart and nothing
could bring them back together except for the . . .

RAIDERS of the LOST SOCKS

STARRING
HARRISON FORD
AND
Your Name Here

THE EPIC THAT ROCKED LAUNDRY ROOMS
AROUND THE WORLD!

NICKELODEON   THE FIRST CHANNEL FOR KIDS

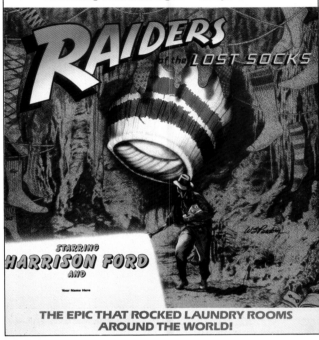

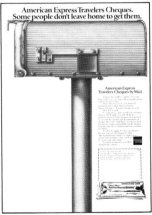

235

Mike Quon
Design Office,
Inc.

568 Broadway
New York, New York 10012
(212) 226-6024

Complete design and
illustration services.

Logos, brochures, posters,
corporate identity, packaging,
catalogues, promotional
material and illustration.

Clients have included:
AT&T, Merrill Lynch, IBM,
Fred S. James Co., Time Inc.,
American Express, Business
Week, CBS Records.

Member Graphic Artists Guild

©Mike Quon 1985

Successful Small Group Insurance
Requires The Strength Of Dun & Bradstreet.

Successful small group insurance requires a strong administrator.
As this nation's largest third party administrator of small group insurance,
Dun & Bradstreet Plan Services has met the test of time. Strong. Stable. Reliable.
And why not. The Dun & Bradstreet name is highly respected for 146 years
of strong service to American business.
Over 500 computer terminals and 200 WATS lines keep the daily flow of
information moving and accessible for response. A portfolio of 23 carriers
permits each plan to be client tailored. Now small group insurance is manage-
able, profitable and a door opener for other forms of insurance.
To find out how to get the strength of Dun & Bradstreet behind your small
group insurance plans, give us a call at 800-237-5561 (in Florida, 800-282-2533).
Strength is being there with the right answers. Consistently.

**Dun & Bradstreet
Plan Services**

Philadelphia • Dallas • Sacramento • Toronto • Tampa

Tim Raglin

138 West 74th Street
New York, New York 10023
(212) 873-0538

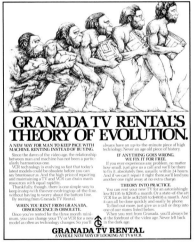

Alan Reingold

Represented by: Anita Grien
155 East 38th Street
New York, New York 10016
(212) 697-6170

Clients include: ABC; CBS; NBC; PBS; Columbia
Pictures; Paramount; Universal; Diener/Hauser/Bates;
Discover; Forbes; Fortune; Gentlemen's Quarterly;
Penthouse; Time; N.W. Ayer; Ted Bates; McCaffrey and
McCall; Ogilvy & Mather; Scali, McCabe, Sloves;
Young & Rubicam; Atlantic Records; RCA; Bantam
Books; Ballantine Books; Reader's Digest; Franklin
Mint; McGraw-Hill; Ziff-Davis; Burlington Industries;
Exxon; Warner Communications.

*The Natural Fabrics for Spring ...
Tropical Worsteds*

David Rickerd

18 University Avenue
Chatham, New Jersey 07928
(201) 635-9513

Clients: Science Digest,
Columbia University, Polydor
Records, East/West Publishing,
Official Airline Guide, View
Communications, Restaurant
Business, Playboy, American
Bookseller, Attenzione, Oui,
Games, Home Video, Sounds
Arts, Home Electronics
and Entertainment, Cycle
Publishing, Video, Gallery,
Scholastic Magazines, Madison
Avenue, The New York Times,
20th Century-Fox, Compton
Advertising, Ziff-Davis, Business
Week, New York Daily News,
Geo, MGM, K-Power, Family
Computers, Paramount, U.S.
Pharmacist, Charles Jourdan,
Fearon O'Leary Kaprielian,
Telepictures Inc., Showtime,
Xerox Corporation.

I specialize in images with a
photographic base, but am not
limited. Other talents include
photo enhancement, air brush,
design involving subjects of
corporate executives, electronics,
computers, and the undefined.

For an up-to-date portfolio
presentation, please call for
an appointment.

Robert Risko

201 West 11th Street
New York, New York 10014
(212) 989-6987

Clients:
Playboy
Time
Vogue
Vanity Fair
Interview
New York Times
New York Magazine
Daily News
Seventeen
Madison Avenue
Scholastic Publications
Fredrick Merrill
  Associates

Richard Romeo

1066 N.W. 96th Avenue
Fort Lauderdale, Florida 33322
(305) 472-0072

Romeo's illustrations have appeared throughout the country in all areas of business, including: Advertising, Publishing, Television, Packaging, Pharmaceuticals, Fashion, Medical and Cartooning. He is extremely versatile, and works in a broad range of media and techniques. He has many years of ad agency experience and an excellent understanding of production.

Clients include:

American Express
Arvida
Barton's
Best Stores
Burdines
Canada Dry
Carrera
Cartier
Celotex
Clairol
Com Bank
Cordis Dow
David's Cookies
Del Monte
Elizabeth Arden
Flagship Bank
Geoffrey Beene
Godiva
Haggar
Hasbro
Hilton Hotels
Hyatt Hotels
Intercontinental Hotels
Jamaica Resort Hotels
Levi Strauss
Miami Magazine
National Distillers
Northeastern Airlines
Panasonic
Personnel Pool
Pierre Cardin
Pepsi Cola
Playboy
Piper Aircraft
Royal Caribbean Cruise Line
Ryder Truck
Salada
Scandinavian World Cruises
Sony
Storer Broadcasting
Talon
Tropic Magazine
Van Heusen
Waterford
Yves Saint Laurent

Samples of B&W Pen Line Illustrations Available Upon Request.

Graduate of Pratt Institute
Member of Graphic Artists Guild

Joe Saffold

Represented by:

Wooden Reps
503 Ansley Villa Drive
Atlanta, Georgia 30324
(404) 892-6303

Studio & Telecopier
(404) 231-2168

Kathy Staico Schorr

Represented by Susan Gomberg
145 East 22nd Street
New York, New York 10010
(212) 473-8747
Studio: (203) 266-4084

ILLUSTRATION

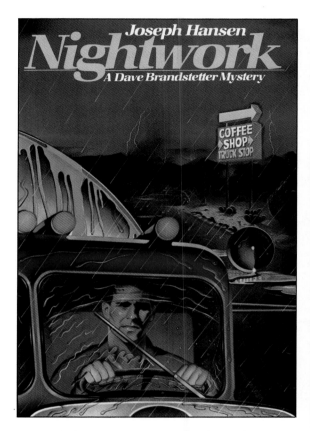

Jeff Seaver

130 West 24th Street, #4B
New York, New York 10011
(212) 255-8299

Clients: ABC; Air Canada; Ally
& Gargano; American Express;
Backer & Spielvogel; BBD&O;
Ted Bates; Book-of-the-Month;
*Business Week; Computers &
Electronics;* Chubb; Doubleday;
Dow Jones; Doyle Dane
Bernbach; Dunkin' Donuts;
Fortune; General Electric; Grey;
GTE; Hertz; IBM; Lever Bros.;
Marshalk; McCaffrey & McCall;
McCann-Erickson; Merrill
Lynch; Miller; *Mother Jones;
National Lampoon; New York;
The New York Times;* Ogilvy &
Mather; *Oui;* Pan Am; Pfizer;
Ralston Purina; Random House;
RCA; Rumrill Hoyt; Sandoz;
Scali, McCabe & Sloves;
Science Digest; Science 83;
Sony; *Sports Afield;* Texaco;
J. Walter Thompson; Touche-
Ross; Tyson; Video Review;
Wells, Rich, Greene; Workman.

Works exhibited in Illustrators
19, 20, 23, 24; Communication
Arts Annual; New York Art
Directors Club; Western Art
Directors Show; National
Lampoon Art Poster Book and
Exhibition; American Humorous
Illustration Exhibit, Tokyo,
Japan; Museum of Art and
Science, Chicago.

Member Graphic Artists Guild

©1984 Jeff Seaver

Joseph Sellars

Represented by:
Barney Kane & Friends
18 East 16th Street
New York, New York 10003
(212) 206-0322

Barclay Shaw
8 Buena Vista Drive
Hastings-on-Hudson, New York 10706
(914) 478-0265

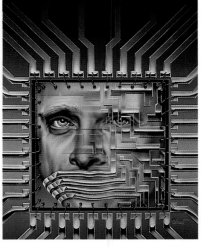

Mary Anne Shea

224 West 29th Street
New York, New York 10001
(212) 239-1076

Represented in Chicago by:
Vincent Kamin & Associates
(312) 787-9138

Photo-illustration, collage, and hand-coloring

Clients include:

AT&T
Avon Books
Connoisseur Magazine

Mobil Oil
Museum of Modern Art
National Lampoon

The Continental Group
Cosmopolitan
Deiner/Hauser/Bates
Doubleday
Doyle Dane Bernbach
Glamour
Bill Gold Advertising
Lever Brothers
Marschalk Advertising
Max Factor

New Yorker Films
New York Times
Official Airline Guides
Polydor Records
PC Magazine
Psychology Today
Seventeen
Sony
Spectrafilm
Young & Rubicam

Member Graphic Artists Guild

Prints available upon request

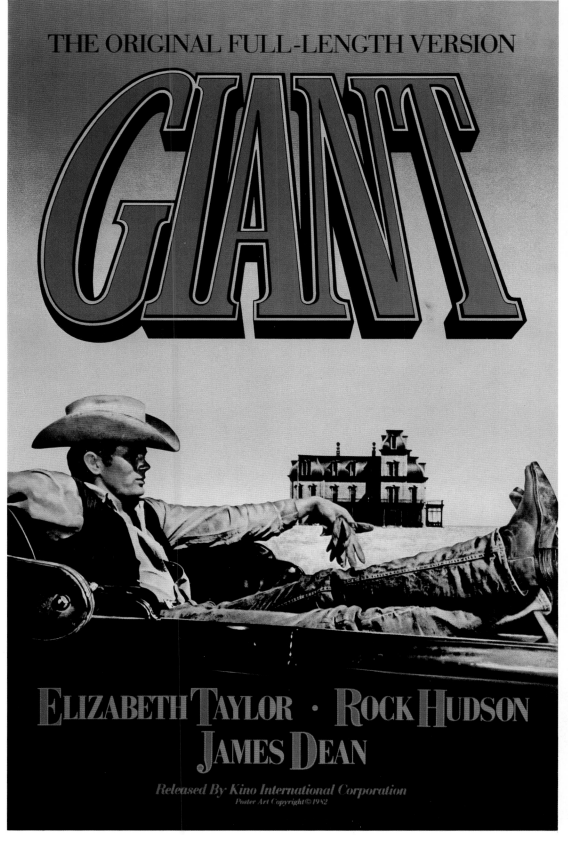

Oren Sherman

30 Ipswich Street
Studio 209
Boston, Massachusetts 02215
(617) 437-7368

Left page; posters, clockwise
from top:

Kentucky Derby
21″ × 30″
Balloons
22″ × 21″
Boston Swan Boats
23″ × 24″
Brooklyn Bridge
Centennial
1883-1983
22″ × 21½″
Duke Ellington
28″ × 21½″
Arnold Arboretum
of Harvard University
17″ × 27″

Right page; illustrations,
clockwise from top:

Copley Place
Houghton Mifflin
SCA Annual Report
Honeywell
SCA Annual Report
SCA Annual Report
South Shore Bank
Copley Place

A SERVICES, INC.

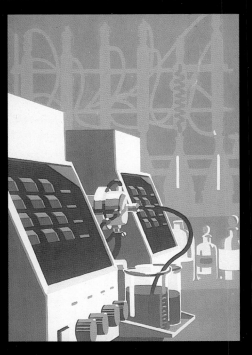

William A. Sloan

Represented by THREE
Contact: John Husak
568 Broadway
Suite 405
New York, New York 10012
(212) 226-8110

Clients include: American Express; Ash LeDonne; Avon; Broadway Play Publishing; Dow Jones; DuPont; Gross, Townsend & Frank; MacMillan Publishing; *Money* Magazine; *The New York Times;* Orient Express; Serino, Coyne, Nappi; Tamotsu; Viking Penguin Publishing; *Vogue.*

Elwood H. Smith

2 Locust Grove Road
Rhinebeck, New York 12572

Represented by:
Maggie Pickard
(914) 876-2358

Hodges Soileau

350 Flax Hill Road
Norwalk, Connecticut 06854
(203) 852-0751

Clients include: Outdoor Life, IT&T, Air Canada, Boy's Life,
Aetna Life, RCA, Wamsutta, Meredith Corp., Unicover Corp.,
Hoechst Fibers, Sony, Spaulding, Reichold Chemicals,
Corporate Annual Reports, Benton & Bowles, Bozell &
Jacobs, Ladies Home Journal, Seventeen, Good Housekeeping,
Fortune, Flying Magazine, Field & Stream, Runner Magazine,
R.J. Reynolds Tobacco Co., Book Publishers: Macmillan
Publishing Co., New American Library, Avon, Bantam, Viking
Penguin, Ballantine, Fawcett, Berkley, Banbury, Reader's
Digest, Doubleday, Coronado, and Franklin Library.

Member: Society of Illustrators
American Portrait Society

Debra Solomon

536 West 111th Street Apt. #55
New York, New York 10025
(212) 662-5619

Clients include:

New American Library
Random House
Ballantine Books
Simon & Schuster
New York Times
Daily News
Vogue
Barron's
Scholastic
Travel & Leisure
Savvy

Jeffrey A. Spear/
Typographic Design

1111 Euclid Street, #302
Santa Monica, California 90403
(213) 395-3939

Clients include:

Tomy Toys; Pacific Southwest Airlines (PSA); Twentieth
Century-Fox Film; Marriott Corporation; Warner
Brothers Records; NBC-TV; CBS-TV; Film Ventures, Inc.;
National Public Radio; Beckman Instruments.

Portfolio and/or other samples available upon request.

Chris Spollen

Moonlight Press
High Contrast Illustration
(718) 979-9695

Clients:
Stanley Tool Company
International Paper
Bell South Company
Mutual Life Insurance
20th Century Fox
Chubb Group Insurance
Digital Computer Co.
Home Box Office
McCaffrey and McCall
MacLean Hunter Media, Inc.
Franklin Library
Consumer Report
Warner Brothers Pubs.
Benton & Bowles
Ziff-Davis
CBS Publishing
Medical Economics Company
Barron's
Popular Mechanics
Hayden Publishing Company
Datamation
Compton Advertising
Acute Care Medicine
Avis
Working Woman
Atlantic Recording

Member:
Graphic Artists Guild
Society of Illustrators

A mini portfolio of samples
sent upon request.

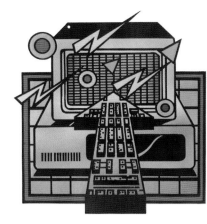

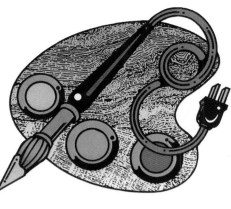

John Sposato

43 East 22nd Street
New York, New York 10010
(212) 477-3909

ILLUSTRATIONS IN OIL PASTEL

Concepts, graphic design and lettering.

Clients have included—Magazines: Newsweek; New York; Industrial Investor; Emergency Medicine; Scholastic. Television: NBC; HBO; ABC. Publishers: Random House; Simon & Schuster; Macmillan; Harcourt Brace Jovanovich; Harper & Row; Holt, Reinhart & Winston; G P Putnam; E P Dutton; Dell; Crown; Doubleday; McGraw-Hill; Bobbs-Merrill; Atheneum. Also: Calvert Distillers; Strathmore Paper; Key Pharmaceuticals; Paramount Pictures; Alcoholics Anonymous; Young & Rubicam; Ted Bates; MGM, Polydor, RCA Records.

Awards have included—Society of Illustrators 19, 21, 22, and 26; Art Directors Club; Graphis Annual; Graphis Posters; American Institute of Graphic Arts; CA Annual; Art Direction's Creativity; Type Directors Club; Advertising Club of New York; New Jersey Art Directors Club.

Sally Springer
317 South Lawrence Court
Philadelphia
Pennsylvania 19106
(215) 925-9697

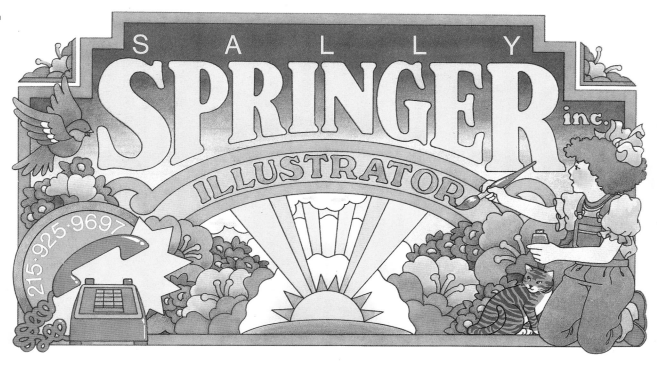

George Stavrinos

76 West 86th Street
New York, New York 10024
(212) 724-1557

Clients:
Bergdorf Goodman
Barney's
New York City Opera
Clinique Cosmetics
New York Times (Sunday
Magazine and Book Review)
Gentlemen's Quarterly
New York Magazine
Cosmopolitan
Random House
EP Dutton
Paper Moon Graphics

Gallery:
Tatistcheff Gallery
50 West 57th Street
New York, New York 10019
(212) 664-0907

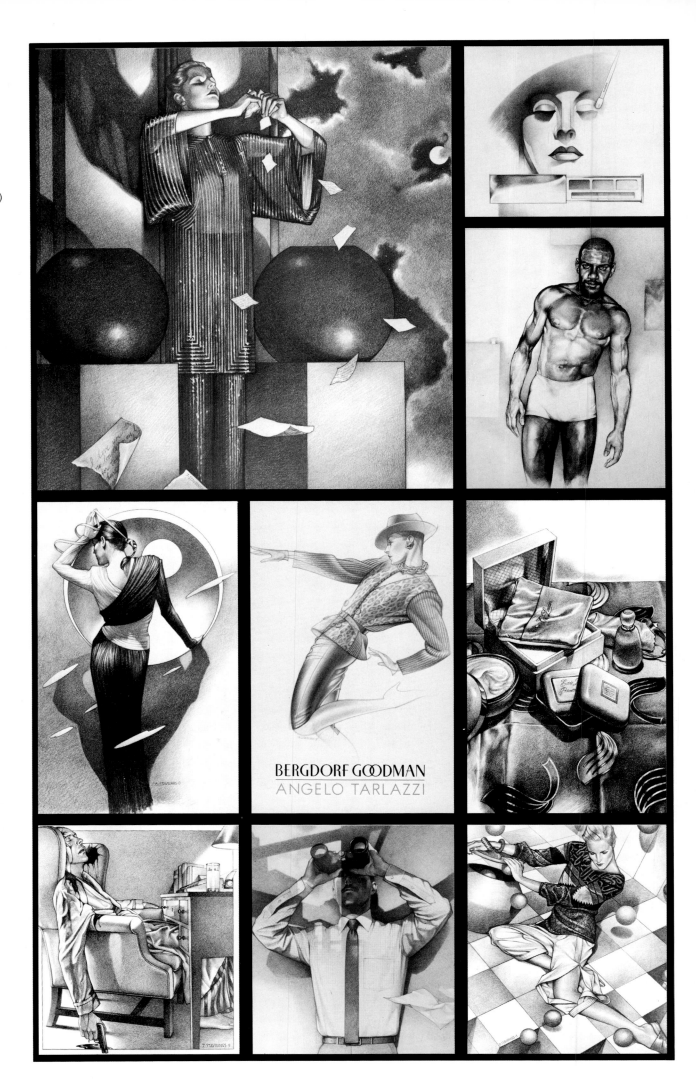

Mary Szilagyi

Illustration/Animated Films
410 Central Park West
New York, New York 10025
(212) 666-7578

Clients include:
Warner Amex-MTV
Macmillan Publishing Company
Parent's Magazine
Children's Television Workshop

1984 CLIO Award Winner

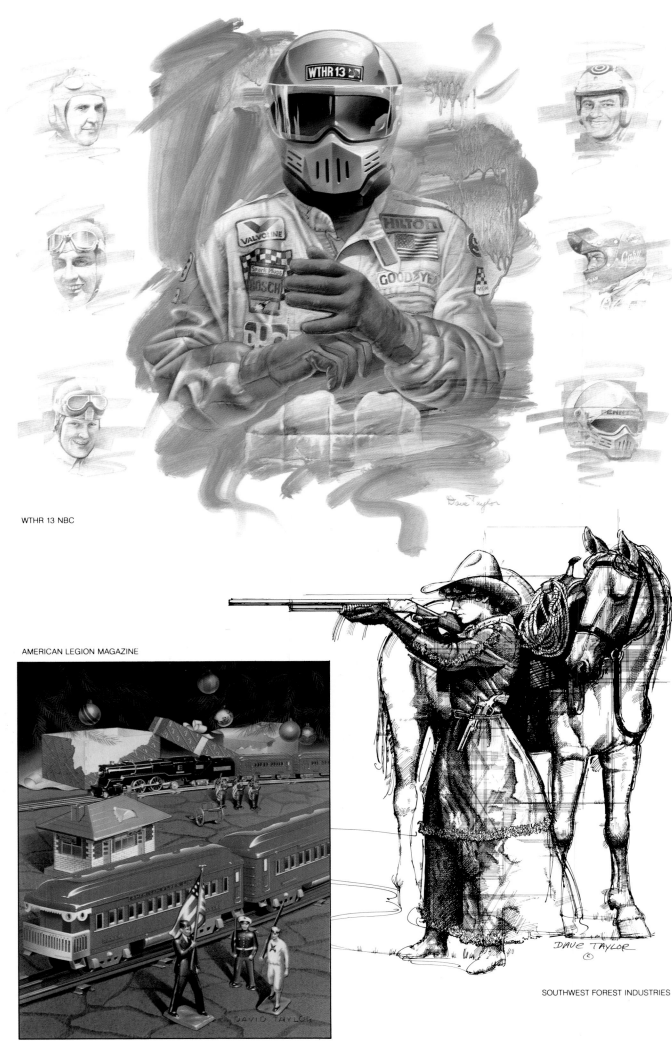

David Taylor

1449 North Pennsylvania Street
Indianapolis, Indiana 46202
(317) 634-2728

Clients include: R.C.A., Sears, *Saturday Evening Post,* Lilly, World Book, N.B.C., *American Legion Magazine,* Gatorade, International Harvester, Burger Chef, McDonald's, Southwest Forest, Coke, American Cablevision, Firestone and Amax Coal Company.

Member Graphic Artists Guild

WTHR 13 NBC

AMERICAN LEGION MAGAZINE

SOUTHWEST FOREST INDUSTRIES

George Tsui Studio

2250 Elliot Street
Merrick, New York 11566
(516) 223-8474

Advertising and editorial illustration.

Clients have included: ABC, CBS, NBC, Film Rite, Universal, Showtime, Creative Alliance, Grey Advertising, J. Walter Thompson, Ogilvy & Mather, Benton & Bowles, McCaffrey & McCall, Jove Books, Bantam Books, Signet, Avon, Dell Books, Reader's Digest, etc.

Member Graphic Artists Guild.

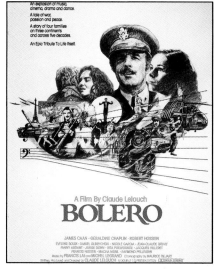

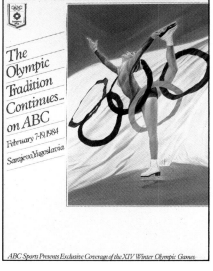

James
Turgeon

233 East Wacker Drive
Suite 1102
Chicago, Illinois 60601
(312) 861-1039

Illustration, lettering, and design.

Clients include: McDonalds, United Airlines, 7UP, Illinois State Lottery, Pizza Hut, WLS, WGN, Jim Beam, Turtle Wax, Quaker Oats, Smirnoff Vodka, Brookfield Zoo, Chicago Sun Times.

Member of the Graphic Artists Guild.

2H Studio—Roger Huyssen and Gerard Huerta

1059 Third Avenue
New York, New York 10021
(212) 753-2918 or 888-9194

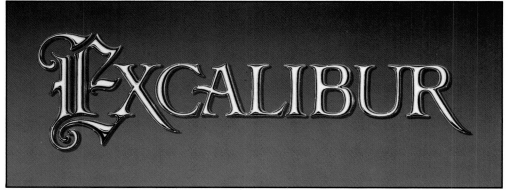

Unicorn

Representing:
GREG HILDEBRANDT
1148 Parsippany Boulevard
Parsippany, New Jersey 07054
(201) 334-0353

Greg Hildebrandt—artist/
illustrator—"My professional
interests center around using
and further developing my
ability to convey, through visual
media, thoughts, ideas and
concepts."

Representative clients:
Omni Magazine
Bantam Books
Ballantine Books
Random House
Golden Books
Simon & Schuster
Warner Brothers Records
MGM
Verkerke Reproductions
Columbia Pictures
Roach Incorporated
William Morrow
3M Corporation
20th Century Fox
Lucas Films
Platt & Munk
Western Publishing
Holt, Rinehart and Winston
The Bill Gold Agency
Young & Rubicam
Dellafemina Travisano
Warner Communications

Lauren Uram

251 Washington Avenue
Brooklyn, New York 11205
(718) 789-7717

Clients include:

NBC, East/West Network, British American Tobacco, Hayden Publishing Company, Facts on File Publications, N.W. Ayer, Cole & Weber, Cunningham & Walsh, American International Pictures, The United States International Communications Agency, Teradyne Inc., The New York Times, The Daily News, The Village Voice, The Washington Post, Life Magazine, Financial World Magazine, Music and Sound Output, Institutional Investor, Health Magazine, Changing Times Magazine, Redbook Magazine, Business Week Magazine.

Bill Vann
1706 South 8th Street
St. Louis, Missouri 63104
(314) 231-2322

Represented by:
• Joseph Mendola
  New York City (212) 986-5680

• Joel Harlib
  Chicago (312) 329-1370

Slide portfolio available upon
request

Telecopier available

Rob Vaughn

P.O. Box 660706
Miami Springs, Florida 33166
(305) 885-1292
Orlando (904) 383-4139

For additional samples
see American Showcase
Volumes 5 and 6.

Member of the Graphic Artists Guild.

Carmine Vecchio Design Inc.

200 East 27th Street
New York, New York 10016
Suite 11-K
(212) 683-2679

A full service graphic design studio specializing in stylized graphics, sales promotion, corporate design, logos and lettering in line or air-brush.

Member Graphic Artists Guild.

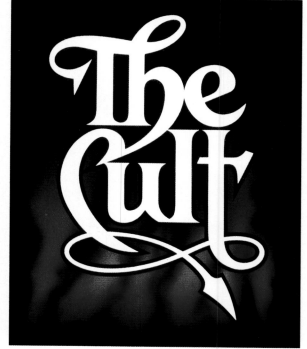

Michael Vernaglia

1251 Bloomfield Street
Hoboken, New Jersey 07030
(201) 659-7750

Artwork is not painted. It is overlays of Presfilm, Zipatone and Letrafilm. A technique 8 years in the making to achieve realistic and sharp graphic images, where colors pop in brilliancy.

Clients include: Sony, RCA Records, Doubleday Books, Lois Fashions, BusinessWeek Magazine, SportsWise Magazine.

Member Graphic Artists Guild

Gary Viskupic

Represented by:

Judy Mattelson

88 Lexington Avenue 12G
New York, New York 10016
(212) 684-2974

Member Graphic Artists Guild

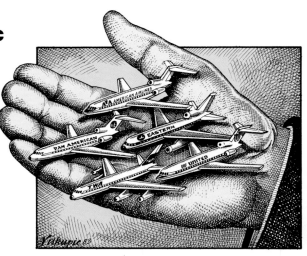

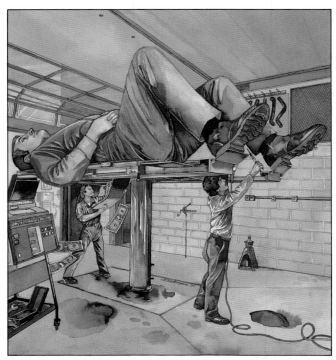

Sam Viviano

25 West 13th Street
New York, New York 10011
(212) 242-1471

Cartoon, caricature and
humorous illustration

Clients: ABC, BBD&O, CBS,
CTW, Citibank, Cunningham &
Walsh, Doyle Dane Bernbach,
Family Weekly, IBM, *Mad
Magazine,* McCaffrey & McCall,
McCann-Erickson, Metromedia,
NBC, N.W. Ayer, *National
Lampoon,* New American
Library, Ogilvy & Mather, PBS,
RCA, *Rolling Stone,* Scholastic,
Showtime, United Artists.

Member Graphic Artists Guild

©Sam Viviano 1984

Michael Waldman

506 West 42nd Street
New York, New York 10036
(212) 239-8245

Neil Waldman

47 Woodlands Avenue
White Plains, New York 10607
(914) 693-2782

Distinctive illustrations with a touch of elegance. Thoughtfully designed watercolor paintings that will enhance annual reports, corporate brochures, advertising and editorial projects, as well as postage stamps.

Clients have included: American Airlines, American Express, AT&T, Benton & Bowles, Business Week, Champion International, Fortune, J. Walter Thompson, Hoffman LaRoche, Merck Sharpe & Dohme, Merrill Lynch, NBC, N.W. Ayer, Playboy, RCA, Sony, Sports Illustrated, Sylvania, Texaco, Young & Rubicam.

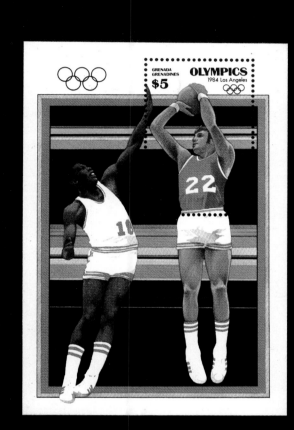

Cameron Wasson

4 South Portland Avenue #3
Brooklyn, New York 11217
(718) 875-8277

Member Graphic Artists Guild

Represented in Chicago by:
Vincent Kamin & Associates
(312) 787-8834

Clients include: Seventeen; Brides; Savvy; Redbook;
Games Magazine; American Health; Glamour;
Working Woman; Texas Monthly; Ladies Home
Journal; Working Mother; 'D' Magazine; Florida Trend;
Young Miss; Fairchild Publications; 13-30 Corp.;

CBS Publications; Ziff-Davis; J. Walter Thompson;
The Martin Agency; Bloomingdale's; Doyle Dane
Bernbach; Hill, Holliday, Connors, Cosmopulos;
Smith/Greenland.

1. Boston Globe
2. Celanese Arnel
3. Ziff-Davis
4. Texas Monthly
5. Family Health Magazine

Richard
Jesse Watson

P.O. Box 1470
Murphys, California 95247
(209) 728-2701

Member Graphic Artists Guild

Ken Westphal

7616 Fairway
Prairie Village, Kansas 66208
(913) 381-8399

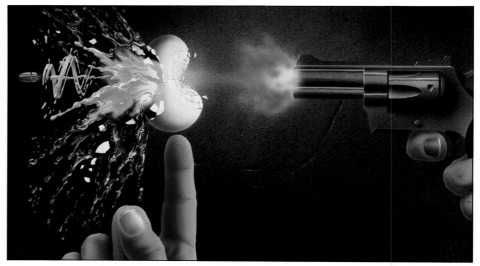

Ken Westphal

7616 Fairway
Prairie Village, Kansas 66208
(913) 381-8399

Clients include: United Telecom, McDonalds, Pizza Hut, Kustom Electronics, Gretsch Drums, Campus Life, Christianity Today, Mobay Chemical, Dekalb, Discwasher, Lee Jeans, Blue Cross.

Member Graphic Artists Guild.

Ed Wexler

11668 Kiowa Avenue #208
Los Angeles, California 90049
(213) 826-1968

Cartoon, caricature, humorous illustration and animation design.

Clients include:
ARCO
Automotive Age
BBDO/West
Burson-Marsteller
Cannon Films
CBS
Chiat/Day
Columbia Pictures
Diener/Hauser/Bates
KROQ-FM
The Ladd Company
Laff Track
Magazine Age
Muscle & Fitness Magazine
NBC
Needham, Harper & Steers
New York Magazine
Olympia Beer
Playboy Publications
Playgirl
Seineger Advertising
Touche-Ross
Transcon
Twentieth Century Fox
USA Cable Network
Warner Brothers
Yamaha
Ziff-Davis Publishing

Slides available upon request

Member Graphic Artists Guild

© Ed Wexler 1984

Samuel B. Whitehead

206 Eighth Avenue
Brooklyn, New York 11215
(718) 965-2047

Client List:
AT&T
The Boston Globe
Crawdaddy
The Detroit Free Press
The Detroit News, Inc.
Donruss Co.
Michigan Bell Telephone
The New Republic
New York Telephone
The New York Times
G.P. Putnam's Sons
Saturday Review
Scholastic Inc.
Topps
United Auto Workers Public
Relations

Kim Whitesides

P.O. Box 2189
Park City, Utah 84060
(801) 649-0490

Represented by:

New York: Madeline Renard
(212) 490-2450

Chicago: Joel Harlib & Assoc.
(312) 329-1370

Dallas: Linda Smith/
Judy Whalen
(214) 521-5156

San Francisco:
Mary VanDamme
(415) 433-1292

Los Angeles: France Aline
(213) 383-0498

Simple, Clean, Exciting Design,
Illustration

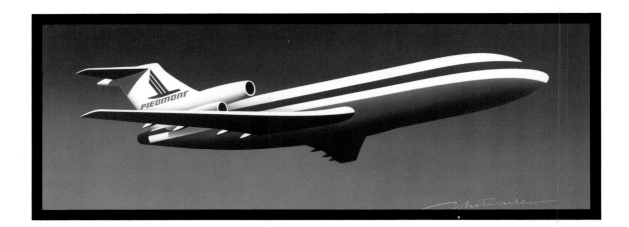

Fredric Winkowski

48 West 71st Street
New York, New York 10023
(212) 724-3136 or
(212) 874-1370

Illustration and design

Clients include:
Xerox Corp., J.C. Penney, Young & Rubicam, N.W.
Ayer, CBS, McCann-Erickson, New York Times,
McGraw-Hill, Macmillan, Backer & Spielvogel, Gannet
Newspapers, Scholastic Publishing, Harper & Row,
Viking Press, Workman Publishing, McCall's Magazine.

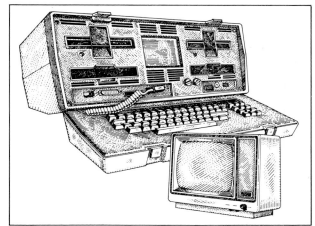

G·E·T   I·N·T·O   B·O·O·K·S

F. WINKOWSKI

Marc Yankus

179 Prince Street
New York, New York 10012
(212) 228-6539

Member of the Graphic Artists Guild

Clients include: AT&T, Ogilvy & Mather, Ruvane &
Leverte, Sudler & Hennessey Agency, McGraw-Hill,
Doubleday & Co., The Brooklyn Museum, The New
York Times, Life Magazine, Science Digest, GEO
Magazine.

Left to right, top to bottom: GEO Magazine; Madison
Avenue Magazine, an article on Creativity in Advertising; cover for Asimov Magazine; Audio Times.

Bruce Young

Atlanta, Georgia
(404) 952-5067

Represented by:
Wooden Reps
503 Ansley Villa Drive
Atlanta, Georgia 30324
(404) 892-6303

Spectron Artist Ltd
5 Dryden Street
London WC2E 9NW
(01) 240-3430

Clients Include: BDA-BBDO; Burton-Campbell;
Cargill; Wilson & Acree; Coca-Cola; D'Arcy-
MacManus & Masius; Delta Airlines; General Foods;
McCann-Erickson; J. Walter Thompson; Six Flags;
Snapper Power Equipment; Wrangler.

John Youssi

Represented by:
Moshier & Maloney
535 North Michigan Avenue
Suite 1416
Chicago, Illinois 60611
(312) 943-1668

Client list:

Kraft Foods
Inland Steel
Philco
Album Graphics
Playboy
McDonald's
Seven-Up
International Harvester
United Airlines
G.D. Searle
Kellogg's
Chicago Tribune
Abbott Labs
Anheuser-Busch
S.C. Johnson
Brunswick
Squibb
McDonnel Douglas
Quaker Oats
Mattel
Sunkist
Atari
Procter & Gamble
AT&T
Fort Howard Paper
Westinghouse

1. Agency: Fletcher-Mayor
   A.D.: Bob Lanning
   Client: Surflan

2. Agency: Waldman &
   Associates, Inc.
   A.D.: Carol Greenan
   Client: WLS-Radio

3. Agency: J. Walter Thompson
   A.D.: Bill Shanahan
   Client: McDonnel Douglas

4. Agency: Tathum-Laird
   & Kudner
   A.D.: Larry Walters
   Client: Procter & Gamble

5. Agency: Leo Burnett
   A.D.: Greg King
   Client: United Airlines

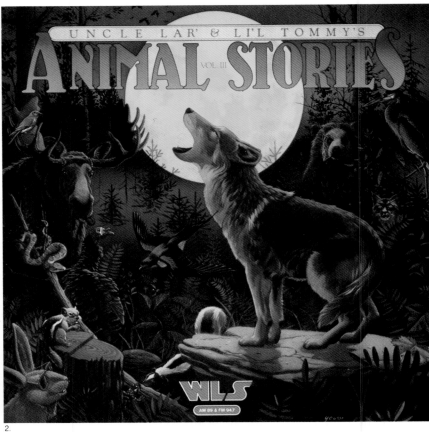

Jerry Zimmerman

48 West 20th Street
New York, New York 10011
(212) 620-7777

Clients include: Geer, DuBois
Inc.; Young & Rubicam;
Needham, Harper & Steers;
William Esty; Wilkerson; Scali,
McCabe, Sloves; Ted Bates;
Cavalieri & Kleier; Random
House; Foote, Cone & Belding;
Cunningham & Walsh;
Dancer Fitzgerald; N.W. Ayer;
Marsteller; Esquire; New York
Times; G.Q.; Games;
Seventeen; Scholastic.

INDEX

continued on page 287

INDEX

continued from page 286

continued on page 288

INDEX

continued from page 287

PHONE LISTINGS & ADDRESSES OF REPRESENTATIVES & VISUAL ARTISTS

Contents

Regions

New York City

Northeast
Connecticut
Delaware
Maine
Maryland
Massachusetts
New Hampshire
New Jersey
New York State
Pennsylvania
Rhode Island
Vermont
Washington, D.C.
West Virginia

Southeast
Alabama
Florida
Georgia
Kentucky
Louisiana
Mississippi
North Carolina
South Carolina
Tennessee
Virginia

Midwest
Illinois
Indiana
Iowa
Kansas
Michigan
Minnesota
Missouri
Nebraska
North Dakota
Ohio
South Dakota
Wisconsin

Southwest
Arizona
Arkansas
New Mexico
Oklahoma
Texas

Rocky Mountain
Colorado
Idaho
Montana
Utah
Wyoming

West Coast
Alaska
British Columbia
California
Hawaii
Nevada
Oregon
Washington

NOTES:

NOTES:

REPRESENTATIVES

Legend
A = Animator
AV = Audio Visual
C = Cartoonist
D = Director
F = Film
G = Graphic Designer
H & MU = Hair & Make-up
I = Illustrator
L = Lettering
M = Music
P = Photographer
R = Retoucher
TV = Television

NEW YORK CITY

A

Abbey, Ken & Assoc/421 Seventh Ave, New York, NY — 212-758-5259
David Greenberg, (P), Hal Oringer, (P), Ted Pobiner, (P), A J Sandone, (P)

Acevedo, Alba/293 Garfield Pl, Brooklyn, NY — 718-622-0246
Adams, Kristine/62 W 45th St, New York, NY — 212-869-4170
Adams, Ray/105 E 29th St, New York, NY — 212-719-5514
American Artists/353 W 53rd St #1W, New York, NY — 212-682-2462
Ed Acuna, (I), Don Almquist, (I), Keith Batcheller, (I), Jim Beigan, (I), Dan Bridy, (I), Bob Byrd, (I), Gary Ciccarelli, (I), Norm Doherty, (I), Alfred D'Ortenzio, (I), Lane DuPont, (I), John Freas, (P), George Gaadt, (I), Jackie Geyer, (I), John Hamagami, (I), John Holm, (I), Chris Hopkins, (I), Sandy Huffaker, (I), Todd Kat, (I), Richard Krieger, (I), Ed Lindlof, (I), Ron Mahoney, (I), Mick McGinty, (I), Steve Miller, (I), Bob Radigan, (I), Ed Renfro, (I), Paul Rogers, (I), Paul Rogers, (I), Mike Ruland, (I), Jan Sawka, (I), Todd Schorr, (P), Kathy S. Schorr, (I), Joe Scrofani, (I), Arthur Shilstone, (I), Eucalyptus Tree Studio, (I), Ron Wolin, (I), Andy Zito, (I)

Anderson, Michael/125 Fifth Ave, New York, NY — 212-620-4075
Anton, Jerry/107 E 38th St #5A, New York, NY — 212-679-4562
Bobbye Cochran, (I), Abe Echevarria, (I), Norman Green, (I), Aaron Rezny, (P), Bob Ziering, (I)

Armona, Fran/35 W 36th St, New York, NY — 212-563-2730
Bruno, (P)

Arnold, Peter Inc/1466 Broadway #1405, New York, NY — 212-840-6928
Fred Bavendam, (P), Bob Evans, (P), Jacques Jangoux, (P), Manfred Kage, (P), Stephen Krasemann, (P), Hans Pfletschinger, (P), David Scharf, (P), Erika Stone, (P), Bruno Zehnder, (P)

Artists Associates/211 E 51st St #5F, New York, NY — 212-755-1365
Norman Adams, (I), Don Braupigam, (I), Michael Deas, (I), Mark English, (I), Alex Gnidziejko, (I), Robert Heindal, (I), Steve Karchin, (I), Dick Krepel, (I), Skip Liepky, (I), Rick McCollum, (I), Fred Otnes, (I), Daniel Schwartz, (I)

Artists International/225 Lafayette St, New York, NY — 212-334-9310
ARTON ASSOCIATES/216 E 45TH ST, NEW YORK, NY (P 54) — **212-661-0850**
Paul Giovanopoulis, (I), Laurent Hubert, (I), Jacob Knight, (I), Carveth Kramer, (I), Michelle Laporte, (I), Karen Laurence, (I), Katrina Taylor, (I)

Asciutto, Mary Anne/99 Madison Ave, New York, NY — 212-679-8660
Ash, Michael/5 W 19th St, New York, NY — 212-741-0015
Azzara, Louise/131 E 17th St, New York, NY — 212-674-8114

B

Backer, Vic/30 W 26th St, New York, NY — 212-620-0944
Badin, Andy/835 Third Ave 4th Fl, New York, NY — 212-986-8833
Jeff Feinen, (I), Vera, (I), Brad Guice, (P), Robert S Levy, (I), George Tsui, (I)

Bahm, Darwin/6 Jane St, New York, NY — 212-989-7074
Joan Landis, (I), Rick Meyerowitz, (I), Don Ivan Punchatz, (I), Arno Sternglass, (I), John Thompson, (I), Robert Weaver, (I)

Barboza, Ken Assoc/853 Broadway #1603, New York, NY — 212-505-8635
Barclay, R Francis/5 W 19th St, New York, NY — 212-255-3440
Basile, Ron/1328 Broadway PH, New York, NY — 212-244-5511
Becker, Noel/150 W 55th St, New York, NY — 212-757-8987
Howard Tangye, (I), Sy Vinopoll, (P)

Beilin, Frank/405 E 56th St, New York, NY — 212-751-3074
Benedict, Brinker/6 W 20th St, New York, NY — 212-675-8067
BERNSTEIN & ANDRIULLI/60 E 42ND ST #505, NEW YORK, NY (P 8-29) — **212-682-1490**
Tony Antonios, (I), Garin Baker, (I), Garie Blackwell, (I), Melinda Bordelon, (I), Graphic Assoc, (I), Airstream, (I), Everett Davidson, (I), Cathy Deeter, (I), Griesbach/Martucci, (I), Victor Gadino, (I), Veronika Hart, (I), Catherine Huerta, (I), Cathy Johnson, (I), Kid Kane, (I), Mary Ann Lasher, (I), Bette Levine, (I), Michael Molkenthon, (I), Frank Moscati, (P), Simpson/Flint, (P), Maria Shega, (I), Chuck Slack, (I), Murray Tinkelman, (I), Clay Turner, (I), Chuck Wilkinson, (I), James B. Wood, (P)

Berthezen, Cyndie/315 W 54th St #12, New York, NY — 212-245-6584
William Garrett, (P), Sydney Shatzky, (I)

Bishop, Lynn/134 E 24th St, New York, NY — 212-254-5737
Irene Stern, (P)

Black Star/450 Park Ave S, New York, NY — 212-679-3288
John W. Alexanders, (P), Nancy Rica Schiff, (P), Arnold Zann, (P)

Bloncourt, Nelson/308 W 30th St, New York, NY — 212-594-3679
Blum, Felice S/79 W 12th St, New York, NY — 212-929-2166
Boghosian, Marty/7 E 35th St #2B, New York, NY — 212-685-8939
James Salzano, (P)

Bohmark Ltd/43 E 30th St 14th Fl, New York, NY — 212-889-9670
Booth, Tom Inc/435 W 23rd St, New York, NY — 212-243-2750
Mike Datoli, (P), Joshua Green, (P), Mats Gustavson, (I), Bob Hiemstre, (I), Jon Mathews, (I), Mike VanHorn, (I)

Brackman, Henrietta/415 E 52nd St, New York, NY — 212-753-6483
Brackman, Selma/251 Park Ave S, New York, NY — 212-777-4210
Brennan, Dan/32 E 38th St, New York, NY — 212-889-6555
Tom Biondo, (P), Knut Bry, (P), Francois Deconnick, (P), Renato Grignaschi, (P), Bob Krieger, (P), Michel Momy, (P)

Brindle, Carolyn/203 E 89th St #3D, New York, NY — 212-831-1572
BRODY, ANNE/55 BETHUNE ST STUDIO 6, NEW YORK, NY (P 55) — **212-242-1407**
John Gampert, (I), John Jamilkowski, (I), Claude Martinot, (I), Harold Pattek, (GD), Debora Whitehouse, (I)

Brody, Sam/230 E 44th St #2F, New York, NY — 212-758-0640
Robert Butler, (P), Fred Hilliard, (I), Elyse Lewin, (P), Sten Svenson, (P), Rudi Tesa, (P)

Brown Ink Assoc/267 Fifth Ave #706, New York, NY — 212-686-5576
Bob Brown, (I), Virginia Curtin, (I), Dariel Kanyok, (I), Jody Silver, (P)

Brown, Doug/400 Madison Ave, New York, NY — 212-980-4971
Andrew Unangst, (P)

Browne, Pema Ltd/185 E 85th St, New York, NY — 212-369-1925
George Angelini, (I), Joe Burleson, (I), Peter Catalanotto, (I), Ted Enik, (I), Ron Jones, (I), Glee LoScalzo, (I), David Plourde, (I), Paul Reott, (I), John Rush, (I), John Sandford, (I)

Bruck, J.S/157 W 57th St, New York, NY — 212-247-1130
Richard Anderson, (I), Peter Caras, (I), Eva Cellini, (I), Joseph Cellini, (I), Michael Dudash, (I), Tom Freeman, (I), Donald Hedin, (I), Jim Mathewuse, (I), Richard Newton, (I), Victoria Vebell, (I), Sally Jo Vitsky, (I), Gary Watson, (I)

Bruck, Nancy/315 E 69th St, New York, NY — 212-288-6023
Morton Beebe, (P)

Bruml, Kathy/262 West End Ave, New York, NY — 212-874-5659
Byrnes, Charles/5 E 19th St, New York, NY — 212-473-3366
Steve Steigman, (P)

C

Cafiano, Charles/140 Fifth Ave, New York, NY — 212-777-2616
Stan Fellerman, (P), Kenro Izu, (P)

Cahill, Joe/135 E 50th St, New York, NY — 212-751-0529
Shig Ikeda, (P), Brad Miller, (P), Howard Sochurek, (P)

Camera 5/6 W 20th St, New York, NY — 212-989-2004
Bob Bishop, (P), Peter Calvin, (P), Karin Epstein, (P), Curt Gunther, (P), Boyd Hagen, (P), Ralph Lewin, (P), Michael Marks, (P), Ralph Pabst, (P), Neal Preston, (P), Ken Regan, (P), Bob Sherman, (P), Ben Weaver, (P), Bob Wiley, (P)

Camp, Woodfin & Assoc/415 Madison Ave, New York, NY — 212-750-1020
Carleo, Teresa/1328 Broadway PH, New York, NY — 212-244-5515
Steve Chenn, (P)

Carmel/69 Mercer St, New York, NY — 212-925-6216
Guy Powers, (P)

Carp, Stanley/11 E 48th St, New York, NY — 212-759-8880
Nick Samardge, (P), Allen Vogel, (P)

Caruso, Frank/523 E 9th St, Brooklyn, NY — 718-854-8346
Casey, Judy/200 W 54th St #3C, New York, NY — 212-757-6144
Michael Doster, (I), Torkil Gudnason, (P), Michael O Brien, (P), Taolo Roversi, (P)

Casey, Marge/245 E 63rd St, New York, NY — 212-486-9575
Chalek, Rick/9 E 32nd St, New York, NY — 212-688-1080
Opticalusions, (I)

REPRESENTATIVES

Chapnick, Ben/450 Park Ave S, New York, NY	212-679-3288
Arnold Zann, (P)	
Chie/15 E 11th St #2M, New York, NY	212-243-2353
CHISLOVSKY, CAROL/420 MADISON AVE #401, NEW YORK, NY (P 30,31)	**212-980-3510**
Randal Birkey, (I), Russell Cobane, (I), Robert Cooper, (I), John Gray, (I), Michael Haynes, (I), Hubert, (I), Tim Herman, (I), William Hosner, (I), Jim Hunt, (I), Joe Lapinski, (I), Felix Marich, (I), Joe Ovies, (I), Vincent Petragnani, (I), Chuck Schmidt, (I), Sandra Shap, (I), Danny Smythe, (I), Nighthawk Studios, (I), Bob Thomas, (I)	
Clarfeld, Suzy/PO Box 455 Murray Hill Station, New York, NY	212-255-0698
COLLIGNON, DANIELE/200 W 15TH ST, NEW YORK, NY (P 56,57)	**212-243-4209**
Bob Aiese, (I), David Gambale, (I), Mel Greifinger, (I), Richard Hughes, (P), Mike Lester, (I), Fran Oelbaum, (I), Barbara Sandler, (I), Varlet-Martinelli, (I)	
Conroy, Chris/124 E 24th St, New York, NY	212-598-9766
Crabb, Wendy/320 E 50th St #5A, New York, NY	212-355-0013
Irene Stern, (P), Norman Walker, (A)	
Creative Freelancers/62 W 45th St, New York, NY	212-398-9540
Harold Brooks, (I), Howard Darden, (I), Claudia Fouse, (I), Arie Hass, (I), Rosanne Percivalle, (I), Alex Tiani, (I)	
CREATIVE TALENT/62 LEROY ST, NEW YORK, NY (P 59)	**212-243-7869**
Marshall Cetlin, (I), Christine Ciesiel, (I), Guy Smalley, (I)	
Cullom, Ellen/55 E 9th St, New York, NY	212-777-1749

D

D P I/521 Madison Ave, New York, NY	212-752-3930
Shorty Wilcox, (P)	
Davies, Nora/370 E 76th St, New York, NY	212-628-6657
DeBacker, Clo/29 E 19th St, New York, NY	212-420-1276
Bob Kiss, (P)	
Dedell, Jacqueline/58 W 15th St, New York, NY	212-741-2539
Ivan Chermayeff, (I), Teresa Fasolino, (I), Chermayeff and Geismar, (I), Ivan Powell, (I), Barry Root, (I), Richard Williams, (I), Henry Wolf, (P)	
DELLACROCE, JULIA/120 W 81ST ST, NEW YORK, NY (P 233)	**212-580-1321**
Bob Bender, (P), Winslow Pinney Pels, (I)	
Delvecchio, Lorraine/3156 Baisley, Bronx, NY	212-829-5194
Des Verges, Diana/73 Fifth Ave, New York, NY	212-691-8674
Deverin, Daniele/226 E 53rd St, New York, NY	212-755-4945
Paul Blakey, (I), Greg Couch, (I), Mort Drucker, (I), Lazlo Kubinyi, (I), Charles Shields, (I), Jeff Smith, (I), Don Weller, (I)	
Devers, Larry/26 Grammercy Park S #9H, New York, NY	212-777-8635
DeVito, Kitty/43 E 30th St 14th Fl, New York, NY	212-889-9670
Bart DeVito, (p)	
DeWan, Michael/250 Cabrini Blvd #2E, New York, NY	212-927-9458
Nancy Bundt, (P), Don Sparks, (P)	
Dewey, Frank & Assoc/420 Lexington Ave, New York, NY	212-986-1249
Di Como, Charles & Assoc Inc/12 W 27th St, New York, NY	212-689-8670
DiCarlo, Barbara/500 E 85th St, New York, NY	212-734-2509
Bob Wolfson, (P)	
Dickinson, Alexis/175 Fifth Ave #1112, New York, NY	212-473-8020
Jim Allen, (P), Robert Cohen, (P), Togashi, (P), Richard Dunkley, (P), Stephan Foster, (I), Jonathon Nix, (I), Elenore Thompson, (P)	
DiMartino, Joseph/200 E 58th St, New York, NY	212-935-9522
Mark Blanton, (I), Sid Evans, (I), Don Rogers, (I), Graphicsgroup, (I), Whistl'n-Dixie, (I)	
Dorman, Paul/419 E 57th St, New York, NY	212-826-6737
Studio DGM, (P)	
Drexler, Sharon/451 Westminister Rd, Brooklyn, NY	178-284-4779
Les Katz, (I)	
DuBane, J J/130 W 17th St, New York, NY	212-982-5201
Peter Castellano, (P), Cy Gross, (P), Bruce Plotkin, (P), Carmen Schiavone, (P), Bob Stone, (P)	
Dubner, Logan/342 Madison Ave, New York, NY	212-883-0242
Charles Kemper, (P), Siorenzo Niccoli, (P)	

E

Eagles, Betsy/130 W 57th St, New York, NY	212-582-1501

East Village Enterprises/231 W 29th St # 807, New York, NY	212-563-5722
Gordon Harris, (I), David Jehn, (G), Carlos Torres, (I)	
Edlitz, Ann/230 E 79th St #14F, New York, NY	212-744-7945
Ellis, Mirjana/176 Westminister Rd, Brooklyn, NY	178-282-6449
Ray Ellis, (P)	
Eng, Barbara/110 E 23rd St, New York, NY	212-254-8334
Erlacher, Bill/211 E 51st St, New York, NY	212-755-1365

F

Feldman, Robert/358 W 18th St, New York, NY	212-741-7254
Alen MacWeeney, (P), Terry Niefield, (P)	
Ficalora, Michael/28 E 29th St, New York, NY	212-679-7700
Finer, Arthur/216 E 45th St, New York, NY	212-661-0850
Fischer, Bob/135 E 54th St, New York, NY	212-755-2131
Bill Siliano, (P)	
Flood, Phyllis Rich/67 Irving Pl, New York, NY	212-674-8080
Istvan Banyai, (I), Christopher Blumrich, (I), Seymour Chwast, (I), Jose Cruz, (I), Vivienne Flesher, (I), Sarah Moon, (P), Elwood H Smith, (I), Stanislaw Zagorski, (I)	
Foster, Peter/870 UN Plaza, New York, NY	212-593-0793
Charles Tracey, (P)	
Freson, Robert/88 Seventh Ave, New York, NY	212-246-0679
Friess, Susan/36 W 20th St, New York, NY	212-675-3021
Richard Goldman, (P)	
Friscia, Salmon/20 W 10th St, New York, NY	212-228-4134
Furst, Franz/420 E 55th St, New York, NY	212-753-3148
Greg Pease, (P)	

G

Galbrand, Lauren/62 Leroy St, New York, NY	212-243-7869
Gamma-Liason/150 E 58th St, New York, NY	212-888-7272
Bruce McAllister, (P)	
Gargagliano, Tony/216 E 45th St, New York, NY	212-661-0850
Gaynin, Gail/147 W 25th St, New York, NY	212-255-3040
Terry Clough, (P)	
Gebbia, Doreen/156 Fifth Ave, New York, NY	212-807-0588
Gelb, Elizabeth/856 West End Ave, New York, NY	212-222-1215
Gelband, Lauren/62 Leroy St, New York, NY	212-243-7869
Ginsburg, Mike/Furer, Doug/145 E 27th St #7L, New York, NY	212-628-2379
Giraldi, Tina/54 W 39th St, New York, NY	212-840-8225
Goldman, David/18 E 17th St, New York, NY	212-807-6627
Norm Bendell, (I), Jay Brenner, (P), Jim Kingston, (I), Joe Marvullo, (P)	
Goldstein, Michael L/107 W 69th St, New York, NY	212-874-6933
Carla Bauer, (P), Fred Schulze, (P)	
Gomberg, Susan/145 E 22nd St, New York, NY	212-473-8747
Richard Fried, (P), Ron Lieberman, (I), Janeart Limited, (P)	
Goodman, Barbara L/435 E 79th St, New York, NY	212-288-3076
Goodwin, Phyllis A/10 E 81st St, New York, NY	212-570-6021
Laurence Bartone, (P), Carl Furuta, (P), Howard Menkin, (P)	
GORDON, BARBARA ASSOC/165 E 32ND ST, NEW YORK, NY (P 60,61)	**212-686-3514**
Ron Barry, (I), Higgins Bond, (I), Bob Clarke, (I), Keita Colton, (I), James Dietz, (I), Glenn Harrington, (I), Nenad Jakesevic, (I), Jackie Jasper, (I), Sonja Lamut, (I), April Lawton, (I), Andrew Nitzberg, (I), Sharleen Pederson, (I), Jas Szygiel, (I)	
Green, Anita/160 E 26th St, New York, NY	212-532-5083
Alan Dolgins, (P), Stuart Peltz, (P)	
Greenblatt, Eunice N/370 E 76th St, New York, NY	212-772-1776
Bob Brody, (P)	
Grey, Barbara L/1519 50th St, Brooklyn, NY	718-851-0332
Grien, Anita/155 E 38th St, New York, NY	212-697-6170
Dolores Bego, (I), Bruce Cayard, (I), Hal Just, (I), Jerry McDaniel, (I), Don Morrison, (I), Marina Neyman-Levikova, (I), Alan Reingold, (I), Ellen Rixford, (I), Bill Wilkinson, (I)	
Griffith, Valerie/10 Sheridan Square, New York, NY	212-675-2089
Groves, Michael/113 E 37th St, New York, NY	212-532-2074
Ulf Skogsbergh, (P)	

H

Hajjar, Rene/220 Park Ave S, New York, NY	212-777-5361
Chris Jones, (P)	
Handwerker, Elise/2752 Whitman Dr, Brooklyn, NY	718-251-9404

REPRESENTATIVES CONT'D.

Please send us your additions and updates.

HANKINS + TEGENBORG LTD/60 E 42ND ST #428, NEW YORK, NY (P 34-43)   212-867-8092
Ralph Brillhart, (I), David Cook, (I), John Dawson, (I), Guy Deel, (I), John Dismukes, (I), John Ennis, (I), David Gaadt, (I), Paul Gleason, (I), James Griffin, (I), Edwin Herder, (I), Michael Herring, (I), Aleta Jenks, (I), Mike Kane, (I), Uldis Klavins, (I), Wendell Minor, (I), Charles Moll, (I), Greg Olanoff, (I), Walter Rane, (I), Kirk Reinert, (I), Robert Sabin, (I), Harry Schaar, (I), Bill Schmidt, (I), Dan Sneberger, (I), Mario Stasolla, (I), Frank Steiner, (I), Robert Travers, (I), Victor Valla, (I), Jeff Walker, (I)

Hansen, Wendy/126 Madison Ave, New York, NY   212-684-7139
Minh, (P)

Hare, Fran/126 W 23rd St, New York, NY   212-794-0043
Peter B Kaplan, (P)

Harmon, Rod/130 W 57th St, New York, NY   212-582-1501
Steve Castagnato, (P), David Hedrick, (P), Stuart McCloud, (P), Ron Nicoleysen, (p), Len Staedler, (P)

Henry, John/237 E 31st St, New York, NY   212-686-6883
Gregory Cannon, (P), Kerry Hayes, (P), Rosemary Howard, (P)

Herron, Pat/829 Park Ave, New York, NY   212-753-0462
Larry Dale Gordon, (P), Malcolm Kirk, (P)

Heyl, Fran/230 Park Ave #2525, New York, NY   212-687-8930

Hoeye, Michael/120 W 70th St, New York, NY   212-362-9546
David Vogel, (P), Richie Williamson, (P)

Hollyman, Audrey/300 E 40th St #19R, New York, NY   212-867-2383
Tom Hollyman, (P), Nancy LeVine, (P), Norman Parkinson, (P), Tobey Sanford, (P)

Holt, Rita/280 Madison Ave, New York, NY   212-683-2002

Hovde, Nob/829 Park Ave, New York, NY   212-753-0462
Malcolm Kirk, (P), J Frederick Smith, (P)

Hurewitz, Gary/5 E 19th St, New York, NY   212-473-3366
Howard Berman, (P), Steve Bronstein, (P), Steve Steigman, (P)

Husak, John/444 E 82nd St #12C, New York, NY   212-988-6267
Frank Marchese, (G), William Sloan, (I)

J
Jacobsen, Vi/333 Park Ave S, New York, NY   212-677-3770
Jaffe, Sandy/15 W 24th St 2nd Fl, New York, NY   212-255-8250
Jedell, Joan/370 E 76th St, New York, NY   212-861-7861
Johnson, Evelyne Assoc/201 E 28th St, New York, NY   212-532-0928
Johnson, Janice/340 E 93rd St #9I, New York, NY   212-722-4964
Judge, Marie/1 W 64th St, New York, NY   212-874-4200

K
Kahn, Harvey/50 E 50th St, New York, NY   212-752-8490
Nicholas Gaetano, (I), Gerald Gersten, (I), Hal Herrman, (I), Wilson McLean, (I), Bob Peak, (I), Robert Peak, (P), Isadore Seltzer, (I), Kirsten Soderlind, (I)

KANE, BARNEY INC/18 E 16TH ST 2ND FL, NEW YORK, NY (P 45-48)   212-206-0322
Margaret Brown, (P), Alan Daniels, (I), Jack DeGraffenried, (I), Joe Denaro, (I), Michael Farina, (I), Nat Giorgio, (I), William Harrison, (I), Steve Hochman, (I), Steven Keyes, (I), Bob Lapsley, (I), Peter Lloyd, (I), Ted Lodigensky, (I), Rich Mahon, (I), Robert Melendez, (I), Sue Rother, (I), Gary Ruddel, (I), Joseph Sellars, (I), Glen Tunstull, (I), Larry Winborg, (I), Jenny Yip, (I)

Keating, Peggy/30 Horatio St, New York, NY   212-691-4654
Georgan Damore, (I), June Grammer, (I), Gerri Kerr, (I), Bob Parker, (I), Frank Paulin, (I), Fritz Varady, (I), Carol Vennell, (I)

Keaton, Liz/40 W 27th St, New York, NY   212-532-2580
Kenney, John/12 W 32nd St, New York, NY   212-697-8370
James McLoughlin, (P)

Kestner, V G/427 E 77th St #4C, New York, NY   212-535-4144
Kim/209 E 25th St, New York, NY   212-679-5628

KIMCHE, TANIA/470 W 23RD ST, NEW YORK, NY (P 64-67)   212-242-6367
Michael Hostovich, (I), Rafal Olbinski, (I), Miriam Schottland, (I), E T Steadman, (I)

Kirchmeier, Susan/160 E 61st St, New York, NY   212-758-4242
Kirchoff-Wohlberg Inc./866 UN Plaza #4014, New York, NY   212-644-2020

Angela Adams, (I), Bob Barner, (I), Esther Baron, (I), Bradley Clark, (I), Brian Cody, (I), Gwen Connelly, (I), Floyd Cooper, (I), Betsy Day, (I), Lois Ehlert, (I), Al Fiorentino, (I), Frank Fretz, (I), Jon Friedman, (I), Jeremy Guitar, (I), Konrad Hack, (I), Pamela Higgins, (I), Ron Himler, (I), Rosekrans Hoffman, (I), Gerry Hoover, (I), Kathleen Howell, (I), Chris Kalle, (I), Mark Kelley, (I), Christa Kieffer, (I), Dora Leder, (I), Tom Leonard, (I), Susan Lexa, (I), Ron Logan, (I), Don Madden, (I), Jane McCreary, (I), Lyle Miller, (I), Carol Nicklaus, (I), Ed Parker, (I), Jim Pearson, (I), Charles Robinson, (I), Bronwen Ross, (I), Robert Steele, (I), Arvis Stewart, (I), Phero Thomas, (I), Pat Traub, (I), Lou Vaccaro, (I), Joe Veno, (I), John Wallner, (I), Alexandra Wallner, (I), Arieh Zeldich, (I)

Klein, Leslie D/130 E 37th St, New York, NY   212-683-5454
Eric Meola, (P), Digital Productions, (P)

KLIMT, BILL & MAURINE/15 W 72ND ST, NEW YORK, NY (P 68,69)   212-799-2231
Jeffrey Adams, (I), Wil Cormier, (I), Ted Detoy, (P), David Febland, (I), Stephen Gorman, (I), Ken Joudrey, (I), Frank Morris, (I), Alan Neider, (I), Michael Rodericks, (I)

Kooyker, Valerie/201 E 12th St, New York, NY   212-673-4333
Kopel, Shelly & Assoc/342 Madison Ave #261, New York, NY   212-986-3282
Bliss Brothers, (I), Penny Carter, (I), Al Hering, (I), Richard Rosenbloom, (I), Meryl Rosner, (I)

Kramer, Joan & Assoc/720 Fifth Ave, New York, NY   212-224-1758
David Cornwell, (P), Tom DeSanto, (P), Clark Dunbar, (P), John Lawlor, (P), Tom Leighton, (P), James McLoughlin, (P), Frank Moscati, (P), Jeff Perkell, (P), John Russell, (P), Ken Whitmore, (P), Bill Wilkinson, (P), Edward Young, (P)

Kreis, Ursula G/63 Adrian Ave, Bronx, NY   212-562-8931
Stephen Green-Armytage, (P), John T. Hill, (P), Bruce Pendleton, (P)

L
Lada, Joe/330 E 19th St, New York, NY   212-254-0253
George Hausman, (P)

Lafayette-Nelson & Assoc/64 W 15th St, New York, NY   212-989-7059
Lamont, Mary/200 W 20th St, New York, NY   212-242-1087
Jim Marchese, (P)

Lander, Jane Assoc/333 E 30th St, New York, NY   212-679-1358
Francois Cloteaux, (I), Patrick Couratin, (I), Phil Franke, (I), Mel Furukawa, (I), Helen Guetary, (I), Cathy Culp Heck, (I), Saul Lambert, (I), Dan Long, (I), Jack Pardue, (I), Frank Riley, (I)

Lane Talent Inc/104 Fifth Ave, New York, NY   212-861-7225
Larkin, Mary/308 E 59th St, New York, NY   212-308-7744
Lynn St John, (I)

Lavaty, Frank & Jeff/50 E 50th St #5, New York, NY   212-355-0910
John Berkey, (I), Tom Blackshear, (I), Jim Butcher, (I), R Crosthwaite, (I), Don Dally, (I), Bernie D'Andrea, (I), Domenick D'Andrea, (I), Roland Descombes, (I), Christine Duke, (I), Gervasio Gallardo, (I), Martin Hoffman, (I), Stan Hunter, (I), Chet Jezierski, (I), David McCall Johnston, (I), Mort Kunstler, (I), Lemuel Line, (I), Robert LoGrippo, (I), Don Maitz, (I), Mara McAfee, (I), Darrell Millsap, (I), Carlos Ochagavia, (I)

Lee, Alan/33 E 22nd St, New York, NY   212-673-2484
Werner Kappes, (I), Peter Vaeth, (P)

Lee, Barbara/307 W 82nd St, New York, NY   212-724-6176
Leff, Jerry/342 Madison Ave #949, New York, NY   212-697-8525
Franco Accornero, (I), James Barkley, (I), Ken Barr, (I), Tom Beecham, (I), Mike Bryan, (I), Mel Crair, (I), Ron DiCianni, (I), Charles Gehm, (I), Penelope Gottlieb, (I), Steve Gross, (I), Gary Lang, (I), Ron Lesser, (I), Dennis Magdich, (I), Michael Nicastre, (I), Roseann Nicotra, (I), John Parsons, (I), Bill Selby, (I), Jon Townley, (I), James Woodend, (I)

Legrand, Jean Yves & Assoc/41 W 84th St #4, New York, NY   212-724-5981
Jim Cherry, (I), Holly Hollington, (I), Barry McKinley, (P), Peter Sato, (I), Jack Ward, (P)

Leone, Mindy/381 Park Ave S #710, New York, NY   212-696-5674

Leonian, Edith/220 E 23rd St, New York, NY	212-989-7670
Philip Leonian, (P)	
Lerman, Gary/40 E 34th St #203, New York, NY	212-683-5777
John Bechtold, (P), Jan Cobb, (P)	
Levy, Leila/4523 Broadway #7G, New York, NY	212-942-8185
Lewin, Betsy/152 Willoughby Ave, Brooklyn, NY	212-622-3882
Ted Lewin, (I)	
Lingren, Patricia/194 Third Ave, New York, NY	212-475-0440
Locke, John Studios Inc/15 E 76th St, New York, NY	212-288-8010
John Cayea, (I), John Clift, (I), Oscar DeMejo, (I), Jean-Pierre Desclozeaux, (I), Blair Drawson, (I), James Endicott, (I), Richard Erdoes, (I), Jean Michel Folon, (I), Michael Foreman, (I), Andre Francois, (I), George Giusti, (I), Edward Gorey, (I), Peter Lippman, (I), Sam Maitin, (I), Richard Oden, (I), William Bryan Park, (I), Colette Portal, (I), Fernando Puigrosado, (I), Hans-Georg Rauch, (I), Ronald Searle, (I), Tim, (I), Roland Topor, (I)	
Locke, John Studios Inc/15 E 76th St, New York, NY	212-288-8010
Longobardi, Gerard/5 W 19th St, New York, NY	212-255-3440
Loshe, Diane/10 W 18th St, New York, NY	212-691-9920
LOTT, PETER & GEORGE/60 E 42ND ST #411, NEW YORK, NY (P 72,73)	**212-687-4185**
Juan Barberis, (I), Ted Chambers, (I), Tony Cove, (I), Jim Dickerson, (I), David Halpern, (I), Ed Kurtzman, (I), Marie Peppard, (I), Steen Svenson, (I)	

M
Mace, Zelda/1133 Broadway, New York, NY	212-929-7017
Madris, Stephen/445 E 77th St, New York, NY	212-744-6668
Gary Perweiler, (P)	
Manasse, Michele/1960 Broadway #2E, New York, NY	212-873-3797
Mangione, Phillip/175 Fifth Ave #1110, New York, NY	212-473-8020
Mann, Ken/20 W 46th St, New York, NY	212-944-2853
Hashi, (P)	
Marchesano, Frank/35 W 36th St, New York, NY	212-563-2730
Marino, Frank/35 W 36th St, New York, NY	212-563-2730
Bruno Benvenuti, (P)	
Mariucci, Marie A/32 W 39th St, New York, NY	212-944-9590
Marks, Don/50 W 17th St, New York, NY	212-807-0457
Mars, Sallie/60 E 42nd St #505, New York, NY	212-682-1490
Don Hamerman, (P), Nobu, (P), J C Suares, (P)	
Marshall, Mel/40 W 77th St, New York, NY	212-877-3921
Marshall, Winifred/2350 Broadway #625, New York, NY	212-874-0478
Mason, Kathy/101 W 18th St 4th Fl, New York, NY	212-675-3809
Don Mason, (P)	
Mathias, Cindy/7 E 14th St, New York, NY	212-741-3191
Vittorio Sartor, (I)	
MATTELSON, JUDY/88 LEXINGTON AVE #12G, NEW YORK, NY (P 127,197, 270	**212-684-2974**
Guy Billout, (I), Karen Kluglein, (I), Marvin Mattelson, (I), Gary Viskupic, (I)	
Mautner, Jane/85 Fourth Ave, New York, NY	212-777-9024
Mayo, Vicki/225 E 31st St, New York, NY	212-686-1690
Harold Krieger, (P)	
McVey, Meg/54 W 84th St # 2F, New York, NY	212-362-3739
Mendelsohn, Richard/353 W 53rd St #1W, New York, NY	212-682-2462
Mendola, Joseph/420 Lexington Ave #2911, New York, NY	212-986-5680
Paul Alexander, (I), Robert Berrar, (I), Dan Brown, (I), Jim Campbell, (I), Carl Cassler, (I), Joe Csatari, (I), Jim Dye, (I), John Eggert, (I), Peter Fiore, (I), Antonio Gabriele, (I), Tom Gala, (I), Hector Garrido, (I), Mark Gerber, (I), Ted Giavis, (I), Dale Gustafson, (I), Chuck Hamrick, (I), Richard Harvey, (I), Dave Henderson, (I), John Holmes, (I), Mitchell Hooks, (I), Joel Iskowitz, (I), Bob Jones, (I), Stuart Kaufman, (I), Michael Koester, (I), Richard Leech, (I), Dennis Lyall, (I), Jeffery Mangiat, (I), Goeffrey McCormack, (I), Ann Meisel, (I), Ted Michner, (I), Mike Mikos, (I), Jonathon Milne, (I), Wally Neibart, (I), Tom Newsome, (I), Mike Noome, (I), Chris Notarile, (I), Kukalis Romas, (I), Mort Rosenfeld, (I), Greg Rudd, (I), Rob Sauber, (I), David Schleinkofer, (I), Mike Smollin, (I), Kip Soldwedel, (I), John Solie, (I), George Sottung, (I), Joel Spector, (I), Cliff Spohn, (I), Jeffrey Terreson, (I), Bill Vann, (I), Mark Watts, (I), Allen Welkis, (I),	

Ben Wohlberg, (I), Ray Yeldman, (I)	
Meneeley, Richard/646 Ninth Ave, New York, NY	212-586-5911
Metz, Bernard/43 E 19th St, New York, NY	212-254-4996
Michalski, Ben/118 E 28th St, New York, NY	212-683-4025
MINTZ, LES/111 WOOSTER ST #PH C, NEW YORK, NY (P 49-51)	**212-925-0491**
Bernard Bonhomme, (I), Robert Burger, (I), Hovik Dilakian, (I), Amy Hill, (I), Susannah Kelly, (I), George Masi, (I), Tina Mercie, (I), Kirsten Soderlind, (I), Dennis Ziemienski, (I)	
Moretz, Eileen P/141 Wooster St, New York, NY	212-254-3766
Charles Moretz, (P), Jeff Morgan, (P)	
MORGAN, VICKI/194 THIRD AVE, NEW YORK, NY (P 75-82,173, 193)	**212-475-0440**
Williardson Associates, (I), Ray Cruz, (I), Joe Heiner, (I), Kathy Heiner, (I), Tim Lewis, (I), Richard Mantel, (I), Wayne McLoughlin, (I), Emanuel Schongut, (I), Nancy Stahl, (I), Bruce Wolfe, (I), Brian Zick, (I)	
Morse, Lauren/78 Fifth Ave, New York, NY	212-807-1551
Alan Zenreich, (P)	
Mosel, Sue/310 E 46th St, New York, NY	212-599-1806
Gerard Gentil, (P), Stan Shaffer, (P)	
Moskowitz, Marion/342 Madison Ave #469, New York, NY	212-719-9879
Diane Teske Harris, (I), Arnie Levin, (I), Geoffrey Moss, (I), Marty Norman, (I), Gary Ruddell, (I)	
MOSS, EILEEN/333 E 49TH ST #3J, NEW YORK, NY (P 145,234)	**212-980-8061**
Bill Cigliano, (I), Tom Curry, (I), Mike Davis, (I), Dennis Gottlieb, (I), Scott Pollack, (I), Norm Siegel, (I)	
Moss, Susan/29 W 38th St, New York, NY	212-354-8024
Louis Mervar, (P)	
Mulvey Associates/1457 Broadway #1001, New York, NY	212-840-8223
Dick Amundsen, (I), Harry Borgman, (I), Roberta Collier, (I), Bill Colrus, (I), Art Cumings, (I), Ric DelRossi, (I), John Dyess, (I), C S Ewing, (I), Leigh Grant, (I), Les Gray, (I), Bill Hartman, (I), Mark Johnson, (I), Phil Jones, (I), John Killgrew, (I), Davis Meltzer, (I), Rebecca Merrilees, (I), Kim Mulkey, (I), Larry Noble, (I), Tom Noonan, (I), Earl Norem, (I), Michael O'Reilly, (I), Taylor Oughton, (I), Tom Powers, (I), Don Pulver, (I), Sandy Rabinowitz, (I), John Rice, (I), Sally Schaedler, (I), Sally Swatland, (I), Bob Taylor, (I), Kyuzo Tsugami, (I), Eric Watts, (I), Jim Woodend, (I), Jack Woolhiser, (I), Jane Yamada, (I)	

NO
National Imagemakers/31 E 17th St, New York, NY	212-475-1050
NEAIL, PAMELA R ASSOC/233 E 82ND ST #3D, NEW YORK, NY (P 83-85)	**212-772-8444**
Sean Daly, (P), Dennis DiVincenzo, (I), Attila Hejja, (I), Thea Kliros, (I), Tony Mascio, (I), Ryuji Otani, (I), Brenda Pepper, (I), Janet Recchia, (I), Linda Richards, (I), Gail Severance, (I), Alex Vosk, (I)	
Newborn, Milton/135 E 54th St, New York, NY	212-421-0050
Stephen Alcorn, (I), John Alcorn, (I), Braldt Bralds, (I), Robert Giusti, (I), Dick Hess, (I), Mark Hess, (I), Edward Sorel, (I), Simms Taback, (I), David Wilcox, (I)	
O'Brien, Fern/201 W 77th St #8C, New York, NY	212-873-8095
Opticalusions/9 E 32nd St, New York, NY	212-688-1080
Stephen Burke, (I), George Kanelous, (I), Rudy Laslo, (I), Kenvin Lyman, (I), Roger Metcalf, (I), George I Parish, (I), Penelope, (I), Mike Robins, (I), Terry Ryan, (I), Ed Scarisbrick, (I), Bruce Young, (I)	
O'Rourke, Gene/200 E 62nd St, New York, NY	212-935-5027
Warren Flagler, (P), Sam Haskins, (P), Art Kane, (P), Douglas Kirkland, (P), Lincoln Potter, (P), Peter Angelo Simon, (P), Smith-Garner, (P), William Sumner, (P), John Thornton, (P), Alexis Urba, (P), Rob VanPetten, (P), John Zimmerman, (P)	

PQ
Palmer-Smith, Glenn Assoc/160 Fifth Ave, New York, NY	212-807-1855
Claude Mougin, Charles Nesbit, (P), John Stember, (P), Michel Teherevkoff, (P)	
PENNY & STERMER GROUP/48 W 21ST ST 9TH FL, NEW YORK, NY (P 91-99)	**212-243-4412**

Please send us your additions and updates.

Bob Alcorn, (I), Manos Angelakis, (I), Deborah Bazzel, (I),
Ron Becker, (I), Jane Clark, (I), Julian Graddon, (I), Rich
Grote, (I), Michael Kanarek, (I), Andy Lackow, (I), Gary
Smith, (I), Page Wood, (I)

Penny, Barbara Assoc/48 W 21st St, New York, NY	212-243-4412
Peretti, Linda/420 Lexington Ave, New York, NY	212-687-7392
Ken Tenabaum, (P)	
Peters, Barbara/One Fifth Ave, New York, NY	212-777-6384
Jacques Dirand, (P), Lizzie Himmel, (P)	
Photo Unique/1328 Broadway PH, New York, NY	212-244-5515
Phyllis/38 E 19th St 8th Fl, New York, NY	212-475-3798
John Weir, (P)	
Plessner International/95 Madison Ave, New York, NY	212-686-2444
Powers, Elizabeth/1414 Ave of Americas, New York, NY	212-832-2343
Di Franza Williams, (P)	
Quercia, Mat/78 Irving Pl, New York, NY	212-477-4491

R

**RAPP, GERALD & CULLEN INC/108 E 35TH ST #1,
NEW YORK, NY (P BACK COVER)** — **212-889-3337**

Michael Brown, (I), Lon Busch, (I), Ken Dallison, (I), Jack
Davis, (I), Bill Delvin, (I), Bob Deschamps, (I), Ray Domingo,
(I), Ginnie Hoffman, (I), Lionel Kalish, (I), Sharon Knettell,
(I), Lee Lorenze, (I), Allan Mardon, (I), Elwyn Mehlman, (I),
Marie Michal, (I), Alex Murawski, (I), Lou Myers, (I), Gary
Overacre, (I), Jerry Pinkney, (I), Charles Santori, (I), Bob
Tanenbaum, (I), Barry Zaid, (I)

Ray, Marlys/350 Central Pk W, New York, NY	212-222-7680
Bill Ray, (P)	
Reese, Kay Assoc/156 Fifth Ave #1107, New York, NY	212-924-5151

Jonathan Atkin, (P), Lev Borodulin, (P), Gerry Cranham, (P),
Scott C Dine, (P), Claudio Edinger, (P), Ashvin Gatha, (P),
Peter Gullers, (P), Arno Hammacher, (P), Jay Leviton, (P),
George Long, (P), George Love, (P), Lynn Pelham, (P),
Richard Saunders, (P), Milkie Studio, (P), T Tanuma, (P)

Reid, Pamela/420 E 64th St, New York, NY	212-832-7589
Thierry des Fontaines, (P), Sandy Hill, (S), Bert Stern, (P)	
Renard, Madeline/501 Fifth Ave #1407, New York, NY	212-490-2450

Chas Wm Bush, (P), John Collier, (I), Etienne Delessert, (I),
Bart Forbes, (I), Tim Girvin, (I), Lamb & Hall, (P), Miles
Hardiman, (I), John Martin, (I), Al Pisano, (I), Robert
Rodriguez, (I), Michael Schwab, (I), Jozef Sumichrast, (I),
Kim Whitesides, (I)

Rhodes, Lela/327 West 89 St, New York, NY	212-787-3885
Riley, Catherine/12 E 37th St, New York, NY	212-532-8326
Riley, Ted/215 E 31st St, New York, NY	212-684-3448

Zevi Blum, (I), William Bramhall, (I), David Gothard, (I),
James Grashow, (I), Paul Hogarth, (I), Edward Koren, (I),
Pierre Le-Tan, (I), Roy McKie, (I), Andrew Parker, (I),
Cheryl Peterson, (I), Jean Jacques Sempe, (I), Patricia
Wynne, (I)

Rindner, Barbara/216 E 45th St, New York, NY	212-661-0850
Rivelli, Cynthia/303 Park Ave S, New York, NY	212-254-0990
Rosenberg, Arlene/200 E 16th St, New York, NY	212-289-7701
Rubin, Elaine R/301 E 38th St #14E, New York, NY	212-725-8313
Rudoff, Stan/271 Madison Ave, New York, NY	212-679-8780

S

S I International/43 East 19th St, New York, NY	212-254-4996

Bob Bass, (I), Jack Brusca, (I), Richard Corben, (I), Richard
Courtney, (I), Robert DeMichiell, (I), Gaetano Liberatore, (I),
Sergio Martinez, (I), Martin Rigo, (I), Doug Rosenthal, (I)

SPAR/1123 Broadway #914, New York, NY	212-490-5895
Sacramone & Valentine/302 W 12th St, New York, NY	212-929-0487
Stephen Ladner, (P), Tohru Nakamura, (P), John Pilgreen, (P), Robin Saidman, (P), Gianni Spinazzola, (P)	
Samuels, Rosemary/39 E 12th St, New York, NY	212-477-3567
Sander, Vicki/48 Gramercy Park North #3B, New York, NY	212-674-8161
Savello, Denise/381 Park Ave S, New York, NY	212-535-4795
Sawyer/Nagakura & Assoc Inc/36 W 35th St, New York, NY	212-764-5944
Schecter Group, Ron Long/430 Park Ave, New York, NY	212-752-4400
Schickler, Paul/135 E 50th St, New York, NY	212-355-1044
Schon, Herb/1240 Lexington Ave, New York, NY	212-249-3236
Schub, Peter & Robert Bear/37 Beekman Pl, New York, NY	212-246-0679

Robert Freson, (P), Alexander Lieberman, (P), Irving Penn,
(P), Rico Puhlmann, (P), Snowdon, (P), Albert Watson, (P)

**SEIGEL, FRAN/515 MADISON AVE 22ND FL,
NEW YORK, NY (P 102-05)** — **212-486-9644**

Leslie Cabarga, (I), Cheryl Cooper, (I), Kinuko Craft, (I),
Peter Cross; (I), Joe English, (I), Earl Keleny, (I)

Shamilzadeh, Sol/1155 Broadway 3rd Fl, New York, NY	212-532-1977
Ryszard Horowitz, (P), The Strobe Studio, (P)	
Shapiro, Elaine/369 Lexington Ave, New York, NY	212-867-8220
Sheer, Doug/29 John St, New York, NY	212-732-4216
Karen Kent, (P)	
Shepherd, Judith/186 E 64th St, New York, NY	212-838-3214
Barry Seidman, (P)	

SIGMAN, JOAN/336 E 54TH ST, NEW YORK, NY (P 106) — **212-832-7980**

Robert Goldstrom, (I), John H Howard, (I), Jeff Seaver, (I)

Simon, Debra/119 Fifth Ave, New York, NY	212-505-5234
Uli Rose, (P)	
Sims, Jennifer/1150 Fifth Ave, New York, NY	212-860-3005
Clint Clemens, (P), Robert Latorre, (P)	
Sjolin, Robert Nils/117 W 13th St, New York, NY	212-242-7238
Richard Brummett, (P)	
Slocum, Linda/15 W 24th St 11th Fl, New York, NY	212-243-0649
Slome, Nancy/342 Madison Ave, New York, NY	212-370-1099
Ed Gallucci, (P), Joe Morello, (P)	
Smith, Emily/30 E 21st St, New York, NY	212-674-8383
Smith, Rose/400 E 56th St #19D, New York, NY	212-758-8711
Solomon, Richard/121 Madison Ave, New York, NY	212-683-1362
Rick Brown, (I), Ray-Mel Cornelius, (I), Jack E. Davis, (I), Elizabeth Koda-Callan, (I), David Palladini, (I), Rodica Prato, (I), Ian Ross, (I), John Svoboda, (I), Shelley Thornton, (I)	
Spencer, Carlene/462 W 23rd St, New York, NY	212-924-2498
Laszlo Studio, (P), Peter Vitale, (P)	
Spiers, Herb/43 E 19th St, New York, NY	212-254-4996
St Pierre, Bernadette/520 E 84th St, New York, NY	212-879-6356
Stein, Jonathan & Assoc/353 E 77th St, New York, NY	212-517-3648
Mitch Epstein, (P), Burt Glinn, (P), Ernst Haas, (P), Nathaniel Lieberman, (P), Alex MacLean, (P), Gregory Murphey, (P), Kim Steele, (P), Joel Sternfeld, (P), Jeffrey Zaruba, (P)	
Steiner, Susan/130 E 18th St, New York, NY	212-673-4704
Stermer, Carol Lee/114 E 32nd St, New York, NY	212-685-2770
Stevens, Norma/1075 Park Ave, New York, NY	212-427-7235
Avedon, Richard, (P)	
Stockland, Bill/7 W 16th St, New York, NY	212-242-7693
Joel Baldwin, (P), Laurence Bartone, (P)	
Stogo, Donald/310 E 46th St, New York, NY	212-490-1034
John Lawlor, (P), Tom McCarthy, (P)	
Susse, Ed/40 E 20th St, New York, NY	212-477-0674
Karl Zapp, (P)	

T

Taylor, Nancy/153 E 57th St, New York, NY	212-223-0744
Therese, Jane/6 W 20th St, New York, NY	212-675-8067
Nancy Brown, (P)	
Thomas, Brenda & Assoc/127 W 79th St, New York, NY	212-873-7236

TISE, KATHERINE/200 E 78TH ST, NEW YORK, NY (P 52,53) — **212-570-9069**

Raphael Boguslav, (I), John Burgoyne, (I), Bunny Carter, (I),
Cheryl Roberts, (I), Cathleen Toelke, (I)

Townsend, Kris/18 E 18th St, New York, NY	212-243-2484
David W Hamilton, (P)	
Tralongo, Katrin/144 W 27th St, New York, NY	212-255-1976
Mickey Kaufman, (P)	

UV

Umlas, Barbara/131 E 93rd St, New York, NY	212-534-4008
Hunter Freeman, (P)	
Uzarski, John/80 Varick St #4B, New York, NY	212-966-6782
Van Arnam, Lewis/154 W 57th St, New York, NY	212-541-4787
Paul Amato, (P), Mike Reinhardt, (P)	
Van Orden, Yvonne/119 W 57th St, New York, NY	212-265-1223
Vance, Joy/515 Broadway #2B, New York, NY	212-219-0808
Al Satterwhite, (P)	
Vollbracht, Michelle/225 E 11th St, New York, NY	212-475-8718
Walter Wick, (P)	

REPRESENTATIVES CONT'D.

Please send us your additions and updates.

Von Schreiber, Barbara/315 Central Pk West, New York, NY   212-873-6594
   Jean Pagliuso, (P), Hiro, (P), Neal Slavin, (P)

W

Walker, Eleanora/120 E 30th St, New York, NY   212-689-4431
Wasserman, Ted/331 Madison Ave #1007, New York, NY   212-867-5360
Waterson, Libby/350 E 30th St, New York, NY   212-696-1461
Watterson, Libby/350 E 30th St, New York, NY   212-696-1461
   Karen Leeds, (P), Karen Leeds, (P)
Wayne, Philip/66 Madison Ave #9C, New York, NY   212-889-2836
   Roberto Brosan, (P)
Wein, Gita/320 E 58th St, New York, NY   212-759-2763
Weissberg, Elyse/299 Pearl St #5E, New York, NY   212-406-2566
   Jack Reznicki, (P), Jack Reznicki, (P), Bill Smith, (P)
West, Beatrix/485 Fifth Ave #407, New York, NY   212-986-2110
Wheeler, Paul/50 W 29th St #11W, New York, NY   212-696-9832
   John Dominis, (P), Greg Edwards, (P), Seth Joel, (P), John McGrail, (P), Joe McNally, (P), Michael Melford, (P), Aaron Rapoport, (P), Steven Smith, (P), Peter Tenzer, (P), Leroy Woodson, (P)
Williamson, Jack/1414 Ave of the Americas, New York, NY   212-832-2343
   Di Franza Williams, (P)

YZ

Yellen, Bert & Assoc/838 Ave of Americas, New York, NY   212-605-0555
   Bill Connors, (P), Joe Francki, (P), Gordon Munro, (P)
Youngs, Maralee/318 E 39th St, New York, NY   212-679-8124
Zanetti, Lucy/139 Fifth Ave, New York, NY   212-473-4999

NORTHEAST

AB

Ackermann, Marjorie/2112 Goodwin Lane, North Wales, PA   215-646-1745
   H Mark Weidman, (P)
Andrews, Carolyn/109 Somerstown Rd, Ossining, NY   914-762-5335
   Whitney Lane, (P)
Bancroft, Carol & Friends/185 Goodhill Rd, Weston, CT   203-226-7674
   Wendy Biggins, (I), Jane Chambless-Rigie, (I), Jim Cummins, (I), Alan Daniel, (I), Andrea Eberbach, (I), Marla Frazee, (I), Jackie Geyer, (I), Fred Harsh, (I), Dennis Hockerman, (I), Ann Iosa, (I), Laurie Jordan, (I), Barbara Lanza, (I), Mila Lazarevich, (I), Karen Loccisano, (I), Jimmy Longacre, (I), Al Lorenz, (I), Bob Masheris, (I), Elizabeth Miles, (I), Yoshi Miyake, (I), Nancy Munger, (I), Rodney Pate, (I), Suzanne Richardson, (I), Gail Roth, (I), Miriam Schottland, (I), Blanche Sims, (I), Jim Spence, (I), Sally Springer, (I), Charles Varner, (I), Linda Boehm Weller, (I), Ann Wilson, (I), Chuck Wimmer, (I), Debby Young, (I)
Bauchner, Susan/774 Lincoln Ave, Bridgeport, CT   203-335-5859
   Jacques Charlas, (P)
Beckelman, Barbara/251 Greenwood Ave, Bethel, CT   203-797-8188
Birenbaum, Molly/7 Williamsburg Dr, Cheshire, CT   203-272-9253
Bloch, Peggy J/464 George Rd #5A, Cliffside Park, NJ   201-943-9435
Brown, Jill/911 State St, Lancaster, PA   717-393-0918
   brt Photo Illustration, (P)

CD

Camp, Woodfin Inc/925 1/2 F St NW, Washington, DC   202-638-5705
Chandoha, Sam/RD 1 PO Box 287, Annandale, NJ   201-782-3666
Correia, Joseph/11 Cabot Rd, Woburn, MA   617-933-3267
   Gorchev & Gorchev, (P)
Crandall, Rob & Marvin Saunders/516 W Boston Post Rd, Mamaroneck, NY   914-381-4400
D'Aquino, Connie/Rt 22, PO Box 64, Bedford Village, NY   914-234-3123
DeBren, Alan/355 Pearl St, Burlington, VT   802-864-5916
   John Goodman, (P)
Donaldson, Selina/37 Hemlock, Arlington, MA   617-646-1687

EG

ELLA/229 BERKELEY #52, BOSTON, MA (P 32,33)   **617-266-3858**
   Norman Adams, (P), Bente Adler, (I), Wilbur Bullock, (I), Rob Cline, (I), Jack Crompton, (I), Anna Davidian, (I), Susan Dodge, (I), Anatoly Dverin, (I), Scott Gordley, (I), Eaton & Iwen, (I), Roger Leyonmark, (I), Ron Toelkey, (I)
Giandomenico, Terry/13 Fern Ave, Collingswood, NJ   609-854-2222
   Bob Giandomenico, (P)

Gidley, Fenton/43 Tokeneke Rd, Darien, CT   212-772-0846
Glover, Cynthia/2502 Eutlaw Pl #2B, Baltimore, MD   301-728-7309
   Susan Fitzhugh, (P)
Gordon, Fran/1654 E 13th St #5A, Brooklyn, NY   212-339-4277
Gruder, Jean/1148 Parsippany Blvd, Parsippany, NJ   201-334-0353

HI

Haas, Ken/717 N Fifth St, Reading, PA   215-374-4431
Hopkins, Nanette/18 North New St, Westchester, PA   215-431-3240
   Rick Davis, (P)
Hubbell, Marian/99 East Elm St, Greenwich, CT   203-629-9629
Imlay, Kathy/41 Upton St, Boston, MA   617-262-5388

KL

Krongard, Paula/1 Riverview Dr W, Upper Montclair, NJ   201-783-6155
   Skip Hine, (P), Bill White, (P)
Kurlansky, Sharon/1400 Worcester Rd, Framingham, MA   617-872-4549
Labonty, Deborah/PO Box 7446, Lancaster, PA   717-291-9843
   Tim Schoon, (P)
LIPMAN, DEBORAH/506 WINDSOR DR, FRAMINGHAM, MA (P 70,71)   **617-451-6528**
   Mark Fisher, (I), Richard A. Goldberg, (I), James Hanlon, (I), Richard M. Joachim, (I), Armen Kojoyian, (I), Carol LaCourse, (I), Katherine Mahoney, (I)

MN

McNamara, Paula B/182 Broad St, Wethersfield, CT   203-563-6159
   Jack McConnell, (P)
Metzger, Rick/186 South St, Boston, MA   617-426-2290
   Steve Grohe, (P)
Morgan, Wendy/5 Logan Hill Rd, Northport, NY   516-757-5609
   Susan Aldrich, (I), Jeff Bravata, (I), Chris Dabrowski, (I), Scott Gordley, (I), Ian LaRoche, (P), Don Landwehrle, (P), Preston Lyon, (P), Al Margolis, (I), Fred Schrier, (I), Art Szabo, (P), Wozniaks, (I), Alan Wallerstein, (I), J. David Wilder, (P)
Nacht, Merle/374 Main St, Weathersfield, CT   203-563-7993
Nichols, Eva/1241 University Ave, Rochester, NY   716-275-9666

OP

OREMAN, LINDA/15 ATKINSON ST, ROCHESTER, NY (P 90)   **716-232-1585**
   Roger DeMuth, (I), Stephen Moscowitz, (I)
Photo-Graphic Agency/58 Pine St, Malden, MA   617-944-3166
Picture That, Inc/880 Briarwood, Newtown Square, PA   215-353-8833

RS

Radxevich Standke/15 Intervale Terr, Reading, MA   617-944-3166
   Christian Delbert, (P)
Reese-Gibson, Jean/4 Puritan Rd, N Beverly, MA   617-927-5006
Ricci, Ron/201 King St, Chappaqua, NY   914-238-4221
Robbins, David Group/256 Arch Rd, Avon, CT   203-673-6530
Rubenstein, Len/One Winthrop Sq, Boston, MA   617-482-0660
   Jim Conaty, (P)
Satterthwaite, Victoria/115 Arch St, Philadelphia, PA   215-925-4233
   Michael Furman, (P)
Schooley & Associates/10 Highland Ave, Rumson, NJ   201-530-1480
   Lorraine Dey, (I), Kevin Dougherty, (I), Geoffrey Gove, (I), William Laird, (I), Gary Smith, (I)
Schoon, Deborah/PO Box 7446, Lancaster, PA   717-291-9483
Smith, Ellen/PO Box 3727, Hartford, CT   203-249-1105
Smith, Wayne R/145 South St Penthouse, Boston, MA   617-426-7262
Spencer, Sandy/700 S 10th St, Philadelphia, PA   215-238-1208
   Anthony Ward, (P)
Stevens, Rick/925 Penn Ave #404, Pittsburgh, PA   412-765-3565

TU

Ternay, Louise/119 Birch Ave, Bala Cynwyd, PA   215-667-8626
   Bruce Blank, (P), Len Epstein, (I), Don Everhart, (I), Geri Grienke, (I), Peter Sasten, (G), Bill Ternay, (I), Kate Ziegler, (I)
UNICORN/1148 PARSIPPANY BLVD, PARSIPPANY, NJ (P 264)   **201-334-0353**
   Greg Hildebrandt, (I)

VW

Valen Assocs/PO Box 8, Westport, CT   203-227-7806
   George Booth, (C), Whitney Darrow, (C), Joe Farris, (C), William Hamilton, (C), Stan Hunt, (C), Anatol Kovarsky, (C), Henry Martin, (C), Frank Modell, (C), Mischa Richter, (C),

REPRESENTATIVES CONT'D.

Please send us your additions and updates.

Charles Saxon, (C), Jim Stevenson, (C), Henry Syverson,
(C), Bob Weber, (C), Rowland Wilson, (I), Bill Ziegler, (I)

Wolfe, Deborah Ltd/731 North 24th St, Philadelphia, PA	215-232-6666

John Collier, (I), Robert Hakalski, (P), Robin Hodgkiss, (I), Ron Lehew, (I),
Bill Margerin, (I), Bruce McAllister, (P), Scott Petters, (I), Bob Schenker, (I),
Jim Sharpe, (I), Charles Weckler, (P), Allan Weitz, (P), Alan White, (P),

Worrall, Dave/125 S 18th St, Philadelphia, PA *Weaver Lilley, (P)*	215-567-2881

SOUTHEAST

AB

Ayres, Beverly/PO Box 11531, Atlanta, GA	404-262-2740
Babcock, Nancy/1496 N Morningside Dr NE, Atlanta, GA	404-876-0117
Beck, Susanne/2721 Cherokee Rd, Birmingham, AL	205-871-6632
Charles Beck, (P)	
Burnett, Yolanda/559 Dutch Vall Rd, Atlanta, GA	404-873-5858
Jim Copland, (P), Charlie Lathem, (P)	
Couch, Tom/1164 Briarcliff Rd NE #2, Atlanta, GA	404-872-5774
Granberry Anderson Studio, (P)	

FJ

Fink, Duncan/437 S Tryon St, Charlotte, NC	704-377-4217
Ron Chapple, (P), Mitchell Kearney, (P)	
Jourdan, Carolyn/520 Brickell Key Dr #1417, Miami, FL	305-372-9425

MP

McGee, Linda/1816 Briarwood Ind Ct, Atlanta, GA	404-633-1286
MCLEAN REPRESENTS/401 W PEACHTREE ST NW #1720, ATLANTA, GA (P 74)	**404-221-0798**
Joe Isom, (I), Jack Jones, (I), Martin Pate, (I), Steve	
Spetseris, (I) , Warren Weber, (I)	
Phelps, Katie/32 Peachtree St NW #201, Atlanta, GA	404-524-1234
Pollard, Kiki/848 Greenwood Ave NE, Atlanta, GA	404-875-1363
Betsy Alexander, (D), John Findley, (I), Dennis Guthrie, (I),	
Mark Stanton, (I)	

ST

Silva, Naomi/100 Bldg Colony Sq #200, Atlanta, GA	404-892-8314
Joe DiNicola, (I), Rob Horn, (G), Christy Sheets Mull, (I),	
Gary Penca, (I), Don Sparks, (P)	
Sumpter, Will/1106 W Peachtree St #106, Atlanta, GA	404-874-2014
Tamara Inc/1900 Emery St NW, Atlanta, GA	404-355-0729
Tom Fleck, (I), Joseph M Ovies, (I), Chuck Passerelli, (I), `	
Larry Tople, (I)	
Torres, Martha/1715 Burgundy, New Orleans, LA	504-895-6570

W

Wells, Susan/51434 Timber Trails, Atlanta, GA	404-255-1430
Wexler, Marsha Brown/6108 Franklin Pk Rd, McLean, VA	703-241-1776
Williams, Phillip/1106 W Peachtree St #201, Atlanta, GA	404-873-2287
Jamie Cook, (P), Chip Jamison, (P), Kenvin Lyman, (GD),	
Bill Mayer, (I), David McKelvey, (I), John Robinette, (I),	
Leroy Woodson, (I)	
Wooden Reps/503 Ansley Villa Dr NE, Atlanta, GA	404-892-6303
Bernard Cohen, (P), Image Electronics, (I), Kevin Hulsey,	
(I), Chris Lewis, (I), Ted Rodgers, (P), Theo Rudnak, (I), Joe	
Saffold, (P), Bruce Young, (I), Cooper-Copeland, (I)	

MIDWEST

AB

Appleman, Norm/679 E Mandoline, Madison Hts, MI	313-589-0066
Art Hansen, (I), Jerry Kolesar, (P), Larry Melkus, (P),	
Glenn Schoenbach, (P)	
Ball, John/203 N Wabash, Chicago, IL	312-332-6041
Bartels, Ceci/111 Jefferson Rd, St Louis, MO	314-961-1670
Berk, Ida/1350 N La Salle, Chicago, IL	312-944-1339
Berntsen, Jim/405 N Wabash #2614, Chicago, IL	312-822-0560
Greg Johannes, (I), Denis Johnson, (I), Josef Sumichrast, (I)	
Blanchette, Dan/645 N Michigan Ave, Chicago, IL	312-280-1077
Brenner, Harriet/660 W Grand Ave, Chicago, IL	312-243-2730
Buermann, Jeri/321 N 22nd St, St Louis, MO	314-231-8690

CD

Chauncey, Michelle/1029 N Wichita #13, Wichita, KS	316-262-6733
Christell, Jim & Assoc/307 N Michigan Ave #1008, Chicago, IL	312-236-2396
Michel Ditlove, (P), Ron Harris, (P)	
Clausen, Bo/643 W Arlington Pl, Chicago, IL	312-871-1242

Cohen, Janice/117 North Jefferson, Chicago, IL	312-454-0680
Coleman, Woody/1295 Old River Rd, Cleveland, OH	216-621-1771
DeWalt & Assoc/3447 N 79th St, Milwaukee, WI	414-449-2263
Tom Fritz, (P)	
Dodge, Tim/2412 E Stratford Ct, Milwaukee, WI	414-964-9558

EF

Emerich Studios/300 W 19th Terrace, Kansas City, MO	816-474-8888
Erdos, Kitty/210 W Chicago, Chicago, IL	312-787-4976
Fiat, Randi/208 W Kinzie, Chicago, IL	312-467-1430
Fleming, Laird Tyler/1 Memorial Dr, St Louis, MO	314-982-1700
John Bilecky, (P), Willardson & White, (P)	
Frost, Brent & Laumer, Dick/4037 Queen Ave S, Minneapolis, MN	612-922-3440

H

Harlib, Joel/405 N Wabash #3203, Chicago, IL	312-329-1370
Bob August, (I), John Casado, (I), Lawrence Duke, (P),	
Peter Elliott, (P), Marty Evans, (P), Ignacio Gomez, (I),	
Barbara Higgins-Bond, (I), DeWitt Jones, (P), Richard	
Leech, (I), Tim Lewis, (I), Peter Lloyd, (I), Bret Lopez, (P),	
David McMacken, (I), Dennis Mukai, (I), Joe Ovies, (I),	
Matthew Rolston, (P), Todd Shorr, (I), Jay Silverman, (P),	
Bill Vann, (I), Allan Weitz, (P), Kim Whitesides, (I), Bruce	
Wolfe, (I), Bob Ziering, (I)	
Hartig, Michael/3620 Pacific, Omaha, NB	402-345-2164
Higgens Hegner Genovese Inc/510 N Dearborn St, Chicago, IL	312-644-1882
Hogan, Myrna & Assoc/333 N Michigan, Chicago, IL	312-372-1616
Terry Heffernan, (P)	
Hoke, Wayne & Assoc/17 N Elizabeth St, Chicago, IL	312-666-0175
Horton, Nancy/939 Sanborn, Palatine, IL	312-934-8966
Hull, Scott/7026 Corporate Way #211, Dayton, OH	513-433-8383
Tracy Britt, (I), Andy Buttram, (I), David Groff, (I), David	
Lesh, (I), John Maggard, (I), Larry Martin, (I), Ernest Norcia,	
(I), Mark Riedy, (I), Don Vanderbeck, (I)	

JK

Jeske, Kurt/612 S Clinton, Chicago, IL	312-922-9200
Kamin, Vince & Assoc/42 E Superior, Chicago, IL	312-787-8834
Ron Lieberman, (I), Mary Anne Shea, (I), Roy Volkman, (P)	
Kapes, Jack/233 E Wacker Dr #1412, Chicago, IL	312-565-0566
Stuart Block, (P), John Cahoon, (P), Jerry Friedman, (P),	
Carl Furuta, (P), Klaus Lucka, (P), Dan Romano, (I), Nicolas	
Sidjakov, (G)	
Kezelis, Elena/215 W Illinois, Chicago, IL	312-644-7108
Koralik, Connie/26 E Huron, Chicago, IL	312-944-5680
Robert Keeling, (P), Kazu, (P)	
Krisher, Deborah/900 N Franklin, Chicago, IL	312-642-2724
Richard Mack, (P)	
Krystal, David/443 King St West, Toronto, ON	416-596-6587

L

Lakehomer & Assoc/307 N Michigan, Chicago, IL	312-236-7885
Tim Schultz, (P)	
Lasko, Pat/452 N Halsted, Chicago, IL	312-243-6696
Ralph King, (P)	
Linzer, Jeff/4001 Forest Rd, Minneapolis, MN	612-926-4390
Lukmann, Geri/314 W Institute Pl, Chicago, IL	312-787-1774
Brent Carpenter, (PH), Steve Nozicka, (P)	

M

McManus, Mike/3423 Devon Rd, Royal Oak, MI	313-549-8196
McMasters, Deborah/157 W Ontario, Chicago, IL	312-943-9007
Richard Foster, (P)	
McNamara Associates/1250 Stephenson Hwy, Troy, MI	313-583-9200
Max Alterruse, (I), Gary Ciccarelli, (I), Garry Colby, (I),	
Hank Kolodziej, (I), Chuck Passarelli, (I), Tony Randazzo,	
(I), Gary Richardson, (I), Dick Scullin, (I), Don Wieland, (I)	
McNaughton, Toni/233 E Wacker #2904, Chicago, IL	312-782-8586
Pam Haller, (P), Rodica Prato, (I), James B. Wood, (P)	
Melkus, Larry/679 Mandoline, Madison Hts, MI	313-589-0066
Miller, Richard/743 N Dearborn, Chicago, IL	312-280-2288
Paul Barton, (P), Morton Beebe, (P), Rebecca Blake, (P),	
Chris Butler, (I), Geoffrey Clifford, (P), Marc Hauser, (P),	
Richard High, (C), Bob Krogle, (I), Jim Krogle, (I), Robert	
Sacco, (P)	

Mohlo, David/ Werremeyer Inc/12837 Flushing Meadow Dr, St Louis, MO — 314-966-3770
Moore, Amanda/1752 N Mohawk, Chicago, IL — 312-337-0880
  Peter Sagara, (P)
Moore, Connie/1540 North Park, Chicago, IL — 312-787-4422
  Richard Shirley, (F)
Moshier & Maloney/535 N Michigan, Chicago, IL — 312-943-1668
  Nicolette Anastas, (I), Steve Carr, (P), Dan Clyne, (I), Ron DiCianni, (I), Pat Dypold, (I), David Gaadt, (I), John Hamagami, (I), Rick Johnson, (I), Bill Kastan, (I), Ed Lindlof, (I), Wilson and Lund, (I), Dennis Luzak, (I), Colleen Quinn, (I), Paul Ristau, (I), Stephen Rybka, (I), Skidmore-Sahratian, (I), Al Stine, (I), Jim Trusilo, (I), John Youssi, (I)
Murphy, Sally/70 W Hubbard, Chicago, IL — 312-346-0720

NO
Nagan, Rita/1514 NE Jefferson St, Minneapolis, MN — 612-788-7923
Newman, Richard/1866 N Burling, Chicago, IL — 312-266-2513
Nicholson, Richard B/2310 Denison Ave, Cleveland, OH — 216-398-1494
  Martin Reuben, (P), Mike Steinberg, (P), Al Teufer, (P), J David Wilder, (P)
Nicolini, Sandra/230 N Michigan #523, Chicago, IL — 312-346-1648
  Elizabeth Ernst, (P), Tom Petroff, (P)
O'Farrel, Eileen/311 Good Ave, Des Plaines, IL — 312-297-5447
O'Grady Advertising Arts/333 North Michigan Ave #2200, Chicago, IL — 312-726-9833
O'Neill, Mary/17006 Woodbury Ave, Cleveland, OH — 216-252-6238
Osler, Spike/2616 Industrial Row, Troy, MI — 313-280-0640
  Mark Coppos, (P), Madison Ford, (P), Rob Gage, (P), Rick Kasmier, (P), Jim Secreto, (P)

P
Parker, Tom/1750 N Clark, Chicago, IL — 312-266-2891
Peterson, Vicki/535 N Michigan Ave #2802, Chicago, IL — 312-467-0780
  Charlie Gold, (P), Elyse Lewin, (P), Howard Menken, (P), Robert Stevens, (P), Charlie Westerman, (P)
Photographic Services Owens-Corning/Fiberglass Towers, Toledo, OH — 419-248-8041
  Jay Langlois, (P), Joe Sharp, (P)
Platzer, Karen & Assoc/535 N Michigan Ave, Chicago, IL — 312-467-1981
  Larry Banner, (P), Michael Caporale, (P), Ray Cioni, (I)
Potts, Carolyn/3 E Ontario #25, Chicago, IL — 312-664-9336
  Barbara Bersel, (P), John Craig, (I), Alan Dolgins, (I), Nelson, Fred, (I), Gregory Murphey, (I), Joe Ovies, (I), Kulp Productions, (P), Leslie Wolf, (I)
Potts, Vicki/139 N Wabash, Chicago, IL — 312-726-5678
  Mitchell Einhorn, (P), Mercer Engelhard, (P), David Gerhardt, (P), Kathy Sanders, (P)

R
Rabin, Bill & Assoc/666 N Lake Shore Dr, Chicago, IL — 312-944-6655
  John Alcorn, (I), Joel Baldwin, (P), Joe Baraban, (P), Roger Beerworth, (I), Guy Billout, (I), Howard Bjornson, (P), Thomas Blackshear, (I), R. O. Blechman, (I), Charles William Bush, (P), JoAnn Carney, (P), Carl Chaplin, (I), John Collier, (I), Etienne Delessert, (I), Nicholas Gaetano, (I), Jackie Geyer, (I), Francois Gillet, (P), Paul Giovanopoulos, (I), Tim Girvin, (GD), Robert Giusti, (I), Lamb&Hall, (P), Milton Glaser, (I), Ernst Haas, (P), Kunio Hagio, (I), Mark Hess, (I), Richard Hess, (I), Walter Ioss, (P), Art Kane, (P), Jacob Knight, (I), Rudy Legname, (P), Daniel Maffia, (I), Alan Magee, (I), Jay Maisel, (P), Dan Malinowski, (P), Jim Matusik, (P), Wayne McLoughlin, (I), Eric Meola, (P), Eugene Mihaesco, (I), Richard Noble, (P), Robert Rodriguez, (I), Reynold Ruffins, (I), Michael Shwab, (I), Ed Sorel, (I), George Stavrinos, (I), Dugald Sterner, (I), Simms Taback, (I), Ezra Tucker, (I), Pete Turner, (P), David Wilcox, (I)
Ray, Rodney/405 N Wabash #3106, Chicago, IL — 312-472-6550

S
Scarff, Signe/22 W Erie, Chicago, IL — 312-266-8352
  Larry Kolze, (P)
Sell, Dan/233 E Wacker, Chicago, IL — 312-565-2701
  Alvin Blick, (I), Paul Bond, (I), Wayne Carey, (I), Justin Carroll, (I), Bobbye Cochran, (I), Wil Cormier, (I), Bill

Ersland, (I), Rick Farrell, (I), Dick Flood, (I), Bill Harrison, (I), Dave LaFleur, (I), Gregory Manchess, (I), Bill Mayer, (I), Frank Morris, (I), Tim Raglin, (I), Ian Ross, (I), Mark Schuler, (I), R J Shay, (I), Jay Songero, (I), Dale Verzaal, (I), Jay, (I), Fran Vuksanovich, (I), Phil Wendy, (I), John Zielinski, (I)
Sharrard, Chuck/1546 N Orleans, Chicago, IL — 312-751-1470
Shulman, Salo/215 W Ohio, Chicago, IL — 312-337-3245
  Stan Stansfield, (P)
Siegel, Gerald & Assoc/506 N Clark, Chicago, IL — 312-661-1818
  Ralph Cowan, (P), Mike Fisher, (I), George Hamblin, (I), John Hulsey, (I), Kevin Hulsey, (I), Jan Jones, (I), Steve Mayse, (I), David Rawcliffe, (P), Elwood Smith, (I), Bill Stebbins, (I)
Skillicorn, Roy/233 E Wacker #29031, Chicago, IL — 312-856-1626
  Tom Curry, (I), David Scanlon, (I)
Stephenson & Taylor/19 N Erie St, Toledo, OH — 419-242-9170
  Tony Duda, (I), Richard Reed, (I)

T V
Timon, Clay & Assoc Inc/405 N Wabash, Chicago, IL — 312-527-1114
  Bob Bender, (P), Michael Fletcher, (P), Larry Dale Gordon, (P), Don Klumpp, (P), Chuck Kuhn, (P), Barry O'Rourke, (P), Al Satterwhite, (P), Michael Slaughter, (P)
Trinko, Genny/126 W Kinzie St, Chicago, IL — 312-222-9242
  Cam Chapman, (P)
Trott, David/32588 Dequiendre, Warren, MI — 313-978-8932
Tuke, Joni/368 W Huron, Chicago, IL — 312-787-6826
  Jay Ahrend, (P), David Beck, (I), Dan Blanchette, (I), Ken Goldammer, (I), Chris Hopkins, (I), Christopher Hopkins, (P), Susan Kindst, (P), Brian Otto, (I), John Welzenbach, (P), Ken Westphal, (I)
Virnig, Janet/3308 Girard Ave S, Minneapolis, MN — 612-822-6444

WYZ
Wilson, Mike/6959 N Hamilton, Chicago, IL — 312-338-4344
Yunker, Kit/4334 N Hazel #1201, Chicago, IL — 312-975-8116
Zann, Sheila/502 N Grove, Oak Park, IL — 312-386-2864
  Arnold Zann, (P)

SOUTHWEST
ABC
Art Rep Inc/3511 Cedar Springs #4A, Dallas, TX — 214-521-5156
Assid, Carol/122 Parkhouse, Dallas, TX — 214-748-3765
Booster, Barbara/4001 Bryn Mawr, Dallas, TX — 214-373-4284
Callahan, Joe/224 N Fifth Ave, Phoenix, AZ — 602-248-0777
  Tom Gerczynski, (P), Mike Gushock, (I), Jon Kleber, (I), Howard Post, (I), Dan Ruiz, (I), Mark Sharpls, (I), Dan Vermillion, (P), Balfour Walker, (P)
Campbell, Patty/2610 Catherine, Dallas, TX — 214-946-6597
  Douglas Doering, (P)
Corcoran, Arlene/224 N 5th Ave, Phoenix, AZ — 602-257-9509
Crowder, Bob/3603 Parry Ave, Dallas, TX — 214-823-9000
  Barry Kaplan, (P), Moses Olmoz, (P), Al Rubin, (P)

DEF
Devereux, Julien/2707 Stemmons Frwy #160, Dallas, TX — 214-634-0222
  Faustino, (P)
DiOrio, Diana/4146 Amherst St, Houston, TX — 713-669-0362
  JoAnn Collier, (I), Ray Mel Cornelius, (I), Regan Dunnick, (I), Richard High, (I), Larry Keith, (I), Dennis Mukai, (I), Patrick Nagel, (I), Thom Ricks, (I), Randy Rogers, (I), Peter Stallard, (I), James Stevens, (I)
Edwards, Nancy/2121 Regency Dr, Irving, TX — 214-438-4114
Fuller, Alyson/5610 Maple Ave, Dallas, TX — 214-688-1855

HL
Hamilton, Chris/3900 Lemmon, Dallas, TX — 214-526-2050
Hooper, Don/PO Box 815443, Dallas, TX — 214-492-1086
  Tim Bowers, (I), Steve Chenn, (P), Bill Craft, (P), Terrell Mashaw, (I)
Lynch, Larry/3317 Montrose #1130, Houston, TX — 713-520-9938
  Morton Beebe, (P), Lee Lee Brazeal, (I), Robert Latorre, (P), Richard Wahlstrom, (P)

REPRESENTATIVES CONT'D.

Please send us your additions and updates.

MPS
McCann, Liz/3000 Carlisle #206, Dallas, TX   214-742-3138
*Bill Crump, (I), Michael Doret, (I), Dan James, (I), Phil
Kretchmar, (P), James B. Wood, (P)*
Production Services/1711 Hazard, Houston, TX   713-529-7916
George Craig, (P), C Bryan Jones, (P), Thaine Manske, (P)
Smith, Linda/3511 Cedar Springs #4A, Dallas, TX   214-521-5156
Kim Whitesides, (I)

VW
Vidal, Jessica/155 Pittsburg, Dallas, TX   214-747-7766
Jerry Segrest, (P)
Washington, Dick/914 Westmoreland, San Antonio, TX   512-342-2009
Willard, Paul Assoc/313 E Thomas Rd #205, Phoenix, AZ   602-279-0119
*Kevin Cruff, (P), Kateri, (I), Matthew Foster, (I), Rick Gayle,
(P), Rick Kirkman, (I), Kevin MacPherson, (I), Curtis Parker,
(I), Nancy Pendleton, (I), Bob Peters, (I), Wayne Watford, (I)*

ROCKY MOUNTAIN

AC
AA Plus/754 International #T-38, Houston, TX
Cornell, Kathleen/90 Corona #508, Denver, CO   303-778-6016
*Nancy Duell, (I), Miles Hardiman, (I), Masami, (I), Daniel
McGowan, (I), Jan Oswald, (P), David Spira, (I), Bonnie
Timmons, (I)*

FK
Foremark Studios/PO Box 10346, Reno, NV   702-786-3150
KELLY, ROB/2215 E MISSISSIPPI, DENVER, CO (P 63)   **303-698-0073**
Pat Fujisaki, (I) Ron Sauter, (I)

NR
**NO COAST GRAPHICS/2544 15TH ST,
DENVER, CO (P 86-89)**   **303-458-7086**
*John Cuneo, (I), Cindy Enright, (I), Tom Nikosey, (I), Mike
Steirnagle, (I)*
Ryan, Patti/550 E 12th Ave #910, Denver, CO   303-832-9214
Bob Fader, (P)

WEST

AB
Albertine, Dotti/202 Westminister Ave #A, Venice, CA   213-392-4877
Aline, France & Marsha Fox/145 N Orange, Los Angeles, CA   213-933-2500
*Guy Billout, (I), Thomas Blackshear, (I), Michael Lamotte,
(P), Bret Lopez, (P), Manuel Nunez, (I), Dave Scanlon, (I),
Michael Schwab, (I), Peggy Sirota, (P), Bob Stevens, (P),
Steve Sulen, (P), Ezra Tucker, (I), Kim Whitesides, (I),
Bruce Wolfe, (I), Bob Zoell, (I)*
Annika/8301 W Third St, Los Angeles, CA   213-655-3527
Bonar, Ellen/1925 S Beverly Glenn, Los Angeles, CA   213-474-7911
Chuck Schmidt, (I)
Brady, Dana/125 N Doheny Dr, Los Angeles, CA   213-275-4455
Braun, Kathy/954 Howard St, San Francisco, CA   415-543-7377
*Tandy Belew, (GD), Michael Bull, (I), Anka, (I), Stan Cacitti,
(P), Jim Fulp, (I), Kathryn Kleinman, (P), Jim Parkinson, (I)*
Broadhurst, Cynde/1850 Union St #254, San Francisco, CA   415-382-1301
Christopher Hopkins, (P), John F Martin, (P)
Brooks/6628 Santa Monica Blvd, Los Angeles, CA   213-463-5678
Mike Chesser, (I)
Brown, Dianne/732 N Highland, Los Angeles, CA   213-464-2775
David LeBon, (P), Bill Werts, (P)
Burlingham, Tricia/8275 Beverly Blvd, Los Angeles, CA   213-651-3212

C
Carroll, J J/PO Box 3881, Manhattan Beach, CA   213-318-1066
Fred Nelson, (I)
Church, Spencer/515 Lake Washington Blvd, Seattle, WA   206-324-1199
*John Fretz, (I), Terry Heffernan, (P), Mits Katayama, (I),
Ann Marra, (G), Scott McDougall, (I), Dale Nordell, (I),
Marilyn Nordell, (I), Rusty Platz, (I), Ted Rand, (I), Diane
Solvang-Angell, (I), Dugald Stermer, (I), West Stock, (S),
Craig Walden, (I), Dale Windham, (P)*
Collier, Jan/166 South Park, San Francisco, CA   415-552-4252
Barbara Banthien, (I)

Conroy, Marie-Anais/222 W Main St #101, Tuscan, CA   714-838-0234
Dean Gerrie, (I)
Cook, Warren/PO Box 2159, Laguna Hills, CA   714-770-4619
Kathleen Norris Cook, (P)
Cormany, Paul/11607 Clover Ave, Los Angeles, CA   213-828-9653
*Mark Busacca, (I), Bryant Eastman, (I), Bryant Eastman, (I),
Dave Eichenberger, (I), Bob Gleason, (I), Lamb & Hall, (P),
Jim Heimann, (I), Bob Krogle, (I), Gary Norman, (I), Ed
Scarisbrick, (I), Stan Watts, (I), Dick Wilson, (I), Andy Zito,
(I)*
Costello/Daley/1317 Maltman St, Los Angeles, CA   213-667-2959
Courie, Jill/Bright & Assoc/8322 Beverly Blvd, Los Angeles, CA   213-658-8844
Courtney, Mary Ellen/1808 Diamond, S Pasadena, CA   213-256-4655
*Douglas Bevans, (I), Bart Doe, (I), Matt Mahurin, (I), Paul
Maxon, (P), Linda Medina, (I), Judy Reed, (I), Jeff Scales,
(P), Chuck Schmidt, (I), Diane Teske-Harris, (I)*
Creative Associates/5233 Bakman Ave, N Hollywood, CA   213-985-1224
*Chris Dellorco, (I), Don Dixon, (I), Derrick Gross, (I), Phillip
Howe, (I), Davin Mann, (I), Pat Ortega, (I), Scott Ross, (I),
Paul Stinson, (I)*
Cross, Anne/10642 Vanora Dr, Sunland, CA   213-934-4443

DE
Denkensohn, Dale/520 N Western Ave, Los Angeles, CA   213-467-2135
Diskin, Donnell/143 Edgemont, Los Angeles, CA   213-383-9157
Drayton, Sheryl/5018 Dumont Pl, Woodland Hills, CA   213-347-2227
DuBow & Hutkin/7461 Beverly Blvd #405, Los Angeles, CA   213-938-5177
Roger Hubbard, (I), Larry Salk, (I)
Epps, Susan/1226 Alameda Padre Serra, Santa Barbara, CA   805-962-2074
Epstein, Rhoni & Assoc/3814 Franklin Ave, Los Angeles, CA   213-663-2388
Ericson, William/1714 N Wilton Pl, Hollywood, CA   213-799-2404

FG
Fleming, Laird Tyler/407 1/2 Shirley Pl, Beverly Hills, CA   213-552-4626
John Bilecky, (P), Willardson & White, (P)
Fletcher, Lois/28956 West Lake Vista Dr, Azoma, CA   213-707-1010
Earl Miller, (P)
Geordell-Faenza & Assoc/2269 Market St #216,
San Francisco, CA   415-750-3079
George, Nancy/360 1/2 N Mansfield Ave, Los Angeles, CA   213-935-4696
*Brent Bear, (P), Justin Carroll, (I), Randy Chewning, (I),
Bruce Dean, (I), Hank Hinton, (I), Gerry Hoover, (I), Andy
Hoyos, (I), Richard Kriegler, (I), Larry Lake, (I), Gary Lund,
(I), Rob Sprattler, (I), Bruce Wilson, (P)*
Gilbert, Sam/410 Sheridan, Palo Alto, CA   415-325-2102
Gray, Connie/248 Alhambra, San Francisco, CA   415-331-9111
*Steven Fucuda, (P), Max Gisko, (I), Bob Gleason, (I), John
Lund, (P), Mark McLandish, (I), Joel Nakamura, (I), Fred
Nelson, (I), Gary Norman, (I), David Oshiro, (GD), Suzanne
Phister, (I), Michael Utterbock, (P), Will Westin, (I), Barry
Wetmore, (I)*
Greenwald, Kim/1115 5th St #202, Santa Monica, CA   213-394-6502
*Livingston Five, (P), Bill Garland, (I), Ron Krisel, (P), Julie
Pace, (I), Teri Sandison, (P), Curt Wastead, (I), Jane
Yamada, (I)*
Grossman, Neal/7618 Melrose Ave, Los Angeles, CA   213-462-7935
Tom Zimberoff, (P)
Group West/5455 Wilshire Blvd #1212, Los Angeles, CA   213-937-4472

H
Hackett, Pat/2030 First Ave #201, Seattle, WA   206-623-9459
*Bill Cannon, (P), Steve Coppin, (I), Larry Duke, (I), Bill
Evans, (I), Norman Hathaway, (I), Ed Hauser, (I), Larry
Lubeck, (P), Bill Mayer, (I), Mike Schumacher, (I), John C
Smith, (I), John Terence Turner, (P)*
Haigh, Nancy/90 Natoma St, San Francisco, CA   415-391-1646
Halcomb, Mark/516 E Maude Ave, Sunnyvale, CA   408-245-1921
Hallowell, Wayne/11046 Mccormick, North Hollywood, CA   213-769-5694
*Dick Birkey, (I), Alden Butcher, (AV),
Emerson/Johnson/MacKay, (I), Dimensional Design, (GD),
Terry Hambright, (I), Ray Howlett, (I), Bill McCormick, (G),
Louis McMurray, (I), Pro/Stock, (P), Lollie Ortiz, (I), Diana
Robbins, (I), Larry Schenkar, (P), Greg Smith, (P), Ed
Vartanian, (I)*

Happe, Michele L/1183 N Michigan, Pasadena, CA — 213-684-3037
Michel Allaire, (I), Chuck Bowden, (L), Chuck Larsen, (I), Rich Mahon, (I), Ken Rosenberg, (I), Randy South, (I), Judy Unger, (I)

Hart, Vikki/409 Bryant St, San Francisco, CA — 415-495-4278
Jim Blakely, (P), Robert Evans, (I), G K Hart, (P), Kevin Hulsey, (I), Aleta Jenks, (I), Tom Kamifuji, (I), Heather King, (I), Julie Tsuchiya, (I), Jonathan Wright, (I)

Harte, Vikki/409 Bryant St, San Francisco, CA — 415-495-4278

Hauser, Barbara/7041 Hemlock St, Oakland, CA — 415-339-1885

Hedge, Joanne/1838 El Cerrito Pl #3, Hollywood, CA — 213-874-1661
Rebecca Archey, (I), Keith Batchellor, (I), Delana Bettoli, (I), Chris Dellorco, (I), Bo Hylen, (P), Jeff Leedy, (I), Bette Levine, (I), Kenvin Lyman, (I), David McMacken, (I), Dennis Mukai, (I), Vida Pavesich, (I), William Rieser, (I)

Hillman, Betsy/2230 Francisco #106, San Francisco, CA — 415-563-2243
Chuck Bowden, (I), Tim Boxell, (I), Hiro Kimura, (I), John Marriott, (P), HKM Productions, (P), Greg Spalenka, (I), Joe Spencer, (I), Jeremy Thornton, (I), Jackson Vereen, (P)

Hunt, Lou/10746 Bluffside Dr, N Hollywood, CA — 213-462-6565
Eric Oxendorf, (P)

Hyatt, Nadine/PO Box 2455, San Francisco, CA — 415-543-8944
Jeanette Adams, (I), Rebecca Archey, (I), Charles Bush, (P), Frank Cowan, (P), Marty Evans, (P), Gerry Gersten, (I), John Hyatt, (I), Bret Lopez, (P), Tom McClure, (I), Jan Schockner, (L), Victor Stabin, (I), Liz Wheaton, (I)

K

Kerz, Valerie/PO Box 480678, Los Angeles, CA — 213-876-6232
Brian Leatart, (P), Ken Nahoun, (P), Jane O'Neill, (P), Matthew Rosen, (P)

Kirsch, Melanie/2643 S Fairfax Ave, Culver City, CA — 213-559-0059

Knable, Ellen/PO Box 67725, Los Angeles, CA — 213-855-8855
Charles Bush, (P), Stan Caplan, (P), Mark Coppos, (P), David Erramouspe, (I), Joe Heiner, (I), Kathy Heiner, (I), John Hyatt, (I), Rudi Legname, (P), Vigon/Nahas/Vigon, (I), Robert Rodriguez, (I), Jonathan Wright, (I), Brian Zick, (I)

Koeffler, Ann/1555 Greenwich #9, San Francisco, CA — 415-885-2714
Randy Berrett, (I), Stewart Daniels, (I), Bob Hickson, (I), Julie Johnson, (I), Rosenberg, Ken, (I), Michael Pearce, (I)

L

Lambert, Ken/10802 White Oak, Granada Hills, CA — 818-363-3791

Laycock, Louise/Storyboards/8800 Venice Blvd, Los Angeles, CA — 213-870-6565

Lee & Lou/618 S Western Ave #202, Los Angeles, CA — 213-388-9465
Rob Gage, (P), Bob Grigg, (P), Richard Leech, (I)

Lilie, Jim/1801 Franklin St #404, San Francisco, CA — 415-441-4384
Lou Beach, (I), Alan Dolgins, (P), Sid Evans, (I), Nancy Freeman, (I), Steve Fukuda, (P), Sharon Harker, (I), Jen-Ann Kirchmeier, (I), Jeff Leedy, (I), Jeff McCaslin, (I), Masami Miyamoto, (I), Mike Murphy, (I), Dennis Ziemienski, (I)

Lippert, Tom/West End Studios/1100 Glendon #732, Los Angeles, CA — 213-279-1539

London, Valerie Eve/820 N Fairfax Ave, Los Angeles, CA — 213-655-4214
Terry Heffernan, (P), Robert Stein, (P)

Luna, Tony/45 E Walnut, Pasadena, CA — 213-681-3130

MO

Marie, Rita/6376 W 5th St, Los Angeles, CA — 213-247-0135

Martha Productions/1830 S Robertson Blvd #203, Los Angeles, CA — 213-204-1771
Bob Brugger, (I), Jacques Devand, (I), Stan Evenson, (I), Tracy Garner, (I), John Hamagami, (I), William Harrison, (I), Arthur Hill, (I), Catherine Leary, (I), Ed Lindlof, (I), Rudy Obrero, (I), Cathy Pavia, (I), Wayne Watford, (I)

Maslansky, Marysa/7927 Hillside Ave, Los Angeles, CA — 213-851-0210
Lisa Tanner, (P)

McBride, Elizabeth/70 Broadway, San Francisco, CA — 415-421-6321
Keith Criss, (I), Robert Holmes, (P), Patricia Pearson, (I), Bill Sanchez, (I), Earl Thollander, (I), Tom Vano, (P)

McCullough, Gavin/638 S Van Ness, Los Angeles, CA — 213-382-6281

McKenzie, Dianne/839 Emerson St, Palo Alto, CA — 415-322-8036
Victor Budnik, (P)

Media Services/Gloria Peterson/10 Aladdin Terr, San Francisco, CA — 415-928-3033

Michaels, Martha/3279 Kifer Rd, Santa Clara, CA — 408-735-8443

Morico, Mike/638 S Van Ness, Los Angeles, CA — 213-382-6281

Morris, Leslie/1062 Rengstorff Ave, Mountain View, CA — 415-966-8301
Paul Olsen, (I)

Ogden, Robin/412 N Doheny Dr, Los Angeles, CA — 213-858-0946
Karen Bell, (I), Rick Brown, (I), Bob Commander, (I), Steve Gray, (I), Richard Milholland, (I), Jim Miller, (P), John Puchalski, (I), Jeannie Winston, (I), Jane vanTamelan, (I)

PQ

Parsons, Ralph/1232 Folsom St, San Francisco, CA — 415-339-1885

Pate, Randy/The Source/5029 Westpark Dr, North Hollywood, CA — 213-985-8181

Pepper, Don/638 S Van Ness, Los Angeles, CA — 213-382-6281

Pierceall, Kelly/25260 Piuma Rd, Malibu, CA — 213-559-4327

Piscopo, Maria Representatives/2038 Calvert Ave, Costa Mesa, CA — 714-556-8133

Quon, Milton/3900 Somerset Dr, Los Angeles, CA — 213-293-0706
Mike Quon, (P)

R

Robbins, Leslie/68 Cumberland St, San Francisco, CA — 415-826-8741
Jim Korte, (I), James LaMarche, (I), Scott Miller, (I), Vida Pavesich, (I), Julie Peterson, (I), David Tise, (P), Tom Wyatt, (P)

Rosenthal, Elise/3443 Wade St, Los Angeles, CA — 213-306-6878
Saul Bernstein, (I), Chris Butler, (I), Jim Deneen, (I), Myron Grossman, (I), Alan Hashimoto, (I), James Henry, (I), Tim Huhn, (I), Jim McKiernan, (I), Kenton Nelson, (I), Peter Palombi, (I), Tom Pansini, (I), Kim Passey, (I), Bill Robles, (I), Tom Tomita, (I), Will Weston, (I), Larry Winborg, (I)

S

Salisbury, Sharon/185 Berry St, San Francisco, CA — 415-495-4665
Keith Batcheller, (I), Craig Calsbeck, (I), Jim Endicott, (I), Bob Graham, (I), Bo Hylen, (P), Larry Keenan, (P), Bette Levine, (I), Dave McMacken, (I), Robert Mizono, (P), Vida Pavesich, (I)

SALZMAN, RICHARD W/1352 HORNBLEND ST, SAN DIEGO, CA (P 101) — 619-272-8147
Tony Baker, (I), Manuel Garcia, (I), Jason Harlem, (P), Denise Hilton-Putnam, (I), Joyce Kitchnell, (I), Bernie Lansky, (C), Gordon Menzie, (P), Dave Mollering, (I), Imagery That Moves, (GD), Dianne O'Quinn-Burke, (I), Everett Peck, (I), Nono Remos, (R), Terry Smith, (I), Walter Stuart, (I), Jonathan Wright, (I)

Sandler, Neil/3443 Wade St, Los Angeles, CA — 213-306-6878

Scott, Freda/1440 Bush St, San Francisco, CA — 415-775-6564

Scroggy, David/2124 Froude St, San Diego, CA — 619-222-2476
Joe Chiado, (I), Joe Chiodo, (I), Rick Geary, (I), Rick Geary, (I), Chris Miller, (I), John Pound, (I)

Slobodian, Barbara/745 N Alta Vista Blvd, Hollywood, CA — 213-935-6668
Bob Greisen, (I), David Kaiser, (I), Tom O'Brien, (P), Forest Sigwart, (I), Scott Slobodian, (I)

Sobol, Lynne/4302 Melrose Ave, Los Angeles, CA — 213-665-5141
Frank Marquez, (I), Arthur Montes de Oca, (P)

Stefanski, Janice/2022 Jones St, San Francisco, CA — 415-928-0457
Michael Jay, (P), Barbara Kelley, (I), George Olson, (P), Christian Ray, (I), Bob Roth, (G), Rolf Seiffe, (P)

Steinberg, John/10434 Corfu Lane, Los Angeles, CA — 213-279-1775
Jay Ahrent, (P), John Alvin, (I), Bo Gehring & Associates, (I), Beau Daniels, (I), Alan Daniels, (I), Precision Illustration, (I), David Kimble, (I), Reid Miles, (P), Richard Moore, (P), Larry Noble, (I), Frank Page, (I), Ed Wexler, (I)

Studio Artists Inc/638 S Van Ness Ave, Los Angeles, CA — 213-382-6281
Chuck Coppock, (I), Carl Crietz, (I), Bill Fleming, (I), George Francuch, (I), Bill Franks, (G), Duane Gordon, (G), Ida O'Malley, (I)

Sullivan, Diane/3727 Buchanan, San Francisco, CA — 415-563-8884
Lawrence Duke, (P)

Sweet, Ron/716 Montgomery St, San Francisco, CA — 415-433-1222
Charles East, (D), John Hamagami, (I), Bob Haydock, (I),

Gregg Keeling, (I), Richard Leech, (I), Walter Swarthout, (P), Don Weller, (I), Bruce Wolfe, (I), James B Wood, (P)

T

Tabke, Tim/35-23 Ryder St, Santa Clara, CA		408-733-5855
Taggard, Jim/PO 4064 Pioneer Square Station, Seattle, WA		206-938-1898
Sjef's-Photographie, (P)		
Todd, Deborah/259 Clara St, San Francisco, CA		415-495-3556
Torrey/11201 Valley Spring Ln, Studio City, CA		213-277-8086

Stewart Daniels, (I), Jim Evans, (I), Bob Hickson, (I), Peter Lloyd, (I), Jim Miller, (P), Michael Schwab, (I), Jackson Vereen, (P), Barry Wetmore, (C), Dick Zimmerman, (P), Lumeni-Productions, (A)

Tos, Debbie/119 N La Brea, Los Angeles, CA		213-932-1291
Carl Furuta, (P)		
TRIMPE, SUSAN/2717 WESTERN AVE,		
SEATTLE, WA (P 107)		**206-382-1100**
Wendy Edelson, (I), Stephen Peringer, (I)		

V

Vandamme, Mary/1165 Francisco #5, San Francisco, CA		415-433-1292

John Blaustein, (P), John Blaustein, (P), John Collier, (I), Robert Giusti, (I), Joe and Kathy Heiner, (I), Alan Krosnick, (P), Kenvin Lyman, (I), Dennis Mukai, (I), Bill Rieser, (I), Ed Scarisbrick, (I), Michael Schwab, (I), Charles Shields, (I), Rick Strauss, (P), Carol Wald, (I), Kim Whitesides, (I)

Varie, Chris/2210 Wilshire Blvd, Santa Monica, CA		213-395-9337
Bill Varie, (P)		
Visages/8228 Sunset Blvd, Los Angeles, CA		213-650-8880

W

Wagoner, Jae/200 Westminister Ave #A, Venice, CA		213-392-4877

Tim Alt, (I), Michael Backus, (I), Roger Beerworth, (I), Stephen Durke, (I), Steve Jones, (I), Steve Jones, (I), Lee MacLeod, (I), Craig Nelson, (I), Robert Tanenbaum, (I), Don Weller, (I)

Wall, Fran/820 N La Brea ave, Los Angeles, CA		213-465-7193
Ron Avery, (P)		
Wiegand, Chris/7106 Waring Ave, Los Angeles, CA		213-931-5942
Williams, Gavin/638 S Van Ness, Los Angeles, CA		213-382-6281
Williams, George A/638 S Van Ness, Los Angeles, CA		213-382-6281

Y

Youmans, Jill/1021 1/2 N La Brea, Los Angeles, CA		213-469-8624

Dan Cooper, (I), Carole Etow, (I), Jeff George, (I), Brian Leng, (P), Jeff Leung, (I)

Young, Jill/Compendium Inc/945 Front St #201, San Francisco, CA		415-392-0542

Judy Clifford, (I), Armondo Diaz, (P), Celeste Ericsson, (I), Marilee Heyer, (I), Rae Huestis, (G), Mary Jew, (G), Bonnie Matza, (G), Barbara Muhlhauser, (G), Martin Schweitzer, (G), Donna Mae Shaver, (P), Cecily Starin, (I), Sarn Suvityasiri, (I), Ed Taber, (I), Carlotta Tormey, (I)

Young, RW/9445 Amboy Ave, Pacoima, CA		213-767-1945

Z

Zank, Elen/262 Donahue St, Sausalito, CA		415-332-3739
Chip Carroon, (P)		
Zimmerman, Delores H/9135 Hazen Dr, Beverly Hills, CA		213-273-2642

NOTES:

ILLUSTRATORS

NEW YORK CITY

A
Abraham, Daniel E/425 Fifth Ave 718-499-4006
ABRAMS, KATHIE/41 UNION SQUARE W #1001 (P 117) **212-741-1333**
Accornero, Franco/620 Broadway 212-674-0068
Accurso, Tony/5309 7th Ave 718-435-1323
Acuna, Ed/353 W 53rd St #1W 212-682-2462
Adams, Angela/866 UN Plaza #4014 212-644-2020
Adams, Jeanette/261 Broadway 212-732-3878
ADAMS, JEFFREY/15 W 72ND ST (P 68) **212-799-2231**
Advertsing Partners/383 Fifth Ave 212-683-5065
AIESE, BOB/200 W 15TH ST (P 56,57) **212-243-4209**
AIRSTREAM/ PAT BAILEY/60 E 42ND ST #505 (P 10) **212-682-1490**
AIRSTREAM/ PAM WALL/60 E 42ND ST #505 (P 11) **212-682-1490**
ALCORN, BOB/48 W 21ST ST 9TH FL (P 92) **212-243-4412**
Alcorn, Stephen/135 E 54th St 212-421-0050
Allaux, Jean Francois/21 W 86th St 212-873-8404
ALLEMAN, ANNIE/38 E 21ST ST (P 120) **212-477-4185**
Allen, Julian/31 Walker St 212-925-6550
Aloise, Frank/NBC, 30 Rockefeller Plaza 212-664-4127
Alpert, Alan/405 E 54th St 212-421-8160
Alpert, Olive/9511 Shore Rd 718-833-3092
Altemus, Robert/401 E 64th St 212-861-5080
Amity, Elena/339 E 77th St 212-879-4690
Amsel, Richard/353 E 83rd St 212-744-5599
Angelakis, Manos/114 E 32nd St #902 212-685-2770
Angerame, Diane/1459 Third Ave 212-353-0502
Antoni, Volker E H/889 Pacific St 718-636-4670
ANTONIOS, TONY/60 E 42ND ST #505 (P 12) **212-682-1490**
Applebaum & Curtis/333 E 49th St 212-752-0679
Arcelle, Joan/430 W 24th St 212-924-1865
Aristovulos, Nick/16 E 30th St 212-725-2454
Arnold, Robert/149 W 14th St 212-989-7049
The Art Farm/420 Lexington Ave 212-688-4555
Arwin, Melanie Gaines/236 W 26th St 212-924-2020
Asch, Howard/21-04 Utopia Pkwy 718-278-7966
Assel, Steven/472 Myrtle Ave 718-789-1725
Azzopardi, Frank/1039 Victory Blvd 718-273-4343

B
Backhaus, R B/280 West End Ave 212-877-4792
BAKER, GARIN/95 W 92ND ST #7A (P 13) **212-865-1975**
Baldus, Fred/29 Jones St 212-620-0423
BALIN, RACQUEL/334 W 87TH ST #PH B (P 123) **212-496-8358**
Ballantyne, Joyce/353 W 53rd St #1W 212-682-2462
Barancik, Cathy/140 Grand St 212-226-2329
BARBERIS, JUAN C/60 E 42ND ST (P 72) **212-687-4185**
Barkley, James/201 King St 914-238-4221
Barner, Bob/866 UN Plaza #4014 212-644-2020
Barr, Ken/342 Madison Ave 212-697-8525
BARRETT, RON/2112 BROADWAY (P 125) **212-874-1370**
Barry, Rick/159 W 23rd St 212-691-0038
BARRY, RON/165 E 32ND ST (P 61) **212-686-3514**
Baruffi, Andrea/72 Barrow St #6G 212-989-8357
Bass, Bob/43 E 19th St 212-254-4996
Bauer, Carla Studio/156 Fifth Ave #1100 212-807-8305
Bauman, Jill/PO Box 152 718-658-3888
BAZZEL, DEBORAH/48 W 21ST ST 9TH FL (P 97) **212-243-4412**
BECKER, RON/265 E 78TH ST (P 95) **212-535-8052**
Beecham, Tom/342 Madison Ave #949 212-697-8525
Beene, Carol/304 W 12th St 212-505-1824
Bego, Dolores/155 E 38th St 212-697-6170
Bellows, Amelia/118 E 25th St 6th Fl 212-777-7012
Bergman, Barbra/41 E 41st St 212-687-6754
Berkey, John/50 E 50th St 212-355-0910
Berns, Ellen S/181 E 93rd St #3A 212-831-0747
Berran, Robert/420 Lexington Ave #2911 212-986-5680
BILLOUT, GUY/88 LEXINGTON AVE #12G (P 127) **212-684-2974**
Blackshear, Tom/50 E 50th St 212-355-0910
BLACKWELL, GARIE/60 E 42ND ST #505 (P 14) **212-682-1490**
Blakey, Paul/226 E 53rd St 212-755-4945
Bloom, Tom/235 E 84th St 212-628-6861

Blum, Zevi/215 E 31st St 212-684-3448
Blumrich, Christopher/67 Irving Pl 212-674-8080
BOGUSLAV, RAPHAEL/200 E 78TH ST (P 53) **212-570-9069**
BONHOMME, BERNARD/111 WOOSTER ST #PH C (P 51) **212-925-0491**
BORDELON, MELINDA/60 E 42ND ST #505 (P 15) **212-682-1490**
Boyd, Harvey/24 Fifth Ave 212-475-5235
Boyd, Kris/318 E 89th St #1D 212-876-4361
Bozzo, Frank/400 E 85th St 212-535-9182
Bralds, Braldt/135 E 54th St 212-421-0050
Bramhall, William/215 E 31st St 212-684-3448
Brautigan, Doris/350 W 30th St 212-736-7698
Brayman, Kari/333 W 55th St 212-582-6137
Breinberg, Aaron/1123 Broadway 212-261-2544
BRICKNER, ALICE/4720 GROSVENOR AVE (P 129) **212-549-5909**
Bridy, Dan/353 W 53rd St #1W 212-682-2462
BRILLHART, RALPH/60 E 42ND ST (P 38) **212-867-8092**
Broderson, Charles/873 Broadway #612 212-925-9392
Brofsky, Miriam/186 Riverside Dr 212-595-8094
Brooks, Andrea/99 Bank St 212-924-3085
Brooks, Harold/62 W 45th St 212-398-9540
BROOKS, LOU/415 W 55TH ST (P 130,31) **212-245-3632**
Brothers, Barry/1922 E 18th St 718-336-7540
Brown, Bob/267 Fifth Ave #706 212-686-5576
Brown, Bradford/151 E 20th St #3A 212-260-1940
Brown, Dan/420 Lexington Ave 212-986-5680
Brown, Judith Gwyn/522 E 85th St 212-288-1599
Brown, Kirk Q/1092 Blake Ave 718-342-4569
Brundage, Dick/142 E 33rd St 212-684-2097
Brusca, Jack/43 E 19th St 212-254-4996
BRYAN, DIANA/200 E 16TH ST #1D (P 132) **212-475-7927**
Bryant, Rick J/18 W 37th St #301 212-594-6718
BUCHANAN, YVONNE/411 14TH ST (P 133) **718-965-3021**
BURGER, ROBERT/111 WOOSTER ST #PH C (P 50) **212-925-0491**
BURGOYNE, JOHN/200 E 78TH ST (P 52) **212-570-9069**
Byrd, Bob/353 W 53rd St #1W 212-682-2462

C
Campbell, Gaither/118 E 28th St #908 212-683-5055
Campbell, Jim/420 Lexington Ave #2911 212-986-5680
Cantarella, Virginia Hoyt/107 Sterling Pl 718-622-2061
Caras, Peter/157 W 57th St 212-247-1130
Carbone, Kye/101 Charles St 212-242-5630
Carr, Noell/30 E 14th St 212-675-1015
CARTER, BUNNY/200 E 78TH ST (P 53) **212-570-9069**
Carter, Penny/342 Madison Ave #261 212-986-3282
Casale, Paul/5304 11th Ave 718-633-7909
Cassler, Carl/420 Lexington Ave #2911 212-986-5680
Cavanagh, Dorothe/135 W 79th St 212-662-1490
Cayard, Bruce/155 E 38th St 212-697-6170
Cellini, Eva/157 W 57th St 212-247-1130
Cellini, Joseph/157 W 57th St 212-247-1130
Ceribello, Jim/35 Holcomb Ave 718-317-5972
CETLIN, MARSHALL/62 LEROY ST (P 59) **212-243-7869**
Chan, Eric/2076 W 9th St 718-266-4573
Chang, Judith/8857 195th St 718-465-5598
Charmatz, Bill/25 W 68th St 212-595-3907
Chen, Tony/53-31 96th St 718-699-4813
Chermayeff, Ivan/58 W 15th St 212-741-2539
CHERRY, JIM/41 W 84TH ST #4 (P 135) **212-724-5981**
Chester, Harry/501 Madison Ave 212-752-0570
Chironna, Ronald/135 Sturges St 718-720-6142
Chorao, Kay/290 Riverside Dr 212-749-8256
Christopher, Tom/342 Madison Ave #261 212-986-3282
Chwast, Seymour/67 Irving Place 212-677-3506
Ciardiello, Joe/203 Center St 718-351-2289
Ciccarielli, Gary/353 W 53rd St #1W 212-682-2462
CIESIEL, CHRISTINE G/62 LEROY ST (P 59) **212-243-7869**
Cieslawski, Steven/321 86th St #F3 718-748-8746
Clark, Bradley/61 Pierrepont St #44 718-237-1869
Clark, Cynthia Watts/61 Pierrepont St #44 718-237-1869
CLARK, JANE/48 W 21ST ST 9TH FL (P 94) **212-243-4412**
Clarke, Bob/159 W 53rd St 212-581-4045
Clifton, John/114-24 200th St 718-464-6746

Please send us your additions and updates.

ILLUSTRATORS

Cloteaux, Francois/333 E 30th St	212-679-1358
COBANE, RUSSELL/420 MADISON AVE #401 (P 30)	**212-980-3510**
Cober, Alan E/50 E 50th St	212-752-8490
Cody, Brian/866 UN Plaza #4014	212-644-2020
Colton, Keita/165 E 32nd St	212-686-3514
Conley, Frank P/14 E 52nd St	212-759-6791
Connelly, Gwen/866 UN Plaza #4014	212-644-2020
Conner, Mona/1 Montgomery Pl #8	718-636-1527
Continuity Graphics Associated, Inc/62 W 45th St	212-869-4170
COOK, DAVID/60 E 42ND ST (P 34)	**212-867-8092**
Cooley, Gary/23 W 35th St	212-695-2426
Cooper, Cheryl/515 Madison Ave	212-486-9644
Cooper, Robert/420 Madison Ave #401	212-980-3510
Corben, Richard/43 E 19th St	212-254-4996
CORNELL, LAURA/118 E 93RD ST #1A (P 137)	**212-534-0596**
Corvi, Donna/91 Fifth Ave 4th Fl	212-620-0610
Couch, Gregg/112 Willow St #5A	718-625-1298
Couratin, Patrick/333 E 30th St	212-679-1358
Courtney, Richard/43 E 19th St	212-254-4996
COVE, TONY/60 E 42ND ST (P 72)	**212-687-4185**
Crair, Mel/342 Madison Ave #949	212-697-8525
Crawford, Margery/237 E 31st St	212-686-6883
CRAWFORD, ROBERT/340 E 93RD ST #9I (P 141)	**212-722-4964**
Crews, Donald/653 Carroll St	718-636-5773
CROSS, PETER/645 WEST END AVE #9E (P 104)	**212-362-3338**
Crosthwaite, Royd C./50 E 50th St	212-355-0910
CRUZ, RAY/162 W 13TH ST (P 78)	**212-243-1199**
Csatari, Joe/420 Lexington Ave #2911	212-986-5680
Cuevos, Stillerman, Plotkin/230 E 44th St	212-661-7149
Cummings, Pat/28 Tiffany Pl	718-834-8584
Cunningham, Jean/177 Waverly Pl #4F	212-675-1731
Cunningham, Robert M/177 Waverly Pl #4F	212-675-1731
CURRY, TOM/333 E 49TH ST (P 145)	**212-980-8061**

D

Dacey,Bob/157 W 57th St	212-247-1130
Dale, Robert/1573 York Ave	212-737-1771
Dallison, Ken/108 E 35th St #1	212-889-3337
DALY, SEAN/85 SOUTH ST (P 83)	**212-668-0031**
D'Andrea, Bernie/50 E 50th St	212-355-0910
D'Andrea, Domenick/50 E 50th St	212-355-0910
Daniels, Alan/120 E 32nd St	212-689-3233
Darden, Howard/62 W 45th St	212-398-9540
DAVIDSON, EVERETT/60 E 42ND ST #505 (P 16)	**212-682-1490**
Davis, Allen/141-10 25th Rd #3A	718-463-0966
Davis, Michael/333 E 49th St	212-980-8061
Davis, Nelle/20 E 17th St	212-807-7737
Davis, Paul/14 E 4th St	212-460-9644
Dawson, Diane/160 West End Ave	212-362-7819
DAWSON, JOHN/60 E 42ND ST (P 43)	**212-867-8092**
Day, Betsy/866 UN Plaza #4014	212-644-2020
Deas, Michael/39 Sidney Pl	718-852-5630
DeCamps, Craig/341 W 38th St	212-564-2691
DEEL, GUY/60 E 42ND ST (P 34)	**212-867-8092**
DEETER, CATHERINE/60 E 42ND ST #505 (P 17)	**212-682-1490**
Degen, Paul/135 Eastern Parkway	718-636-8299
DEGRAFFENRIED, JACK/18 E 16TH ST (P 46)	**212-206-0322**
Deigan, Jim/353 W 53rd St #1W	212-682-2462
Del Rosso, Richard/33 W 89th St #1A	212-580-8387
DeLattre, Georgette/100 Central Park South	212-247-6850
DeMichiell, Robert/43 E 19th St	212-254-4996
DENARO, JOSEPH/18 E 16TH ST (P 48)	**212-206-0322**
Deschamps, Bob/108 E 35th St #1	212-889-3337
Descombes, Roland/50 E 50th St 5th Fl	212-355-0910
Dewey, Kenneth F/226 E 53rd St	212-755-4945
Diamond Art Studio/11 E 36th St	212-685-6622
Diaz, Pablo/173 Lafayette St #5N	212-219-3643
DiCione, Ron/342 Madison Ave #949	212-697-8525
DiComo Comp Art/12 W 27th St	212-689-8670
DIETZ, JIM/165 E 32ND ST (P 60,61)	**212-686-3514**
DiFranza-Williamson, Inc/1414 Ave of the Americas	212-832-2343
DILAKIAN, HOVIK/111 WOOSTER ST #PH C (P 51)	**212-925-0491**
Dillon, Leo & Diane/221 Kane St	718-624-0023

Dinnerstein, Harvey/933 President St	718-783-6879
DITTRICH, DENNIS/42 W 72ND ST #12B (P 149)	**212-595-9773**
DiVincenzo, Dennis/128 E 91st St	212-772-8444
DODDS, GLENN/392 CENTRAL PARK WEST (P 150,151)	**212-679-3630**
Domingo, Ray/108 E 35th St #1	212-889-3337
Domino, Bob/60 Sutton Pl So	212-935-0139
D'Onofrio, Alice/866 UN Plaza #4014	212-644-2020
DORET, MICHAEL/12 E 14TH ST (P 152)	**212-929-1688**
DORET/ SMITH STUDIOS/12 E 14TH ST (P 152,153)	**212-929-1688**
D'Ortenzio, Alfred/353 W 53rd St #1W	212-682-2462
Drovetto, Richard/355 E 72nd St	212-861-0927
Drucker, Mort/226 E 53rd St	212-755-4945
Duarte, Mary/350 First Ave	212-674-4513
Dubanevich, Arlene/866 UN Plaza #4014	212-644-2020
Dudash, Michael/157 W 57th St	212-247-1130
Dudzinski, Andrzej/52 E 81st St	212-628-6959
Dupont, Lane/353 W 53rd St #1W	212-682-2462
Durke, Stephen/9 E 32nd St	212-688-1080
Dyess, John/157 W 57th St	212-247-1130

E

Eagle, Cameron/440 Prospect Ave #3R	718-499-7250
Eggert, John/420 Lexington Ave #2911	212-986-5680
Egielski, Richard/463 West St	212-255-9328
Ehlert, Lois/866 UN Plaza #4014	212-644-2020
Ellis, Dean/30 E 20th St	212-254-7590
Elmer, Richard/504 E 11th St	212-598-4024
Ely, Richard/207 W 86th St	212-874-4816
Emerson, Carmela/110-20 71st Ave #519	718-210-5570
Emerson, Matt (Emerson-Wajdowicz)/1123 Broadway	212-807-8144
Emmett, Bruce/285 Park Pl	718-636-5263
Endewelt, Jack/50 Riverside Dr	212-877-0575
Enik, Ted/82 Jane St #4A	212-620-5972
Ennis, John/310 Madison Ave #1225	212-867-8092
Ettlinger, Doris/73 Leonard St	212-226-0331
Eutemy, Loring/51 Fifth Ave	212-741-0140
Evcimen, Al/305 Lexington Ave	212-889-2995

F

Familton, Herb/59 W 10 St #1D	212-254-2943
Farina, Michael/120 E 32nd St	212-689-3233
Farley, Eileen M/383 First Ave	212-674-3602
Farmakis, Andreas/835 Third Ave	212-758-5280
Farrell, Marybeth/644 E 24th St	718-859-1824
Fasolino, Teresa/58 W 15th St	212-741-2539
Fassell, Beatrice/785 West End Ave #11D	212-865-2144
FEBLAND, DAVID/670 WEST END AVE (P 155)	**212-580-9299**
FEIGELES, NEIL/920 E 17TH ST (P 156)	**718-377-4418**
FEINEN, JEFF/835 THIRD AVE 4TH FL (P 157)	**212-986-8833**
Fennimore, Linda/808 West End Ave	212-866-0279
FERNANDES, STANISLAW/35 E 12TH ST (P 158)	**212-533-2648**
Fichera, Maryanne/12 W 27th St	212-689-8670
FILIPPUCCI, SANDRA/270 PARK AVE S #9B (P 159)	**212-477-8732**
Fiore, Peter/420 Lexington Ave #2911	212-986-5680
Fiorentino, Al/866 UN Plaza #4014	212-644-2020
Fitzgerald, Frank/212 E 89th St	212-722-6793
Flesher, Vivienne/23 E 10th St	212-505-6731
Foster, B Lynne/540 Ft Washington Ave #3D	212-781-1055
Fouse, Claudia/124 Riverside Dr	212-724-5412
Fox, Barbara/301 W 53rd St	212-245-7564
FRANCIS, JUDY/110 W 96TH ST (P 160)	**212-866-7204**
Franke, Phil/333 E 30th St	212-679-1358
Fraser, Betty/240 Central Park South	212-247-1937
Freeman, Irving/145 Fourth Ave	212-674-6705
Freeman, Tom/157 W 57th St	212-247-1130
Fretz, Frank/866 UN Plaza #4014	212-644-2020
Fricke, Warren/15 W 72nd St	212-799-2231
Fried, Janice/51 W 46th St #3B	212-398-0067
Friedman, Jon/866 UN Plaza #4014	212-644-2020
Froom, Georgia/62 W 39th St #803	212-944-0330
Furukawa, Mel/116 Duane St	212-349-3225

G

Gaadt, George/353 W 53rd St #1W	212-682-2462
Gabriele, Antonio J/420 Lexington Ave #2911	212-986-5680

Please send us your additions and updates.

GADINO, VICTOR/1601 THIRD AVE (P 20)	**212-534-7206**
Gahan, Nancy Lou/3 Washington Square Village	212-674-2644
Gala, Tom/420 Lexington Ave #2911	212-986-5680
Gale, Cynthia/229 E 88th St	212-860-5429
Gallardo, Gervasio/50 E 50th St	212-355-0910
Galub, Meg/405 W 57th St	212-489-8544
Gampert, John/55 Bethune St	212-242-1407
Garrido, Hector/420 Lexington Ave #2911	212-986-5680
Garrison, Barbara/12 E 87th St	212-348-6382
Gayler, Anne/320 E 86th St	212-734-7060
Geatano, Nicholas/821 Broadway	212-674-5749
Gehm, Charles/342 Madison Ave #949	212-697-8525
Geller, Martin/105 Montague St	718-237-1733
Gem Studio/420 Lexington Ave #220	212-687-3460
Genova, Joe/60 E 42nd St #505	212-682-1490
Gentile, John & Anthony/850 Seventh Ave #1006	212-757-1966
Gerber, Mark & Stephanie/159 Madison Ave	212-684-7137
Gershinowitz, George/PO Box 204 Chelsea Sta	212-691-1376
Gersten, Gerry/1380 Riverside Dr	212-928-7957
Geyer, Jackie/353 W 53rd St #1W	212-682-2462
Giavis, Ted/420 Lexington Ave #2911	212-986-5680
Giglio, Richard/299 W 12th St	212-675-7642
Gignilliat, Elaine/150 E 56th St	212-935-1943
Gillot, Carol/162 W 13th St	212-243-6448
GIORGIO, NATE/18 E 16TH ST (P 47)	**212-206-0322**
GIOVANOPOULIS, PAUL/216 E 45TH ST (P 54)	**212-661-0850**
GIUSTI, ROBERT/350 E 52ND ST #80 (P 163)	**212-752-0179**
Gleason, Paul/310 Madison Ave #1225	212-867-8092
GOLDSTROM, ROBERT/471 FIFTH ST (P 106)	**718-832-7980**
Goodell, Jon/866 UN Plaza #4014	212-644-2020
GOODRICH, CARTER/708 BROADWAY 10TH FL (P 165)	**212-477-3015**
Gordon, Rebecca/201 W 16th St	212-989-5762
GORMAN, STEPHEN/15 W 72ND ST (P 68)	**212-799-2231**
Gothard, David/215 E 31st St	212-684-3448
Gottlieb, Penelope/342 Madison Ave #949	212-679-8525
Graboff, Abner/310 Madison Ave	212-687-2034
GRADDON, JULIAN/48 W 21ST ST 9TH FL (P 93)	**212-243-4412**
GRAHAM, MARIAH/670 WEST END AVE (P 166)	**212-580-8061**
Grammer, June/126 E 24th St #3B	212-475-4745
GRAPHIC ASSOC/ CLAY TURNER/60 E 42ND ST #505 (P 19)	**212-682-1490**
GRAPHIC ASSOC/ RON FLEMING/60 E 42ND ST #505 (P 18)	**212-682-1490**
Grashow, David/215 E 31st St	212-684-3448
Gray, John/264 Van Duzer St	718-447-6466
GRAY, SUSAN/42 W 12TH ST #5 (P 167)	**212-675-2243**
GREIFINGER, MEL/200 W 15TH ST (P 56,57)	**212-243-4209**
GRIESBACH/MARTUCCI/35 STERLING PL (P 22,23)	**718-622-1831**
Griffel, Barbara/8006 47th Ave	718-446-0285
GRIFFIN, JAMES/60 E 42ND ST (P 41)	**212-867-8092**
Gross, Mort/2 Park Ave #1804	212-686-4788
Gross, Steve/342 Madison Ave	212-697-8525
Grossman, Robert/19 Crosby St	212-925-1965
GROTE, RICH/48 W 21ST ST 9TH FL (P 98)	**212-243-4412**
Grunfeld Graphics Ltd/80 Varick St	212-431-8700
Guarnaccia, Steven/89 Bleecker St #6B	212-420-0108
Guetary, Helen/333 E 30th St	212-563-4172
Guitar, Jeremy/866 UN Plaza #4014	212-644-2020

H

Haas, Arie/62 W 45th St	212-382-1677
Hack, Konrad/866 UN Plaza #4014	212-644-2020
HALL, DEBORAH ANN/105-28 65TH AVE #6B (P 169)	**718-896-3152**
HALL, JOAN/155 BANK ST #H954 (P 170)	**212-243-6059**
HALLGREN, GARY/6 W 37TH ST (P 171)	**212-947-1054**
Hamrick, Chuck/420 Lexington Ave #2911	212-986-5680
HARRINGTON, GLENN/165 E 32ND ST (P 61)	**212-686-3514**
Harris, Diane Teske/315 E 68th St	212-719-9879
Harrison, Sean/1349 Lexington Ave	212-369-3831
HARRISON, WILLIAM/18 E 16TH ST (P 45)	**212-689-3233**
Hart, Veronika/60 E 42nd St #505	212-682-1490
Harvey, Ned/129 W 22nd St	212-807-7043

Harvey, Richard/420 Lexington Ave #2911	212-986-5680
Harwood, Laurel/90 Lexington Ave #3A	212-532-0248
Haynes, Michael/420 Madison Ave #401	212-980-3510
Hays, Michael/43 Cheever Pl	718-852-2731
Heck, Cathy/30 W 74th St #1D	212-874-0913
Hedin, Donald/157 W 57th St	212-247-1130
Heindel, Robert/353 W 53rd St #1W	212-755-1365
HELLER, KAREN/300 W 108TH ST (P 174)	**212-866-5879**
Henderson, Alan/31 Jane St	212-243-0693
Henderson, Dave/420 Lexington Ave #2911	212-986-5680
Henrie, Cary/34 Hillside Ave #1C	212-942-6838
Henry, Paul/157 W 57th St	212-247-1130
HERBICK, DAVID/5 MONTAGUE TERRACE (P 175)	**718-852-6450**
HERDER, EDWIN/60 E 42ND ST (P 35)	**212-867-8092**
HERING, AL/342 MADISON AVE #261 (P 176)	**212-986-3282**
Herman, Tim/420 Madison Ave #401	212-980-3510
Hernandez, Richard/144 Chambers St	212-732-3474
Herrmann, Hal/50 E 50th St	212-752-8490
Hess, Mark/135 E 54th St	212-421-0050
Higgins, Pamela/866 UN Plaza #4014	212-644-2020
HILL, AMY/111 WOOSTER ST #PH C (P 51)	**212-925-0491**
Himmler, Ron/866 UN Plaza #4014	212-644-2020
Hochman, Steve/120 E 32nd St	212-689-3233
Hoffman, Ginnie/108 E 35th St #1	212-889-3337
Hoffman, Rosekrans/866 UN Plaza #4014	212-644-2020
Hogarth, Paul/215 E 31st St	212-684-3448
Holland, Brad/96 Greene St	212-226-3675
Holmes, John/420 Lexington Ave #2911	212-986-5680
Hooks, Mitchell/321 E 83rd St	212-737-1853
Hoover, Gerry/866 UN Plaza #4014	212-644-2020
Hortens, Walter/154 E 64th St	212-838-0014
Hosner, William/420 Madison Ave #401	212-980-3510
HOSTOVICH, MICHAEL/470 W 23RD ST (P 64)	**212-242-6367**
HOWARD, JOHN/336 E 54TH ST (P 106)	**212-832-7980**
The Hub/16 E 52nd St #504	212-421-5807
Hubert, Laurent/216 E 45th St	212-661-0850
Huerta, Catherine/60 E 42nd St #505	212-682-1490
Huffman, Tom/130 W 47th St #6A	212-819-0211
Hughes, Mary Ellen/403 E 70th St	212-288-8375
Hull, Cathy/236 E 36th St	212-683-8559
HUNT, JIM/420 MADISON AVE #401 (P 31)	**212-980-3510**
Hunter, Stan/50 E 50th St	212-355-0910
HUYSSEN, ROGER/1059 THIRD AVE (P 263)	**212-888-9193**

I

Idelson, Joyce/11 Riverside Dr	212-877-6161
Image Network Inc/645 West End Ave	212-877-1734
Incandescent Ink Inc/111 Wooster St #PH C	212-925-0491
Incisa, Monica/141 E 56th St	212-752-1554
INOUE, IZUMI/311 E 12TH ST (P 182)	**212-689-5148**
Iskowitz, Joel/420 Lexington Ave #2911	212-986-5680
Ivenbaum, Elliott/267 W 90th St	212-664-5656

J

JABEN, SETH/47 E 3RD ST #3 (P 185)	**212-260-7859**
JAMIESON, DOUG/42-20 69TH ST (P 186)	**718-565-6034**
Jampel, Judith/148 Columbus Ave	212-873-5234
JASPER, JACKIE/165 E 32ND ST (P 60,61)	**212-686-3514**
JEFFERS, KATHY/106 E 19TH ST 12TH FL (P 189)	**212-475-1756**
Jetter, Frances/390 West End Ave	212-580-3720
Jezierski, Chet/50 E 50th St	212-355-0910
Jobe, Jody/875 W 181st St	212-795-4941
JOHNSON, DOUG/45 E 19TH ST (P 192)	**212-260-1880**
JOHNSON, KRISTIN/902 BROADWAY #1609 (P 193)	**212-477-4033**
Jones, Bob/420 Lexington Ave #2911	212-986-5680
Joseph, Paula/147 W.13th St #2F	212-242-6137
JOUDREY, KEN/15 W 72ND ST (P 69)	**212-799-2231**
Just, Hal/155 E 38th St	212-697-6170

K

Kahn, Sandra/344 E 49th St #7A	212-759-0630
Kallan, Elizabeth Kada/67 Irving Pl	212-674-8080
Kampmier, Jill/320 E 22nd St	212-674-8379
KANAREK, MICHAEL/48 W 21ST ST 9TH FL (P 99)	**212-243-4412**
Kane, Harry/310 E 49th St	212-486-0180

KANE, KID/60 E 42ND ST #505 (P 21)	**212-682-1490**
KANE, MICHAEL/15 W 72ND ST (P 37)	**212-799-2231**
Kanelous, George/9 E 32nd St	212-688-1080
Kappes, Werner/345 E 73rd St	212-673-2484
Karlin, Bernie/41 E 42nd St	212-687-7636
Karlin, Eugene/39-73 48th St	718-457-5086
Katsin, Nancy/417 E 72nd St # 3B	212-535-7786
KATZ, LES/451 WESTMINSTER (P 195)	**718-284-4779**
Kaufman, Curt/215 W 88th St	212-873-9841
Kaufman, Stuart/420 Lexington Ave #2911	212-986-5680
KELENY, EARL/515 MADISON AVE 22ND FL (P 105)	**212-486-9644**
Kelley, Mark/866 UN Plaza #4014	212-644-2020
KELLY, SUSANNAH/111 WOOSTER ST # PH C (P 51)	**212-925-0491**
Kendrick, Dennis/99 Bank St	212-924-3085
KEYES, STEVEN/18 E 16TH ST (P 48)	**212-206-0322**
Kibbee, Gordon/6 Jane St	212-989-7074
Kidd, Tom/19 Broadway Terrace	212-942-5146
Kieffer, Christa/866 UN Plaza #4014	212-644-2020
King, Jean/315 Riverside Dr	212-866-8488
Kingsley, Melinda/120 E 79th St	212-879-2042
Kingston, James/31 E 31st St	212-685-2520
Kirk, Daniel/85 South St #6N	212-825-0190
KLAVINS, ULDIS/60 E 42ND ST (P 39)	**212-867-8092**
KLUGLEIN, KAREN/88 LEXINGTON AVE #12G (P 197)	**212-684-2974**
Knettell, Sharon/108 E 35th St #1	212-889-3337
KNIGHT, JACOB/216 E 45TH ST (P 54)	**212-661-0850**
Koester, Michael/420 Lexington Ave #2911	212-986-5680
Korda, Leslie/150 W 80th St	212-595-3711
Koren, Edward/215 E 31st St	212-684-3448
Kotzky, Brian/132-42 Booth Memorial Ave	718-353-5480
Krakovitz, Harlan/343 E 30th St #8B	212-679-4054
Kramer, Carveth/216 E 45th St	212-661-0850
Krantz Fieramosca, Kathy/9 Wirt Ave	718-777-9446
Kretschmann, Karin/323 W 75th St #1A	212-724-5001
Kriegler, Richard/353 W 53rd St #1W	212-682-2462
Kubinyi, Laszlo/41 Union Sq W #1228	212-691-5296
Kuester, Bob/353 W 53rd St #1W	212-682-2462
Kukalis, Romas/420 Lexington Ave #2911	212-986-5680
Kunstler, Mort/50 E 50th St	212-355-0910
Kursar, Ray/1 Lincoln Plaza #43R	212-873-5605
KURTZMAN, EDWARD/60 E 42ND ST (P 73)	**212-687-4185**
L Lacey, Lucille/77-07 Jamaica Ave	718-296-1813
Lackow, Andy/114 E 32nd St #902	212-685-2770
Lakeman, Steven/115 W 85th St	212-877-8888
LAMUT,SONJA & JAKESEVIC, NENAD/165 E 32ND ST (P 60)	**212-686-3514**
Landis, Joan/6 Jane St	212-989-7074
Lang, Gary/342 Madison Ave	212-697-8525
LAPINSKI, JOE/420 MADISON AVE #401 (P 31)	**212-980-3510**
LAPORTE, MICHELLE/216 E 45TH ST (P 54)	**212-661-0850**
Lasasso, Gary/2881 Coney Islnd Ave	718-646-6226
LASHER, MARY ANN/60 E 42ND ST #505 (P 24)	**212-682-1490**
Laslo, Larry/179 E 71st St	212-737-2340
Laslo, Rudy/9 E 32nd St	212-688-1080
Laurence, Karen/216 E 45th St	212-661-0850
Lauter, Richard/157 W 57th St	212-247-1130
Lawton, Nancy/601 W 113 St #9B	212-222-0210
Lazarevich, Mila/225 E 63rd St	212-371-9173
Leach, Richard/62 W 39th St #803	212-944-0330
Leake, Don/124 W 80th St	212-877-8405
LEBBAD, JAMES A/220 FIFTH AVE #1707 (P 202)	**212-679-2234**
Leder, Dora/866 UN Plaza #4014	212-644-2020
Lee, Bryce/246 Mott St #1	212-219-3782
Leonard, Richard/212 W 17th St #2B	212-243-6613
Leonard, Tom/866 UN Plaza #4014	212-644-2020
Lesser, Ron/342 Madison Ave #949	212-697-8525
LeTan, Pierre/215 E 31st St	212-684-3448
Lettick, Birney/121 E 35th St	212-532-0535
Levin, Arnie/315 E 68th St	212-472-9474
LEVINE, BETTE/60 E 42ND ST #505 (P 25)	**212-682-1490**
Levine, Ron/1 W 85th St #4D	212-787-7415
Levirne, Joel/151 W 46th St	212-869-8370
LEVY, ROBERT S/835 THIRD AVE (P 205)	**212-986-8833**
Lewin, Ted/152 Willoughby Ave	718-622-3882
LEWIS, HOWARD B/708 BROADWAY (P 207)	**212-477-3015**
LEWIS, TIM/194 THIRD AVE (P 81)	**212-475-0440**
Lexa, Susan/866 UN Plaza #4014	212-644-2020
Liberatore, Gaetano/43 E 19th St	212-254-4996
LIEBERMAN, RON/109 W 28TH ST (P 208)	**212-947-0653**
Lilly, Charles/56 W 82nd St #15	212-873-3608
Lindberg, Jeffery K/449 50th St	718-492-1114
Lindlof, Ed/353 W 53rd St #1W	212-682-2462
Line, Lemuel/50 E 50th St	212-355-0910
LITTLE APPLE ART/409 SIXTH AVE (P 209)	**718-499-7045**
LLOYD, PETER/18 E 16TH ST (P 46,47)	**212-206-0322**
LoGrippo, Robert/50 E 50th St #5	212-355-0910
LODIGENSKY, TED/18 E 16TH ST (P 47)	**212-206-0322**
Logan, Ron/866 UN Plaza #4014	212-644-2020
Long, Dan/333 E 30th St	212-679-1358
Lopez, Antonio/31 Union Square W #10A	212-924-2060
Lozner, Ruth/155 W 68th St	212-724-9403
Luce, Ben/200 Seventh Ave	718-768-8710
Lundgren, Ray Graphics/122 E 42nd St #216	212-370-1686
Lustig, Loretta/99 Madison Ave	212-679-8660
Lyall, Dennis/420 Lexington Ave #2911	212-986-5680
Lynch, Alan/60 Pineapple St #26	718-624-7979
Lyons, Robert/130 Willoughby Ave	718-622-0712
M Mack, Stan/226 E 53rd St	212-755-4945
Maddalone, John/1123 Broadway #310	212-807-6087
Madden, Don/866 U N Plaza #4014	212-644-2020
Magagna, Anna Marie/2 Tudor City Pl	212-840-1234
MAHON, RICH/18 E 16TH ST (P 47)	**212-206-0322**
Mahoney, Ron/353 W 53rd St #1W	212-682-2462
Maitz, Don/50 E 50th St	212-355-0910
Mambach, Alex/102-35 64th Rd	718-275-4269
Mandel, Saul/342 Madison Ave #949	212-697-8525
Manders, John/98 Bergen St	718-596-5468
Mangiat, Jeffrey/420 Lexington Ave #2911	212-986-5680
Mann, Patrick/220 W 98th St #3A	212-222-6854
Manos, Jim/342 Madison Ave #261	212-986-3282
MANTEL, RICHARD/194 THIRD AVE (P 76)	**212-475-0440**
Manyum, Wallop/37-40 60th St	718-476-1478
Marcellino, Fred Studio/432 Park Ave S #601	212-532-0150
Mardon, Allan/108 E 35th St #1	212-889-3337
MARGARET & FRANK & FRIENDS INC/124 HOYT ST (P 215)	**718-237-0145**
Marich, Felix/420 Madison Ave #401	212-980-3510
Marinelli, Robert/165 Bryant Ave	718-979-4018
Martin, Bruce Rough Riders/389 Ave of Americas	212-620-0539
Martinez, Sergio/43 E 19th St	212-254-4996
MARTINOT, CLAUDE/55 BETHUNE ST (P 55)	**212-242-1407**
MASI, GEORGE/111 WOOSTER ST #PH C (P 51)	**212-925-0491**
MASLEN, BARBARA/226 E 29TH ST (P 217)	**212-686-6559**
Mason, Brick/349 E 14th St #3R	212-777-4297
Mathewuse, James/157 W 57th St	212-247-1130
Mathieu, Joseph/215 E 31st St	212-684-3448
Mattelson, Marvin/88 Lexington Ave	212-684-2974
Mattingly, David/466 Washington St	212-219-0689
Maxwell, Brookie/53 Irving Pl	212-475-6909
Maye, Warren/3621 DeReimer Ave	212-655-7116
McCormack, Geoffrey/420 Lexington Ave #2911	212-986-5680
McCoy, Steve/514 E 83rd St	212-866-9536
McDaniel, Jerry/155 E 38th St	212-697-6170
McKie, Roy/75 Perry	212-989-5186
McLean, Wilson/50 E 50th St	212-752-8490
MCLOUGHLIN, WAYNE/194 THIRD AVE (P 80)	**212-475-0440**
Mead, Kimble Pendleton/125 Prospect Park West	718-768-3632
Mehlman, Elwyn/108 E 35th St #1	212-889-3337
Meisel, Ann/420 Lexington Ave #2911	212-986-5680
Melendez, Robert/120 E 32nd St	212-689-3233
Mercie, Tina/111 Wooster St #PH C	212-925-0491
MERRELL, PATRICK/48 W 20TH ST (P 221)	**212-620-7777**
Metcalf, Roger/9 E 32nd St	212-688-1080

Please send us your additions and updates.

Meyerowitz, Rick/68 Jane St	212-989-2446
Michaels, Bob/304 E 49 St	212-752-1185
Michal, Marie/108 E 35th St #1	212-889-3337
Michner, Ted/420 Lexington Ave #2911	212-986-5680
Mikos, Mike/420 Lexington Ave #2911	212-986-5680
Miller, Lyle/866 UN Plaza #4014	212-644-2020
Miller, Steve/11-18 47th Ave	718-784-3351
Milne, Jonathon/420 Lexington Ave	212-986-5680
MINOR, WENDELL/277 W 4TH ST (P 34)	**212-691-6925**
Mitchell, Maceo/446 Central Park West #4E	212-865-1059
Mitsuhashi, Yoko/43 E 29th St	212-683-7312
Miyamoto, Linda/484 Warren St	718-596-4787
MOLL, CHARLES/60 E 42ND ST (P 36)	**212-867-8092**
Montague, Andrea/19 Broadway Terrace	212-569-1421
MONTIEL, DAVID/115 W 16TH ST #211 (P 223)	**212-989-7426**
Mooney, Gerry/158-18 Riverside Dr W	212-781-3209
Moraes, Greg/310 Madison Ave #1225	212-867-8092
MORGAN, JACQUI/315 E 58TH ST (P 226)	**212-421-0766**
MORGEN, BARRY/337 W 87TH ST (P 227)	**212-595-6835**
MORRIS, FRANK/15 W 72ND ST (P 69)	**212-799-2231**
Morrison, Don/155 E 38th St	212-697-6170
Moseley, Marshall/409 Sixth Ave	718-499-7045
Moseley, Richie/409 Sixth Ave	718-499-7045
Moss, Geoffrey/315 E 68th St	212-472-9474
Murawski, Alex/108 E 35th St #1	212-889-3337
MYERS, DAVID/228 BLEECKER ST #8 (P 228)	**212-989-5260**
Myers, Lou/108 E 35th St #1	212-889-3337
N Nakai Sacco & Crowell/466 Lexington Ave	212-210-6905
Neff, Leland/506 Amsterdam Ave #61	212-724-1884
Nessim, Barbara/240 E 15th St	212-677-8888
Neubecker, Robert/395 Broadway #14C	212-219-8435
Neumann, Ann/444 Broome St	212-431-7141
Newsome, Tom/420 Lexington Ave #2911	212-986-5680
Newton, Richard/157 W 57th St	212-247-1130
NEYMAN-LEVIKOVA, MARINA/155 E 38TH ST (P 229)	**212-697-6170**
Ng, Michael/84-20 60th Ave	718-651-1913
Nicastre, Michael/342 Madison Ave #949	212-697-8525
NICHOLAS, JESS/18 E 16TH ST (P 48)	**212-206-0322**
Nicklaus, Carol/866 UN Plaza #4014	212-644-2020
Nicotra, Roseann/342 Maison Ave #949	212-697-8525
NIGHTHAWK STUDIO/420 MADISON AVE #401 (P 31)	**212-980-3510**
Nix, Jonathon J/175 Fifth Ave #1112	212-447-8027
Noftsinger, Pamela/7 Cornelia St	212-807-8861
Noome, Mike/420 Lexington Ave #2911	212-986-5680
Noonan, Julia/873 President St	718-622-9268
Notarile, Chris/420 Lexington Ave #2911	212-986-5680
O Oberheide, Heide/295 Washington Ave #5B	718-622-7056
Ochagavia, Carlos/50 E 50th St	212-355-0910
Odom, Mel/252 W 76th St	212-724-9320
OELBAUM, FRAN/200 W 15TH ST (P 56)	**212-243-4209**
OLANOFF, GREG/60 E 42ND ST (P 41)	**212-867-8092**
OLBINSKI, RAFAL/470 W 23RD ST (P 65)	**212-242-6367**
Olson, Maribeth/75 Huntington Ave	914-472-2384
Olson, Richard A/85 Grand St	212-925-1820
Orlin, Richard/2550 Olinville Ave	212-882-6177
Orloff, Dennis/682 Carroll St #1	718-965-0385
OVIES, JOE/420 MADISON AVE #401 (P 31)	**212-980-3510**
PQ Pahmer, Hal/8 W 30th St 7th Fl	212-889-6202
Parker, Robert Andrew/215 E 31st St	212-684-3448
Parle Portraits/100 LaSalle St	212-663-7361
Parrish, George I Jr/9 E 32nd St	212-688-1080
Parsons, John/342 Madison Ave #949	212-697-8525
Paslavsky, Evan/510-7 Main St N	212-759-3985
Passons, John/342 Madison Ave	212-697-8525
Pasternak, Robert/114 W 27th St	212-675-0002
Paul, Tony/235 E 49th St	212-307-6188
Peak, Bob/50 E 50th St	212-752-8490
Peele, Lynwood/344 W 88th St	212-799-3305
PELAVIN, DANIEL/45 CARMINE ST (P 232)	**212-929-2706**

PELS, WINSLOW PINNEY/120 W 81ST ST (P 233)	**212-580-1321**
Percivalle, Rosanne/211 E 11th St	212-254-6161
Petersen, Victoria/16 W 71st St	212-799-7021
Peterson, Cheryl/215 E 31st St	212-684-3448
Peterson, Robin/411 West End Ave	212-724-3479
Petragnani, Vincent/420 Madison Ave #401	212-980-3510
Pettingill, Ondre/295 Bennett Ave #4E	212-942-1993
Piscopia, Joe/114 Beadel St	718-384-2206
Plastic Triangle/146 W 16th St #4B	212-875-9345
Podwill, Jerry/108 W 14th St	212-255-9464
Powell, Ivan/58 W 15th St	212-741-2539
Powers, Christine/198 Berkeley Pl	718-783-1266
Pribula, Jo/59 First Ave	212-260-4548
Pu, Shirley/2 Horatio St	212-807-7069
PURDOM, BILL/780 MADISON AVE #7A (P 235)	**212-988-4566**
Quartuccio, Dom/5 Tudor City Pl #2201	212-661-1173
QUON, MIKE DESIGN OFFICE/53 SPRING ST (P 236)	**212-226-6024**
R Racz, Michael/224 Ave B #23	212-477-0401
Radigan, Bob/353 W 53rd St #1W	212-682-2462
RAGLIN, TIM/138 W 74TH ST (P 237)	**212-873-0538**
Rainbow Grinder/353 W 53rd St #1W	212-682-2462
RANE, WALTER/60 E 42ND ST (P 39)	**212-867-8092**
Realo, Perry A/155 E 2nd St #4B	212-254-5635
Reddin, Paul/120 Windsor Pl	718-965-0647
Reed, Chris/14 E 4th St #817	212-677-7198
REINGOLD, ALAN/155 E 38TH ST (P 238)	**212-697-6170**
Renfro, Ed/250 E 83rd St	212-879-3823
Reott, Paul/51-10 Van Horn St	718-426-1928
RICHARDS, LINDA/128 E 91ST ST (P 85)	**212-348-3781**
Rigo, Martin/43 E 19th St	212-254-4996
RISKO, ROBERT/201 W 11TH ST (P 240)	**212-989-6987**
Rixford, Ellen/308 W 97th St	212-865-5686
ROBERTS, CHERYL/200 E 78TH ST (P 53)	**212-570-9069**
Robins, Mike/9 E 32nd St	212-688-1080
Robinson, Charles/866 UN Plaza #4014	212-644-2020
Rogers, Paul/353 W 53rd St #1W	212-682-2462
Romer, Dan/125 Prospect Park W	718-768-3632
Root, Barry/265 Riverside Dr #4F	212-662-2290
Rosenblum, Richard/392 Fifth Ave	212-279-2068
Rosenfeld, Mort/420 Lexington Ave #2911	212-986-5680
Rosenthal, Doug/24 Fifth Ave	212-475-9422
Rosenwald, Laurie/45 Lispenard St	212-966-6896
Rosner, Meryl/342 Madison Ave #261	212-986-3282
Ross Design Assoc/27 W 20th St	212-206-0044
Ross, Barry/211 W 102nd St #5A	212-663-7386
Ross, Peter Design Assoc/10 E 23rd St 3rd Fl	212-206-0044
Roy, Frederick/205 W 14th St	212-206-8789
Rudd, Greg/420 Lexington Ave #2911	212-986-5680
Rudenjack, Phyllis/245 E 72nd St	212-772-2813
Ruff, Donna/42 E 23rd St	212-505-6913
Ruffins, Reynold/38 E 21st St	212-674-8150
Russell, Billy D/152 W 58th St #6D	212-246-0965
Ryan, Terry/9 E 32nd St	212-688-1080
S SABIN, ROBERT/60 E 42ND ST (P 42)	**212-867-8092**
Salaverry, Phillip/333 E 49th St	212-980-8061
Saldutti, Denise/463 West St #354H	212-255-9328
Salerno, Steve/226 E 53rd St # 3C	212-673-2298
Samuels, Mark/163 Corson Ave	718-447-8536
Sandler, Barbara/221 W 20th St	212-691-2052
Sargent, Claudia K/15-38 126th St	212-461-8280
Saris, Anthony/103 E 86th St	212-831-6353
Sauber, Rob/420 Lexington #2911	212-986-5680
Sawka, Jan/353 W 53rd St #1W	212-682-2462
Scarisbrick, Ed/9 E 32nd St	212-688-1080
Schaare, Harry/310 Madison Ave #1225	212-867-8092
Schimoler, Thomas/181 Baltic St #1	718-237-1586
Schleinkofer, David/420 Lexington Ave #2911	212-986-5680
SCHMIDT, BILL/60 E 42ND ST (P 39)	**212-867-8092**
Schmidt, Chuck/420 Madison Ave #401	212-980-3510
Schneegass, Martin/35 Carmine #9	212-675-5710

Please send us your additions and updates.

SCHONGUT, EMANUEL/ 353 W 53RD ST (P 79)	**212-682-2462**
SCHORR, KATHY STAICO/116 LEXINGTON AVE (P 243)	**212-684-3598**
Schorr, Todd/116 Lexington Ave	212-684-3598
SCHOTTLAND, MIRIAM/470 W 23RD ST (P 66)	**212-242-6367**
Schwarz, Jill Karla/80 N Moore St	212-227-2444
Scrofani, Joe/353 W 53rd St #1W	212-682-2462
SEAVER, JEFFREY/130 W 24TH ST #4B (P 244)	**212-255-8299**
Selby, Bill/342 Madison Ave #949	212-697-8525
Sell, Michael/253 W 72nd St	212-724-3406
Seltzer, Isadore/336 Central Park West	212-666-1561
Sempe, J J/215 E 31st St	212-684-3440
Shap, Sandra/342 Madison Ave #261	212-986-3282
SHEA, MARY ANNE/224 W 29TH ST (P 247)	**212-239-1076**
Shefts, Joelle/24 Bond St	212-228-7640
SHEGA, MARLA/60 E 42ND ST #505 (P 26)	**212-682-1490**
Sherman, Mary/165 E 32nd St	212-686-3514
Shields, Charles/226 E 53rd St	212-755-4945
Shub, Steve/114 E 32nd St #902	212-685-2770
Siegel, Norm/333 E 49th St	212-980-8061
Silverman, Burt/324 W 71st St	212-799-3399
Singer, Alan D/672 Fourth Ave	718-768-6664
Singer, Paul Design/494 14th St	718-499-8172
SLACK, CHUCK/60 E 42ND ST #505 (P 27)	**212-682-1490**
Slackman, Charles B/320 E 57th St	212-758-8233
Slavin, Fran/452 Myrtle Ave	718-403-9643
SLOAN, WILLIAM/444 E 82ND ST #12C (P 250)	**212-988-6267**
SMALLEY, GUY/62 LEROY ST (P 59)	**212-243-7869**
Smallwood, Steve/50 W 34th St #6C1	212-564-7923
Smith, Brett/353 W 53rd St #1W	212-682-2462
Smith, Edward/114 E 32nd St	212-686-5818
SMITH, GARY/48 W 21ST ST 9TH FL (P 96)	**212-243-4412**
Smith, Jeffrey/226 E 53rd St	212-755-4945
Smith, Joseph/159 John St #6	212-825-1475
SMITH, LAURA/12 E 14TH ST (P 153)	**212-206-9162**
Smith, Trudi/866 UN Plaza #4014	212-644-2020
Smollin, Mike/420 Lexington Ave #2911	212-986-5680
Smythe, Danny/420 Madison Ave #401	212-980-3510
SNEBERGER, DAN/60 E 42ND ST (P 34,39)	**212-867-8092**
SODERLIND, KIRSTEN/111 WOOSTER ST # PH C (P 51)	**212-925-0491**
Soldwedel, Kip/420 Lexington Ave #2911	212-986-5680
Solie, John/420 Lexington Ave #2911	212-986-5680
SOLOMON, DEBRA/536 W 111TH ST #55 (P 253)	**212-662-5619**
Sorel, Ed/135 E 54th St	212-421-0050
Sottung, George/420 Lexington Ave #2911	212-986-5680
Spector, Joel/420 Lexington Ave #2911	212-986-5680
SPOLLEN, CHRIS/203 CENTER ST (P 255)	**718-979-9695**
SPOSATO, JOHN/43 E 22ND ST (P 256)	**212-477-3909**
Stabin, Victor/100 W 15th St #4I	212-243-7688
STAHL, NANCY/194 THIRD AVE (P 77)	**212-475-0440**
Stamaty, Mark Alan/118 MacDougal St	212-475-1626
STAVRINOS, GEORGE/76 W 86TH ST (P 258)	**212-724-1557**
Steadman, Barbara/330 E 33rd St #10A	212-684-6326
STEADMAN, E T/470 W 23RD ST (P 67)	**212-242-6367**
STEINER, FRANK/60 E 42ND ST (P 40,42)	**212-867-8092**
Sterrett, Jane/160 Fifth Ave #700	212-929-2566
Stewart, Arvis/866 UN Plaza #4014	212-644-2020
Stillerman, Robbie/230 E 44th St #2F	212-661-7149
Stillman, Susan/126 W 71st St	212-724-5634
Stone, Gilbert/58 W 15th St	212-741-2539
Strimban, Robert/349 W 20th St	212-243-6965
Swanson, Robert/17 W 45th St 6th Fl	212-840-8516
Sweny, Stephen/217 E 29th St #52	212-532-4072
Szabo, Gustav/440 West End Ave	212-362-7376
SZILAGYI, MARY/410 CENTRAL PARK WEST (P 259)	**212-666-7578**
SZYGIEL, JAS/165 E 32ND ST (P 60)	**212-686-3514**

T Taback, Simms/38 E 21st St — 212-674-8150

Taleporos, Plato/401 First Ave	212-689-3138
Tankersley, Paul/29 Bethune St	212-924-0015
Taylor, Curtise/29 E 22nd St	212-473-6886
Taylor, Doug/106 Lexington Ave	212-674-6346
Taylor, Katrina/216 E 45th St	212-661-0850

Taylor, Stan Inc/6 E 39th St	212-685-4741
Tedesco, Michael/47 Joralemon St	718-596-4179
Ten, Arnie/446 62nd St	718-745-8477
Terreson, Jeffrey/420 Lexington Ave #2911	212-986-5680
Theakston, Greg/15 W 72nd St	212-799-2231
Thomas, Bob/420 Madison Ave #401	212-980-3510
Thomas, Phero/866 UN Plaza #4014	212-644-2020
Thornton, Shelley/121 Madison Avenue	212-683-1362
Tiani, Alex/142 E 37th St	212-683-3310
TINKELMAN, MURRAY/60 E 42ND ST #505 (P 28)	**212-682-1490**
Tobre, Marie/342 Madison Ave #949	212-697-8525
Tocchet, Mark/1071 Arnow Ave	212-654-4667
Tod-Kat Studios/353 W 53rd St #1W	212-682-2462
TRAVERS, ROBERT/60 E 42ND ST (P 36,42)	**212-867-8092**
Trossman, Michael/337 W 20th St	212-243-8839
Trull, John/1573 York Ave	212-535-5383
Tucker, Ezra/267 Fifth Ave #803	212-686-5576
TUNSTULL, GLENN/47 STATE ST (P 48)	**718-226-9356**
2-H STUDIO/1059 THIRD AVE (P 263)	**212-753-2918**

U V Uhler, Ms Kimane/47-25 40th St — 718-729-0635

Underwood, Beth/449 W 43rd St #3C	212-246-9788
URAM, LAUREN/251 WASHINGTON AVE (P 265)	**718-789-7717**
Vaccaro, Lou/866 UN Plaza #4014	212-644-2020
VALLA, VICTOR/60 E 42ND ST (P 41,42)	**212-867-8092**
Van Horn, Michael/49 Crosby St	212-226-8341
Vargo, Kurt/111 E 12th St Loft #4	212-982-6098
Varlet-Martinelli/200 W 15th St	212-243-4209
Vebell, Victoria/157 W 57th St	212-247-1130
VECCHIO, CARMINE/200 E 27TH ST (P 268)	**212-683-2679**
Velasquez, Eric/226 W 113th St	212-866-2209
Ventura, Dana/134 W 32nd St	212-244-4270
Vermont, Hillary/218 East 17th St	212-674-3845
Victor, Joan B/863 Park Ave #11E	212-988-2773
VIVIANO, SAM/25 W 13TH ST (P 271)	**212-242-1471**
Vizbar, Milda/529 E 84th St	212-944-9707

W Wajdowicz, Jurek/1123 Broadway — 212-807-8144

Wald, Carol/57 E 78th St	212-737-4559
WALDMAN, MICHAEL/506 W 42ND ST (P 272)	**212-239-8245**
WALKER, JEFF/60 E 42ND ST (P 40,41)	**212-867-8092**
Walker, Norman/535 E 86th St	212-355-0013
Waller, Charles/154 E 61st St	212-752-4392
Wallner, Alexandra/866 UN Plaza #4014	212-644-2020
Wallner, John/866 UN Plaza #4014	212-644-2020
Ward, Wendy/200 Madison Ave #2402	212-684-0590
Wasserman, Randi/28 W 11th St	212-254-0468
WASSON, CAMERON/4 S PORTLAND AVE #3 (P 274)	**718-875-8277**
Weaver, Robert/42 E 12th St	212-254-4289
Weiman, Jon/147 W 85th St #3F	212-787-3184
Weisser, Carl/38 Livingston St #38	718-834-0952
Weissman, S Q/2510 Fenton Ave	212-654-5381
Welkis, Allen/420 Lexington Ave #2911	212-986-5680
Wells, Skip/244 W 10th St	212-242-5563
Whistl'N Dixie/200 E 58th St	212-935-9522
WHITEHEAD, SAMUEL B/206 EIGHTH ST (P 279)	**718-965-2047**
Whitehouse, Debora/55 Bethune St	212-242-1407
Wilcox, David/135 E 54th St	212-421-0050
Wilkinson, Bill/155 E 38th St	212-697-6170
WILKINSON, CHUCK/60 E 42ND ST #505 (P 29)	**212-682-1490**
Williams, Richard/58 W 15th St	212-741-2539
Wilson, Deborah C/339 E 53rd St #1R	212-532-5205
WINKOWSKI, FRED/48 W 71ST ST (P 281)	**212-724-3136**
Wohlberg, Ben/43 Great Jones St	212-254-9663
WOLFF, PUNZ/151 E 20TH ST #5G (P 116)	**212-254-5705**
Wolin, Ron/353 W 53rd St #1W	212-682-2462
WOOD, PAGE/48 W 21ST ST 9TH FL (P 91)	**212-243-4412**
Woodend, James/342 Madison Ave #949	212-697-8525
Word-Wise/325 W 45th St	212-246-0430
Wynne, Patricia/446 Central Pk West	212-865-1059

Y Z YANKUS, MARC/179 PRINCE ST (P 282) — **212-228-6539**

ILLUSTRATORS

Please send us your additions and updates.

Yeldham, Ray/420 Lexington Ave #2911	212-986-5680
YIP, JENNY/18 E 16TH ST (P 48)	**212-206-0322**
York, Judy/165 E 32nd St	212-686-3514
Yule, Susan Hunt/176 Elizabeth St	212-226-0439
Zagorski, Stanislaw/142 E 35th St	212-532-2348
Zaid, Barry/108 E 35th St #1	212-889-3337
Zann, Nicky/210 E 29th St	212-689-6144
Zeldrich, Arieh/866 UN Plaza #4014	212-644-2020
ZIEMIENSKI, DENNIS/121 W 3RD ST (P 49)	**212-254-0233**
Ziering, Bob/151 W 74th St	212-873-0034
ZIMMERMAN, JERRY/48 W 20TH ST (P 285)	**212-620-7777**
Zitting, Joel/333 E 49th St #3J	212-980-8061
Zwarenstein, Alex/15 W 72nd St	212-799-2231

NORTHEAST

A

Abel, Ray/18 Vassar Pl, Scarsdale, NY	914-725-1899
Adam Filippo & Moran/1206 Fifth Ave, Pittsburgh, PA	412-261-3720
ADAMS, NORMAN/229 BERKELEY. #52, BOSTON, MA (P 33)	**617-266-3858**
Addams, Charles/PO Box 8, Westport, CT	203-227-7806
ADLER, BENTE/103 BROAD ST, BOSTON, MA (P 33)	**617-266-3858**
Ahmed, Ghulan Hassan/5738 Edgepark Rd, Baltimore, MD	301-444-8246
Aiese, Bob/12 Charles, Lynnbrook, NY	516-887-1367
Alcorn, John/RFD #2 Box 179, Lyme, CT	203-434-8533
ALEXANDER, PAUL R/37 PINE MOUNTAIN RD, REDDING, CT (P 119)	**203-544-9293**
Allen, Christina/289 Main St, Hingham, MA	617-749-0264
Almquist, Don/166 Grovers Ave, Bridgeport, CT	203-336-5649
AMICOSANTE, VINCENT/33 ROUTE 5, EDGEWATER, NJ (P 121)	**201-886-9354**
Ancas, Karen/7 Perkins Sq #11, Jamaica Plain, MA	617-522-2958
Archambault, David/56 Arbor St, Hartford, CT	203-523-9876
The Art Source/201 King St, Chappaqua, NY	914-238-4221
Ashmead, Hal/39 Club House Dr, Woodbury, CT	203-263-3466
Avati, Jim/10 Highland Ave, Rumson, NJ	201-530-1480

B

Babij, Oksanna/PO Box 1411, Norwalk, CT	203-226-3950
Bakley, Craig/68 Madison Ave, Cherry Hill, NJ	609-667-0022
Ball, Harvey/340 Main St, Wooster, MA	617-752-9154
Bang, Molly Garrett/43 Drumlin Rd, Falmouth, MA	617-540-5174
Banta, Susan/72 Newbern Ave, Medford, MA	617-396-1792
Barkely, James/25 Brook Manor, Pleasantville, NY	914-769-5207
Barrett, Tom/90 Myrtle St #4, Boston, MA	617-742-5143
Bass & Goldman/RD 3 Gypsy Trail Rd, Carmel, NY	914-225-8611
Baxter, Robert/Conte Pl #2, Westport, CT	203-226-3011
Bedard, Rob Ms/10215 Fernwood Rd, Bethesda, MD	301-530-9624
Bek-Gran, Phyllis/259 Vivien Ct, Paramus, NJ	201-261-5510
Belser, Burkey/1636 R St NW, Washington, DC	202-462-1482
Berry, Sheila & Richard/42 Phillips, Boston, MA	617-742-4246
Berstein, Steve/48 Arrandale Ave, Great Neck, NY	516-466-4730
Biggins, Wendy/185 Goodhill Rd, Weston, CT	203-226-7674
Birmingham, Lloyd P/Peekskill Hollow Rd, Putnam Valley, NY	914-528-3207
Bomzer, Barry Assoc/66 Canal St, Boston, MA	617-227-5151
Booth, George/PO Box 8, Westport, CT	203-227-7806
Boynton, Lee A/3 Weems Creek Dr, Annapolis, MD	301-263-6336
Brandt, Joan/PO Box 861, Stratford, CT	203-377-6735
Brautigan, Don/29 Cona Ct, Haledon, NJ	201-956-7710
Breeden, Paul M/Sullivan Harbor Farm, Sullivan Harbor, ME	207-422-3007
Breiner, Joanne/11 Webster St, Medford, MA	617-354-8378
Brickman, Robin/381 Morris Ave, Providence, RI	401-273-7372
Bridy, Dan Visuals Inc/119 First Ave, Pittsburgh, PA	412-288-9362
Brier, David/6 Cameron Ln, Valley Stream, NY	516-791-2662
Brown, Michael David/932 Hungerford Dr Bldg 24, Rockville, MD	301-762-4474
Bucella, Martin/72 Martinique Dr, Cheektowaga, NY	716-668-0040
BULLOCK, WILBUR/229 BERKELEY #52, BOSTON, MA (P 32)	**617-266-3858**
Burroughs, Miggs/Box 6, Westport, CT	203-227-9667
Burrows, Bill & Assoc/103 E Read St, Baltimore, MD	301-752-4615
Buschini, Maryanne/602 N 16th St #O, Philadelphia, PA	215-235-7838
Butcher, Jim/1357 E Macphail Rd, Bel Air, MD	301-879-6380

C

CABARGA, LESLIE/258 W TULPEHOCKEN, PHILADELPHIA, PA (P 102)	**215-438-9954**
Callahan, Kevin/26 France St, Norwalk, CT	203-847-2046
Calver, Dave/71 Henrietta St, Rochester, NY	716-271-6208
Caporale, Wendy/Studio Hill Farm Rte 116, N Salem, NY	914-669-5653
Carlson, Frederick H/2335 Meadow Dr, Pittsburgh, PA	412-371-8951
Carpenter, Sheldon/9 Sparhank St, Brighton, MA	617-782-6827
Carson, Jim/18 Orchard St, Cambridge, MA	617-661-3321
Casilla, Robert/36 Hamilton Ave, Yonkers, NY	914-963-8165
Catalano, Sal/114 Boyce Pl, Ridgewood, NJ	201-447-5318
Chambless-Rigie, Jane/185 Goodhill Rd, Weston, CT	203-226-7674
Chandler, Jean/385 Oakwood Dr, Wyckoff, NJ	201-891-2381
CHENG, JUDITH/88-57 195TH ST, HOLLIS, NY (P 134)	**718-465-5598**
CLINE, ROB/229 BERKELEY ST #52, BOSTON, MA (P 33)	**617-266-3858**
Cober, Alan/95 Croton Dam Rd, Ossining, NY	914-941-8696
Codd, Mary/1 Richmond Square, Providence, RI	401-273-9898
Cohen, Susan D/208 Park Ave #3R, Hoboken, NJ	201-659-5472
Collier, John/731 N 24th St, Philadelphia, PA	215-232-6666
Concept One/Gizmo/366 Oxford St, Rochester, NY	716-461-4240
CONGE, BOB/28 HARPER ST, ROCHESTER, NY (P 136)	**716-244-0183**
Console, Carmen/8 Gettysburg St, Voorshis, NJ	215-463-6110
Cooper, Bob/311 Fern Dr, Atco Post Office, NJ	609-767-0967
Cornell, Jeff/58 Noyes Rd, Fairfield, CT	203-259-7715
Cosatt, Paulette/60 South St, Cresskill, NJ	201-568-1436
CRAFT, KINUKO/RFD #1 PO BOX 167, NORFOLK, CT (P 103)	**203-542-5018**
CRAMER, D L/10 BEECHWOOD DR, WAYNE, NJ (P 140)	**201-628-8793**
CROFUT, BOB/225 PEACEABLE ST, RIDGEFIELD, CT (P 142,143)	**203-431-4304**
CROMPTON, JACK/229 BERKELEY #52, BOSTON, MA (P 32)	**617-266-3858**

D

Daily, Don/57 Academy Rd, Bala Cynwyd, PA	215-664-5729
Daly, Tom/47 E Edsel Ave, Palisades Park, NJ	201-943-1837
Daniel, Alan/185 Goodhill Rd, Weston, CT	203-226-7674
Darrow, Whitney/PO Box 8, Westport, CT	203-227-7806
DAVIDIAN, ANNA/229 BERKELEY #52, BOSTON, MA (P 32)	**617-266-3858**
Davis, Gary/33 Vincent St, Saugus, MA	617-233-3523
Dawes, Joseph/20 Church Ct, Closter, NJ	201-685-9670
Dedini, Eldon/PO Box 8, Westport, CT	203-227-7806
Deigen, Jim and Assoc/625 Stanwick St, Pittsburgh, PA	412-391-1698
DeKiefte, Kees/185 Goodhill Rd, Weston, CT	203-226-7674
Demarest, Robert/87 Highview Terr, Hawthorne, NJ	201-427-9639
Demers, Donald/15 Liberty St, Waltham, MA	617-893-6388
DEMUTH, ROGER TAZE/2627 DEGROFF RD, NUNDA, NY (P 90)	**716-468-2685**
Devlin, Bill/3393 Lufberry, Wantagh, NY	516-785-0376
Dey, Lorraine/10 Highland Ave, Rumson, NJ	201-530-1480
Dior, Jerry/9 Old Hickory Ln, Edison, NJ	201-561-6536
Dodge, Paul/731 N 24th St, Philadelphia, PA	215-232-6666
Dodge, Plunkett/79A Atlantic Ave, Cohasset, MA	617-383-6951
DODGE, SUSAN/229 BERKELEY #52, BOSTON, MA (P 33)	**617-266-3858**
Dougherty, Kevin/10 Highland Ave, Rumson, NJ	201-530-1480
Drescher, Joan/23 Cedar, Hingham, MA	617-749-5179
Duke, Christine/R D #1, Millbrook, NY	914-677-9510
Duke, W E Illustration/216 Walnut St, Holyoke, MA	413-536-8269
Dunne, Tom/16 Cherry St, Locust Valley, NY	516-676-3641
DVERIN, ANATOLY/229 BERKELEY #52, BOSTON, MA (P 33)	**617-266-3858**

E

Eagle, Mike/7 Captains Ln, Old Saybrook, CT	203-388-5654
Ebel, Alex/30 Newport Rd, Yonkers, NY	914-961-4058
Echevarria, Abe/Box 98 Anderson Rd, Sherman, CT	203-355-1254
Eichen, Ellen/1337 Corcoran St NW, Washington, DC	202-462-1482
Einsel, Naiad/26 S Morningside Dr, Westport, CT	203-226-0709
Einsel, Walter/26 S Morningside Dr, Westport, CT	203-226-0709
Enos, Randall/11 Court of Oaks, Westport, CT	203-227-4785
Epstein, Dave/Dows Ln, Irvington-on-Hudson, NY	914-591-7470
Epstein, Len/720 Montgomery Ave, Narbeth, PA	215-664-4700
Estey, Peg/7 Garden Ct, Cambridge, MA	617-876-1142
Eucalyptus Tree Studio/2220 N Charles St, Baltimore, MD	301-243-0211

Please send us your additions and updates.

F

Farris, Joe/PO Box 8, Westport, CT	203-227-7806
Fiedler, Joseph D/500 Sampsonia Way, Pittsburgh, PA	412-322-7245
FISHER, MARK/506 WINDSOR DR,	
FRAMINGHAM, MA (P 70,71)	**617-451-6528**
Ford, Pam/49 Richmondville Ave, Westport, CT	203-797-8188
Frazee, Marla/5114 1/2 La Roda Ave, Los Angeles, CA	213-258-3846
Frinta, Dagmar/87 Hope St, Providence, RI	401-273-6125
Frost, Ralph/170-6 Polk St, Syracuse, NY	315-445-0064
Fuchs, Bernard/3 Tanglewood Ln, Westport, CT	203-227-4644
Fulkerson, Chuck/Box 7 North St, Roxbury, CT	203-354-1365

G

Gaadt, George/888 Thorn, Sewickley, PA	412-741-5161
GARLAND, MICHAEL/78 COLUMBIA AVE,	
HARTSDALE, NY (P 161)	**914-946-4536**
Gerlach, Cameron/2644 N Calvert St, Baltimore, MD	301-889-3093
Gist, Linda E/224 Madison Ave, Fort Washington, PA	215-643-3757
Giuliani, Alfred/10 Woodland Terrace, Lincroft, NJ	201-741-8756
Glanzman, Louis S/154 Handsome Ave, Sayville, NY	516-589-2613
GLASBERGEN, RANDY J/34 SOUTH MAIN,	
EARLVILLE, NY (P 164)	**315-691-2424**
Glazer, Ted/28 West View Rd, Spring Valley, NY	914-354-1524
Glessner, Marc/24 Evergreen Rd, Somerset, NJ	201-249-5038
Gnatek, Michael Assoc/6642 Barnaby St NW, Washington, DC	202-363-6803
Gnidziejko, Alex/37 Alexander Ave, Madison, NJ	201-377-2664
GOLDBERG, RICHARD/368 CONGRESS ST 5TH FL,	
BOSTON, MA (P 70,71)	**617-338-6369**
Goldman, Marvin/RD 3 Gypsy Trail Rd, Carmel, NY	914-225-8611
GORDLEY, SCOTT/229 BERKELEY #52, BOSTON, MA (P 33)	**617-266-3858**
Gottfried, Max/82-60 116th St #CC3, Kew Gardens, NY	718-441-9868
Gove, Geoffrey/10 Highland Ave, Rumson, NJ	201-530-1480
Grashow, James/14 Diamond Hill Rd, West Redding, CT	203-938-9195
Green, Norman/11 Seventy Acres Rd, W Redding, CT	203-438-9909
Gustafson, Dale/56 Fourbrooks Rd, Stamford, CT	203-322-5667

HI

Haffner, Marilyn/185 Holworthy St, Cambridge, MA	617-354-0696
Hallman, Tom/38 S 17th St, Allentown, PA	215-776-1144
Hamilton, William/PO Box 8, Westport, CT	203-227-7806
Handelsman, Bud/PO Box 8, Westport, CT	203-227-7806
Handville, Robert T/99 Woodland Dr, Pleasantville, NY	914-769-3582
Haney, William/16 River Road RD #3, Neshanic Station, NJ	201-369-3848
Harden, Laurie/20 Overlook Rd, Boonton Township, NJ	201-335-4578
Hardy, Neil O/2 Woods Grove, Westport, CT	203-226-4446
Harris, Ellen/125 Pleasant St #602, Brookline, MA	617-739-1867
Harris, Peter/37 Beech St, Wrentham, MA	617-384-2470
Harsh, Fred/185 Goodhill Rd, Weston, CT	203-226-7674
Hazelton, Betsey/106 Robbins Dr, Carlisle, MA	617-369-5309
Healy, Deborah/72 Watchung Ave, Upper Montclair, NJ	201-746-2549
Hearn, Walter/22 Spring St, Pauling, NY	914-855-1152
Heath, R Mark/4338 Roland Springs Dr, Baltimore, MD	301-366-4633
HEJJA, ATTILA/300 EDWARD ST,	
ROSLYN HEIGHTS, NY (P 84)	**516-621-8054**
Henderson, David/7 Clover Ln, Verona, NJ	201-783-5791
Herrick, George W/384 Farmington, Hartford, CT	203-527-1940
HERRING, MICHAEL/5 OVERLOOK RD, OSSINING, NY (P 40)	**914-762-5045**
Hess, Richard/Southover Farms RT 67, Roxbury, CT	203-354-2921
Heyck, Edith/92 Water St, Newburyport, MA	617-462-9027
HILDEBRANDT, GREG/1148 PARSIPPANY BLVD,	
PARSIPPANY, NJ (P 264)	**201-334-0353**
Hildebrandt, Tim/10 Jackson Ave, Gladstone, NJ	201-234-2149
Hockerman, Dennis/185 Goodhill Rd, Weston, CT	203-226-7674
Hoffman, Martin/RD 2 Box 50, Worcester, MA	607-638-5472
Huehnergarth, John/196 Snowden Ln, Princeton, NJ	609-921-3211
Huelsman, Amy/24 S Calumet Ave, Hastings on Hudson, NY	914-478-0596
Huffaker, Sandy/375 Snowden Lane, Princeton, NJ	609-924-2883
Hulsey, John/Rte 9D, Garrison, NY	914-424-3544
Humphrey, John J Jr/5506 Namakagan Rd, Bethesda, MD	301-229-1116
Hunt, Stan/PO Box 8, Westport, CT	203-227-7806
Iosa, Ann/185 Goodhill Rd, Weston, CT	203-226-7674
Irwin, Virginia/174 Chestnut Ave #2, Jamaica Plain, MA	617-522-0580

JK

Jaeger Design Studio/2025 I St NW #622,	
Washington, DC	202-785-8434
Jean, Carole/45 Oriole Dr, Roslyn, NY	516-742-3322
Johne, Garrett/84-35 Lander St #4F, Briarwood, NY	212-523-5558
JOHNSON, B E/366 OXFORD ST,	
ROCHESTER, NY (P 190,191)	**716-461-4240**
Johnson, David A/299 South Ave, New Canaan, CT	203-966-3269
Jones, George/52 Old Highway, Wilton, CT	203-762-7242
Jones, John R/335 Town St, East Haddam, CT	203-873-9950
Jones, Robert/47 W Stewart, Lansdowne, PA	215-626-1245
Jones, Roger/15 Waldo Ave, Somerville, MA	617-628-1487
Jordan, Laurie/185 Goodhill Rd, Weston, CT	203-226-7674
Kalish, Lionel/Box 559, Woodstock, NY	914-679-8156
Kingham, Dave/42 Blue Spruce Circle, Weston, CT	203-226-3106
Kinstrey, Jim/35 Bryant Pl, Lodi, NJ	201-772-1781
Koeppel, Gary/368 Congress, Boston, MA	617-426-8887
Kossin, Sanford/143 Cowneck Rd, Port Washington, NY	516-883-3038
KOVALCIK, TERRY/15 1/2 VAN HOUTEN ST #307,	
PATERSON, NJ (P 198)	**201-345-2155**
Kovarsky, Anatol/PO Box 8, Westport, CT	203-227-7806

L

LACAOURSE, CAROL/506 WINDSOR DR,	
FRAMINGHAM, MA (P 70,71)	**617-451-6528**
LaGrone, Roy/25 Indiana Rd, Somerset, NJ	201-463-4515
Laird, William/10 Highland Ave, Rumson, NJ	201-530-1480
Lambert, Saul/153 Carter Rd, Princeton, NJ	609-924-6518
Lane, Jack/177 San Juan Dr, Hauppauge, NY	516-361-6051
LANGDON, JOHN/106 S MARION AVE,	
WENONAH, NJ (P 201)	**609-468-7868**
Lanza, Barbara/PO Box 118, Pine Island, NY	914-258-4601
Laquatra, Jack/1221 Glencoe Ave, Pittsburgh, PA	412-279-6210
Lawton, April/31 Hampshire Dr, Farmingdale, NY	516-454-0868
Layman, Linda J/35 Ware Rd, Auburndale, MA	617-965-0519
Lazarevich, Mila/185 Goodhill Rd, Weston, CT	203-226-7674
Leamon, Tom/18 Main St, Amherst, MA	413-256-8423
Lefevre, Joe/238 N High St, East Haven, CT	203-467-0135
Lehew, Ron/17 Chestnut St, Salem, NJ	609-935-1422
Leibow, Paul/369 Lantana Ave, Englewood, NJ	201-567-2561
Levine, Ned/301 Frankel Blvd, Merrick, NY	516-378-8122
Lewis, Alex/1527 16th St NW, Washington, DC	202-462-5326
LEYONMARK, ROGER/229 BERKELEY ST #52,	
BOSTON, MA (P 32)	**617-266-3858**
Lidbeck, Karin/185 Goodhill Rd, Weston, CT	203-226-7674
Loccisano, Karen/185 Goodhill Rd, Weston, CT	203-226-7674
Longacre, Jimmy/185 Goodhill Rd, Weston, CT	203-679-1358
LORENZ, AL/49 PINE AVE, FLORAL PARK, NY (P 210)	**516-354-5530**
Lorenz, Lee/PO Box 8, Westport, CT	203-227-7806
Lose, Hal/533 W Hortter St, Philadelphia, PA	215-859-7635
Lowes, Tom/72 Ridgeview Ln, Glenwood, NY	716-592-7353
Lubey, Dick/726 Harvard, Rochester, NY	716-442-6075
LUZAK, DENNIS/PO BOX 342,	
REDDING RIDGE, CT (P 212,213)	**203-938-3158**
Lynch, Don/532 N Broadway, Upper Nyack, NY	914-358-3939
Lyon, Lynne/9 Castleton St, Jamaica Plain, MA	617-522-4533

M

MacArthur, Dave/147 E Bradford Ave #B, Cedar Grove, NJ	201-857-1046
MacDonald, Susan/PO Box 25, S Londonderry, VT	802-824-6309
MacFarland, Jean/Laurel Lake Rd, Lenox, MA	413-637-3647
Maffia, Daniel/44 N Dean St, Englewood, NJ	201-871-0435
Maglio, Mark/PO Box 872, Plainville, CT	203-793-0771
Mahoney, Katherine/60 Hurd Rd, Belmont, MA	617-489-0406
Mandel, Saul/163 Maytime Dr, Jericho, NY	516-681-3530
Mariuzza, Pete/146 Hardscrabble Rd, Briarcliff Manor, NY	914-769-3310
Marmo, Brent/15A St Mary's Ct, Brookline, MA	617-395-8977
Martin, Henry/PO Box 8, Westport, CT	203-227-7806
Mascio, Tony/4 Teton Ct, Voorhees, NJ	609-567-1585
Mayforth, Hal/19 Irma Ave, Watertown, MA	617-923-4668
Mayo, Frank/265 Briar Brae, Stamford, CT	203-322-3650
McCanlish, Joan/327A Highland Ave, Somerville, MA	617-666-4546
McElfish, Susan/5725 Phillips Ave, Pittsburgh, PA	412-521-6041
McGinnis, Robert/13 Arcadia Rd, Old Greenwich, CT	203-637-5055

McGuire, Arlene Phoebe/The Cambridge #509/Alden Pk, Philadelphia, PA	215-844-0754
McIntosh, Jon C/268 Woodward St, Waban, MA	617-964-6292
McManimon, Tom/2700 Route 22, Union, NJ	201-688-2700
McVicker, Charles/4 Willow St, Princeton, NJ	609-924-2660
Menn, Jennifer J/28-4 Beacon St, Chelsea, MA	617-884-6267
Miles, Elizabeth/185 Goodhill, Weston, CT	203-226-7674
Miller, Warren/PO Box 8, Westport, CT	203-227-7806
Milnazik, Kim/210 Locust St #3F, Philadelphia, PA	215-922-5440
Mistretta, Andrea/5 Bohnert Pl, Waldwick, NJ	201-652-5325
Mitchell & Company/1029 33rd St NW, Washington, DC	202-342-6025
Miyake, Yoshi/185 Goodhill Rd, Weston, CT	203-226-7674
Modell, Frank/PO Box 8, Westport, CT	203-227-7806
Moore, Jack/14 Smull Ave, Caldwell, NJ	201-228-2334
MORALES, MANUEL/PO BOX 1763, BLOOMFIELD, NJ (P 224,225)	**201-429-0848**
MOSCOWITZ, STEPHEN/1239 UNIVERSITY AV E, ROCHESTER, NY (P 90)	**716-442-8433**
Munger, Nancy/185 Goodhill Rd, Weston, CT	203-226-7674
Myers, Lou/58 Lakeview Ave, Peekskill, NY	914-737-2307

NO

Nachbar, Amy/57 Lorimar Ave, Providence, RI	401-274-4591
Neibart, Wally/1715 Walnut St, Philadelphia, PA	215-564-5167
Newman, Robert/570 W Dekalb Pike #111, King of Prussia, PA	215-337-2745
Norman, Marty/5 Radcliff Blvd, Glen Head, NY	516-671-4482
Noyes, David/506 Windsor Dr, Framingham, MA	617-451-6528
Noyse, Janet/118 Woodland Rd, Wincote, PA	215-572-6975
Oh, Jeffrey/2635 Ebony Rd, Baltimore, MD	301-661-6064
O'Leary, John/547 N 20th St, Philadelphia, PA	215-561-7377
Olsen, Jimmy/50 New York Ave, Clark, NJ	201-388-0967
Olson, Victor/Santon Meadows, West Redding, CT	203-938-2863
Oni/3514 Tulip Dr, Yorktown Hts, NY	914-245-5862
Otnes, Fred/Chalburn Rd, West Redding, CT	203-938-2829
Oughton, Taylor/Jamison, Bucks County, PA	215-598-3246

P

Paine/ Bluett/ Paine/4617 Edgefield Rd, Bethesda, MA	301-493-8445
Palulian, Dickran/18 McKinley St, Rowayton, CT	203-866-3734
Papitto, Aurelia/PO Box 1454 GMS, Boston, MA	617-451-5362
Parker, Ed Assoc/45 Newbury St, Boston, MA	617-437-7726
Parry, Ivor A/4 Lorraine Dr, Eastchester, NY	212-889-0619
Passalacqua, David/325 Versa Pl, Sayville, NY	516-589-1663
Pate, Rodney/185 Goodhill Rd, Weston, CT	203-226-7674
PAYNE, THOMAS/11 COLONIAL AVE, ALBANY, NY (P 231)	**518-482-1756**
Perina, Jim/33 Regent St, N Plainfield, NJ	201-757-3010
Pierson, Mary Louise/743 Bedford Rd, Tarrytown, NY	914-631-3711
Pinkney, Jerry/41 Furnace Dock Rd, Croton-on-Hudson, NY	914-271-5238
Pisano, Al/21 Skyline Dr, Upper Saddle River, NJ	201-327-6716
Plotkin, Barnett/126 Wooleys Ln, Great Neck, NY	516-487-7457
Plumridge Artworks Inc/10215 Fernwood Rd, Bethesda, MD	301-530-9624
POLLACK, SCOTT/11 TRINITY PL, HEWLETT, NY (P 234)	**516-295-4026**
Porzio, Ed/131 Bartlett Rd, Winthrop, MA	617-846-3875
Price, George/PO Box 8, Westport, CT	203-227-7806
Provensen, Alice/Meadowbrook Ln Box 171, Staatsburg, NY	914-266-3245
Pruyn, Glen/800 Cottman #105A, Philadelphia, PA	215-722-1323
Puccio, Jim/32 Rugg Rd, Allston, MA	617-783-2719

R

Rabl, Lorraine/249 Queen Anne Rd, Bogota, NJ	201-342-4647
Ramage, Alfred/29 Tewksbury St, Winthrop, MA	617-846-5955
Recchia, Dennis/191 Engle St, Englewood, NJ	201-569-6136
Recchia, Janet/191 Engle St, Englewood, NJ	201-569-6136
Reeser, Tracy P/254 Andover Rd, Glenmoore, PA	215-942-2597
Regnier, Mark/31 Glenville Ave, Allston, MA	617-782-4399
Reiner, John/27 Commander Ln, Nesconset, NY	516-360-3049
Richardson, Suzanne/185 Goodhill Rd, Weston, CT	203-226-7674
Richter, Mische/Box 8, Westport, CT	203-227-7806
RICKERD, DAVID/18 UNIVERSITY AVE, CHATHAM, NJ (P 239)	**201-635-9513**
Riley, Frank/108 Bamford Ave, Hawthorne, NJ	201-423-2659
Rodericks, Michael/129 Lounsbury Rd, Trumbull, CT	203-268-1551
Rogers, Howard/18 Walnut Ln, Weston, CT	203-227-2273
Roman, Barbara/25 Franklin Blvd #6T, Long Beach, NY	516-431-5872

Roman, Irena & John/369 Thom Clapp Rd Box 571, Scituate, MA	617-545-6514
Ross, Jeremy/26 Vautrinot Ave, Hull, MA	617-925-0176
Ross, Larry/53 Fairview Ave, Madison, NJ	201-377-6859
Ross, Richard/71 Redbrook Rd, Great Neck, NY	516-466-3339
Roth, Gail/185 Goodhill Rd, Weston, CT	203-226-7674
Rutherford, Jenny/185 Goodhill Rd, Weston, CT	203-226-7674

S

Saint John, Bob/320 South St, Portsmouth, NH	603-431-7345
Sanderson, Ruth/185 Goodhill Rd, Weston, CT	203-226-7674
Santa, Monica/185 Goodhill Rd, Weston, CT	203-226-7674
Santore, Charles/138 S 20th St, Philadelphia, PA	215-563-0430
Saxon, Charles/Box 8, Westport, CT	203-227-7806
Schleinkofer, David/344 Crown St, Morrisville, PA	215-295-8622
Schneider, Rick/260 Montague Rd, Leverett, MA	413-549-0704
Schreck, John/29 Commonwealth Ave, Boston, MA	617-236-4269
Schroeppel, Richard/31 Walnut Hill Rd, Amherst, NH	603-673-0997
Selwyn, Paul/1 Norton Ln, Farmington, CT	203-677-7320
Sharpe, Jim/5 Side Hill Rd, Westport, CT	203-226-9984
SHAW, BARCLAY/8 BUENA VISTA DR, HASTINGS-ON-HUDSON, NY (P 246)	**914-478-0265**
SHERMAN, OREN/30 IPSWICH #209, BOSTON, MA (P 248,249)	**617-437-7368**
Shiff, Andrew Z/153 Clinton St, Hopkinton, MA	617-435-3607
Sierra, Dorthea/5 Bridge St, Watertown, MA	617-924-5100
Simmonds, Oz/236 W Grand St #A5, Elizabeth, NJ	201-289-1714
Sims, Blanche/185 Goodhill Rd, Weston, CT	203-226-7674
Skibinski, Ray/694 Harrell Ave, Woodbridge, NJ	201-634-3074
Smith, Douglas/405 Washington St #2, Brookline, MA	617-566-3816
SMITH, ELWOOD H/2 LOCUST GROVE RD, RHINEBECK, NY (P 251)	**914-876-2358**
Smith, Marcia/112 Linden St, Rochester, NY	716-461-9348
Smith, Susan B/22 Henchman St, Boston, MA	617-266-4441
Snyder, Diane/3 Underwood Rd, Wyncote, PA	215-572-1192
SOILEAU, HODGES/350 FLAX HILL RD, NORWALK, CT (P 252)	**203-852-0751**
Solomon, Shimon Josef/754 Scotland Rd #G2, Orange, NJ	201-672-1898
Soyka, Ed/231 Lafayette Ave, Peekskill, NY	914-737-2230
Spanfeller, Jim/Mustato Rd, Katonah, NY	914-232-3546
Sparkman, Gene/15 Bradley Lane, Sandy Hook, CT	203-426-0061
Sparks, Richard & Barbara/2 W Rocks Rd, Norwalk, CT	203-866-2002
Spence, Jim/185 Goodhill Rd, Weston, CT	203-226-7674
Spitzmiller, Walter/24 Lee Lane Rd 2, West Redding, CT	203-938-3551
SPRINGER, SALLY/317 S LAWRENCE CT, PHILADELPHIA, PA (P 257)	**215-925-9697**
Stahl, Benjamin F/East Hill, Litchfield, CT	203-567-8005
STASOLLA, MARIO/LAUREL RIDGE, TUXEDO, NY (P 37)	**914-676-8373**
Steig, William/Box 8, Westport, CT	203-227-7806
Steinberg, Herb/PO Box 65, Roosevelt, NJ	609-448-4724
Sternglass, Arno/16 Linden Blvd, Great Neck, NY	516-487-9886
Stevenson, James/PO Box 8, Westport, CT	203-227-7806
Stirweis, Shannon/31 Fawn Pl, Wilton, CT	203-762-7058
Stone, David K/6 Farmview Rd, Port Washington, NY	516-627-7040
Stump, Greg/2 Upton Hall, Newark, DE	302-737-0813
Sturrock, Walt/57 E Shawnee Trail, Wharton, NJ	201-663-0069
Syverson, Henry/PO Box 8, Westport, CT	203-227-7806
Szabo, Leslie/7 Buck Hill Rd, Westport, CT	203-227-4338

TV

Taktakajian, Asdur/17 Merlin Ave, North Tarrytown, NY	914-631-5553
Tandem Graphics/5313 Waneta Rd, Bethesda, MD	301-320-5008
Tantillo, Leonard F/PO Box 320 RD1, Nassau, NY	516-766-4542
Tatore, Paul/10 Wartburg Pl, Valhalla, NY	914-769-1061
Tauss, Herb/S Mountain Pass, Garrison, NY	914-424-3765
Tayler, Dahl/120 1st St, Troy, NY	518-274-6379
Thomas, Anne/8 Steephill Rd, Weston, CT	203-227-5672
Thompson, Arthur/39 Prospect Ave, Pompton Plains, NJ	201-835-3534
Thompson, John M/River Road, W Cornwall, CT	203-672-6163
Tinkelman, Murray/75 Lakeview Ave W, Peekskill, NY	914-737-5960
TOELKEY, RON/229 BERKELEY #52, BOSTON, MA (P 32)	**617-266-3858**
Tolke, Cathleen/234 W Canton St, Boston, MA	617-266-8790
Toulmin-Rothe, Ann/49 Richmondville Rd, Westport, CT	203-226-3011
Traub, Patricia/25-30 Aspen St, Philadelphia, PA	215-769-1378

Treatner, Meryl/721 Lombard St, Philadelphia, PA	215-627-2297
TSUI, GEORGE/2250 ELLIOT ST, MERRICK, NY (P 261)	**516-223-8474**
Valeho, Boris/24 St Andrews Pl, Yonkers, NY	914-423-8694
Veno, Joe/20 Cutler Rd, Hamilton, MA	617-468-3165
VERNAGLIA, MICHAEL/1251 BLOOMFIELD ST,	
HOBOKEN, NJ (P 269)	**201-659-7750**
VISKUPIC, GARY/7 WESTFIELD DR,	
CENTER PORT, NY (P 270)	**516-757-9021**
Vissichelli, Joe/34-40 Church St #21, Malverne, NY	516-599-2562

WYZ WALDMAN, NEIL/47 WOODLANDS AVE,

WHITE PLAINS, NY (P 273)	**914-693-2782**
Wallerstein, Alan/61 Tenth St, Ronkonkoma, NY	516-981-3589
Watson, Karen/100 Churchill Ave, Arlington, MA	617-641-1420
Watts, Mark/616 Iva Ln, Fairless Hills, PA	215-945-9422
Weber, Robert/PO Box 8, Westport, CT	203-227-7806
Weissman, Bari/41 Atkins St, Brighton, MA	617-783-0230
Weller, Linda Boehm/185 Goodhill Rd, Weston, CT	203-226-7674
Whelan, Michael/172 Candlewood Lake Rd, Brookfield, CT	203-775-4430
Williams, Frank/130 Bainbridge St, Philadelphia, PA	215-625-2408
Wilson, Gahan/PO Box 8, Westport, CT	203-227-7806
Witschonke, Alan/28 Tower St #2, Somerville, MA	617-628-5601
Woodman, Bill/PO Box 8, Westport, CT	203-227-7806
Wright, Bob Creative/247 N Goodman St, Rochester, NY	716-271-2280
Yalowitz, Paul/598 Freeman Ave, Brentwood, NY	516-273-7782
Young, Debby/185 Goodhill Rd, Weston, CT	203-226-7674
Young, Robert Assoc/78 North Union St, Rochester, NY	716-546-1973
Young, Wally/8 Steephill Rd, Weston, CT	203-227-5672
Ziegler, Bill/PO Box 8, Westport, CT	203-227-7806
Zimmerman, Robert/191 Stadley Rough Rd, Danbury, CT	203-792-0783

SOUTHEAST
AB Adams, Lisa/161 Aragon Ave, Coral Gables, FL

Adams, Lisa/161 Aragon Ave, Coral Gables, FL	305-444-4080
Advertising Artists/880 W 53rd Terrace, Hialeah, FL	305-557-4631
Andrew, Joan/9315 Glenbrook Rd, Fairfax, VA	703-385-0126
Armstrong, Lynn/7325 Chattaho. Bluff Dr, Atlanta, GA	404-396-0742
Art Directions/2907 Bird Ave, Coconut Grove, FL	305-446-3697
Arunski, Joe & Assoc/8264 SW 184th Terr, Miami, FL	305-387-2130
Bailey, R.C./255 Westward Dr, Miami Springs, FL	305-888-6309
Boatright, John/PO Box 171382, Memphis, TN	901-683-1856
Boone, Joe/ PW Inc/PO Box 99337, Louisville, KY	502-499-9220

CD Carey, Mark/1209 Anne Ave, Chesapeake, VA

Carey, Mark/1209 Anne Ave, Chesapeake, VA	804-545-2669
Carey, Wayne/532 Hardendorp Ave, Atlanta, GA	404-378-0426
Carter, Zane/1008 N Randolph St #100, Arlington, VA	703-527-7338
Chaisson, Brant/1420 Lee Ave, Houma, LA	504-868-7423
Cooper-Copeland Inc./1151 W Peachtree St NW, Atlanta, GA	404-892-3472
Davis, Mike/1461 Rockspring Cir #3, Atlanta, GA	404-872-5525
DeBro, James/2725 Hayden Dr, Eastpoint, GA	404-344-2971

FG Faure, Renee/600 Second St, Neptune Beach, FL

Faure, Renee/600 Second St, Neptune Beach, FL	904-246-2781
Findley, John/213 Elizabeth St, Atlanta, GA	404-659-7103
Fleck, Tom/One Park Pl #120, Atlanta, GA	404-355-0729
GAADT, DAVID/3500 FOX PL, GREENSBORO, NC (P 37,40)	**919-288-9727**
George, Eugene/2905 Saint Anne St, New Orleans, LA	504-482-3774
Gordon, Jack/5716 S 2nd St, Arlington, VA	703-820-0145
Gorman, Martha/3057 Pharr Ct Nrth NW #E6, Atlanta, GA	404-261-5632
Graphics Group/6111 PeachtreeDunwdy Rd #G101,	
Atlanta, GA	404-261-5146
Greathead, Ian/2975 Christopher's Court, Marietta, GA	404-952-5067
Guthrie, Dennis/645 Raven Springs Tr, Stone Mtn, GA	404-469-8770

HIJ Hamilton, Marcus/12225 Ranburne Rd, Charlotte, NC

Hamilton, Marcus/12225 Ranburne Rd, Charlotte, NC	704-545-3121
Havaway, Jane/806 Briarcliff Rd, Atlanta, GA	404-872-7284
Hicks, Richard Edward/3635 Pierce Dr #76, Chamblee, GA	404-457-8928
Hinojosa, Albino/2101 Mesa Dr, Ruston, LA	318-255-2820
IMAGE ELECTRONIC INC/2030 POWERS FERRY RD #226,	
ATLANTA, GA (P 181)	**404-951-9580**
IRVIN, TREVOR/330 SOUTHERLAND TERRACE,	
ATLANTA, GA (P 183)	**404-337-4574**

Ison, Diana/4212 E Knob Oak Lane, Charlotte, NC	704-553-2864
J H ILLUSTRATION/3832 LANGLEY RD,	
CHARLOTTE, NC (P 184)	**704-568-8137**
JONES, JACK/104 ARDMORE PL #1, ATLANTA, GA (P 74)	**404-355-6357**

KL Kerns, Jeffrey/48 Peachtree Ave, Atlanta, GA

Kerns, Jeffrey/48 Peachtree Ave, Atlanta, GA	404-233-5158
Lee, Kelly/3511 N 22nd St, Arlington, VA	703-527-4089
LESTER, MIKE/1001 EULALIA RD, ATLANTA, GA (P 204)	**404-233-3093**
LEWIS, CHRIS/1115 N VIRGINIA AVE, ATLANTA,	
GA (P 206)	**404-876-0288**
LOVELL, RICK/745 KIRK RD, DECATUR, GA (P 211)	**404-371-0681**

MN Martin, Don/5110 S W 80th St, Miami, FL

Martin, Don/5110 S W 80th St, Miami, FL	305-665-2376
Mayer, Bill/240 Forkner Dr, Decatur, GA	404-378-0686
McGary, Richard/180 NE 39th St #125, Miami, FL	305-573-0490
McGurren Weber Ink/104 S Alfred St #C, Alexandria, VA	703-548-0003
MCKELVEY, DAVID/2702 FRONTIER COURT,	
ATLANTA, GA (P 218)	**404-457-3615**
McKinney, Deborah/95-50 Regency Sq Blvd, Jacksonville, FL	904-723-6000
MCKISSICK, RANDALL/PO BOX 21811,	
COLUMBIA, SC (P 219)	**803-798-3688**
Nelson, Bill/1402 Wilmington Ave, Richmond, VA	804-358-9637

OP Olson, Linda/1 Charter Plaza, Jacksonville, FL

Olson, Linda/1 Charter Plaza, Jacksonville, FL	904-723-6000
Overacre, Gary/RD 2, 3802 Vineyard Trace, Marietta, GA	404-973-8878
OVIES, JOE/1900 EMERY ST NW #120,	
ATLANTA, GA (P 31)	**404-355-0729**
Pardue, Jack/2307 Sherwood Hall Ln, Alexandria, VA	703-765-2622
Pate, Martin/401 W Peachtree NW, Atlanta, GA	404-221-0700
Penca, Gary/3184 NW 39th Ct, Lauderdale Lakes, FL	305-733-5847
Profancik, Larry/ PW Inc/PO Box 99337, Louisville, KY	502-499-9220

RS Robinette, John/1147 S Prescott, Memphis, TN

Robinette, John/1147 S Prescott, Memphis, TN	901-452-9853
ROMEO, RICHARD/1066 NW 96TH AVE,	
FT LAUDERDALE, FL (P 241)	**305-472-0072**
SAFFOLD, JOE/719 MARTINA DR NE, ATLANTA, GA (P 242)	**404-231-2168**
Salmon, Paul/5826 Jackson's Oak Ct., Burke, VA	703-250-4943
Sams, B B/PO Box A, Social Circle, GA	404-464-2956
Shelly, Ron/6396 Manor Lane, S Miami, FL	305-667-0154
Soper, Pat/214 Stephens, Lafayette, LA	318-233-1635
SPETSERIS, STEVE/401 W PEACHTREE NW #1720,	
ATLANTA, GA (P 74)	**404221-0798**
Stanton, Mark/67 Jonesboro St, McDonough, GA	404-957-5966

TUV Thomas, Steve Design/141 Brevard Ct, Charlotte, NC

Thomas, Steve Design/141 Brevard Ct, Charlotte, NC	704-332-4624
Turner, Pete/938 Pamlico Dr, Cary, NC	919-467-8466
Utz, David/1733 Spring Creek Dr, Sarasota, FL	813-365-1269
Vander Weg, Phil/Box 450 MTSU, Murfreesboro, TN	615-896-4239
VAUGHN, ROB/PO BOX 660706, MIAMI SPRINGS, FL (P 267)	**305-885-1292**
Vintson, Sherry/1361 Snell Isle Blvd #10, St Petersburg, FL	813-822-2512
Vondracek, Woody/420 Lincoln Rd #408, Old Miami Beach, FL	305-531-7558

WY Wasiluck Associates/1333 Tierra Cir, Winter Park, FL

Wasiluck Associates/1333 Tierra Cir, Winter Park, FL	305-678-6964
Webber, Warren/401 W Peachtree NW, Atlanta, Ga	404-221-0700
Whitver, Harry K/208 Reidhurst Ave, Nashville, TN	615-320-1795
Whole Hog Studios Ltd/1205 Spring St, Atlanta, GA	404-873-4021
The Workshop Inc/735 Bismark Rd NE, Atlanta, GA	404-875-0141
YOUNG, BRUCE/503 ANSLEY VILLA DR,	
ATLANTA, GA (P 283)	**404-892-6303**

MIDWEST
AB Ahearn, John D/151 S Elm, St Louis, MO

Ahearn, John D/151 S Elm, St Louis, MO	314-721-3997
Anastas, Nicolette/535 N Michigan Ave, Chicago, IL	312-943-1668
Art Force Inc/21700 NW Hwy #570, Southfield, MI	313-569-1074
Art Staff Inc/1200 City Nat Bank Bldg, Detroit, MI	313-963-8240
Artist Studios/666 Euclid Ave, Cleveland, OH	216-241-5355
August, Bob/405 N Wabash #3203, Chicago, IL	312-329-1370
Baker, Strandell/233 E Wacker Dr #3609, Chicago, IL	312-664-7525
Behum, Cliff/26384 Aaron Ave, Euclid, OH	216-261-9266
Bowman, Bob/163 Cedarwood Ct, Palatine, IL	312-966-2770

Please send us your additions and updates.

Braught, Mark/629 Cherry St #18, Terre Haute, IN	812-234-6135
Busch, Lonnie/11 Meadow Dr, Fenton, MO	314-343-1330
Butler, Chris/743 N Dearborn, Chicago, IL	312-280-2288
Buttram, Andy/1636 Hickory Glen Dr, Miamisburg, OH	513-859-7428

CD

Call, Ken/520 N Michigan Ave, Chicago, IL	312-644-3017
Carroll, Michael/1321 W Fargo Ave, Chicago, IL	312-274-5592
Centaur Studios/10 Broadway, St Louis, MO	314-421-6485
Cigliano, William/832 W Gunnison, Chicago, IL	312-878-1659
Clay, Steve/245 W North Ave, Chicago, IL	312-280-7945
Clyne, Dan/535 N Michigan Ave #1416, Chicago, IL	312-943-1668
Cobane, Russell/8291 Allen Rd, Clarkston, MI	313-623-1675
Cochran, Bobbye/730 N Franklin #403, Chicago, IL	312-943-5912
Collier, John/2309 Willow Creek Ln, Lawrence, KS	913-841-6442
Collins & Lund Studios/11 S Meramec, Clayton, MO	314-725-0344
COSGROVE, DAN/405 N WABASH #4307, CHICAGO, IL (P 138)	**312-527-0375**
CRAIG, JOHN/RT 2 BOX 81 TOWER RD, SOLDIERS GROVE, WI (P 139)	**608-872-2371**
Creative Source/360 N Michigan, Chicago, IL	312-649-9777
Crnkovich, Tony/5706 S Narragansett, Chicago, IL	312-586-9696
Csicsko, David/2350 N Cleveland, Chicago, IL	312-935-1707
Deal, Jim/2558 W Wilson Ave, Chicago, IL	312-242-3846
DeShetler, Steven A/291,4 Allen, St Louis, MO	314-772-8685
DiCianni, Ron/340 Thompson Blvd, Buffalo Grove, IL	312-634-1848
Duggan, Lee/405 N Wabash #4307, Chicago, IL	312-527-0375
Dypold, Pat/26 E Huron St, Chicago, IL	312-337-6919

EF

EATON & IWEN/307 N MICHIGAN, CHICAGO, IL (P 112, 113)	**312-332-3256**
Eberbach, Andrea/6215 N Carrollton Ave, Indianapolis, IN	317-253-0421
Elbie/PO Box 1225, St Louis, MO	314-343-6568
English, Mark/5013 A Walnut St, Kansas City, MO	816-635-4433
Flood, Dick/2210 S Lynn, Urbana, IL	217-328-3642

GHI

Gieseke, Thomas/7909 W 61st St, Merriam, KS	913-677-4593
Goldammer, Ken/405 N Wabash #3001, Chicago, IL	312-836-0143
Graham, Bill/2350 N Cleveland, Chicago, IL	312-935-1707
Groff, David/2527 Crauder Ave, Kettering, OH	513-294-7700
Handelan-Pedersen/333 N Michigan #1005, Chicago, IL	312-782-6833
Harabe, Curt/2944 Greenwood Ave, Highland Park, IL	312-432-4632
Harritos, Pete/225 E Sixth St, Cincinnati, OH	513-241-6330
Izold, Donald/20475 Bunker Hill Dr, Fairview Park, OH	216-333-9988

J

Jacobsen, Bill/405 N Wabash #1801, Chicago, IL	312-321-9558
Jamerson, David/6367 N Guilford Ave, Indianapolis, IN	317-257-8752
JAY/15119 WOODLAWN AVE, DOLTON, IL (P 187)	**312-849-5676**
JOHNSON, RICK/323 S FRANKLIN, CHICAGO, IL (P 194)	**312-943-1168**
Johnston, David McCall/26110 Carol St, Franklin, MI	313-626-9546
Juenger, Richard/1324 S 9th St, St Louis, MO	314-231-4069

K

Kahl, Konrad/26039 German Hill, Franklin, MI	313-851-7064
Kalisch, John W/4201 Levenworth, Omaha, NE	402-734-5064
Kauffman, George/1232 W 70th Terrace, Kansas City, MO	816-523-0223
Kecman, Milan/2730 Somia Dr, Cleveland, OH	216-888-3256
Kocar, George F/2141 W 98th St, Cleveland, OH	216-651-8171
Kock, Carl/311 N Desplaines Ave, Chicago, IL	312-559-0440
Kordic, Vladimar/3535 Grovewood Dr, East Lake, OH	216-951-4026
KRIEGSHAUSER, SHANNON/111 JEFFERSON RD, ST LOUIS, MO (P 199)	**314-961-1670**

L

Langeneckert, Donald/4939 Ringer Rd, St Louis, MO	314-487-2042
Langeneckert, Mark/704 Dover Pl, St Louis, MO	314-752-0199
Langton, Bruce/53145 Kinglet, South Bend, IN	219-277-6137
Laurent, Richard/1132 W Columbia Ave, Chicago, IL	312-761-1436
Lawson, Robert/1523 Seminole, Kalamazoo, MI	616-345-7607
LEE, JARED D/2942 OLD HAMILTON RD, LEBANON, OH (P 203)	**513-932-2154**
Lesh, David/6332 Guilford Ave, Indianapolis, IN	317-253-3141
Loveless, Jim/4137 San Francisco, St Louis, MO	314-533-7914
Lueck, Craig/1016 W 41st Pl #3, Kansas City, MO	816-756-1326

MN

Magdich, Dennis/1914 N Dayton, Chicago, IL	312-248-6492
MAHAN, BENTON/PO BOX 66, CHESTERVILLE, OH (P 214)	**419-768-2204**
Mayes, Kevin/1414 Alturas, Wichita, KS	316-522-6742
McInturff, Steve/6174 Joyce Ln #2, Cincinnati, OH	513-731-8017
McMahon, Mark/2620 Highland Ave, Evanston, IL	312-869-6491
MEADE, ROY/240 TENTH ST, TOLEDO, OH (P 220)	**419-244-9074**
Miller, Bill/1355 N Sandburg Terr #2, Chicago, IL	312-787-4093
Miller, Doug/1180 Chambers Rd #103C, Columbus, OH	614-488-3987
Nichols, Gary/1449 N Pennsylvania St, Indianapolis, IN	317-637-0250
NIGHTHAWK STUDIO/1250 RIVERBED RD, CLEVELAND, OH (P 31)	**216-522-1809**
Norcia, Ernest/3451 Houston Rd, Waynesville, OH	513-862-5761
Novack, Bob/6809 Mayfield Gates Mills Twrs, Mayfield Hts, OH	216-442-0456

OPQ

O'Neill, Brian/17006 Woodbury Ave, Cleveland, OH	216-252-6238
Pigalle Studios Inc/314 N Broadway #1936, St Louis, MO	314-241-4398
Pitt Studios/1370 Ontario St #1430, Cleveland, OH	216-241-6720
Pope, Kevin/2310 W Nichols Rd #B, Arlington Hgts, IL	312-392 9245
Quinn, Colleen/535 N Michigan, Chicago, IL	312-943-1668

RS

Rawson, Jon/750 N Dearborn #2703, Chicago, IL	312-266-4884
Reinert, Kirk/10600 Clifton Blvd #14, Cleveland, OH	216-631-7193
Roth, Hy/1300 Ashland St, Evanston, IL	312-491-1937
Rybka, Stephen/535 N Michigan, Chicago, IL	312-943-1668
Sahratian, John/2100 W Big Beaver Rd, Troy, MI	313-643-6000
Sanford, John/5038 W Bertean, Chicago, IL	312-685-0656
Schenker, Bob/10 E Ontario St, Chicago, IL	312-787-1573
Schmelzer, J P/1002 S Wesley Ave, Oak Park, IL	312-386-4005
Schrag, Allan/8530 W Ninth, Wichita, KS	316-722-4585
Schrier, Fred/9058 Little Mtn Rd, Kirtland Hills, OH	216-255-7787
Scibilia, Dom/2902 Franklin Blvd, Cleveland, OH	216-861-2561
Selfridge, Mary/3317 N Sheffield, Chicago, IL	516-757-5609
SELLARS, JOSEPH/2423 W 22ND ST, MINNEAPOLIS, MN (P 245)	**612-377-8766**
Sereta, Bruce/3010 Parklane Dr, Cleveland, OH	216-842-9251
Shay, RJ/3301 S Jefferson, St Louis, MO	314-773-9989
Slack, Chuck/9 Cambridge Ln, Lincolnshire, IL	312-948-9226
Smith, Raymond/1546 West Sherwin, Chicago, IL	312-973-2625
Smithback, Jes/2013 E 7th St Box 556, Wellington, KS	316-326-8631
Songero, Jay/15119 Woodlawn, Dalton, IL	312-849-5676
Stearney, Mark/5415 N Sheridan Rd, Chicago, IL	312-769-4059
Stephens Biondi Decicco/230 E Ohio, Chicago, IL	312-944-3340
Streff, Michael/2766 Wasson Rd, Cincinnati, OH	513-731-0360
Sumichrast, Jozef/860 N Northwoods, Deerfield, IL	312-945-6353

T

TAYLOR, DAVID/1449 N PENNSYLVANIA ST, INDIANAPOLIS, IN (P 260)	**317-634-2728**
Thiewes, Sam/111 N Andover Ln, Geneva, IL	312-232-0980
Thomas, Bob/3737 N Meridian St #200, Indianapolis, IN	317-923-7373
Thumbtac Studio/2013 E 7th St Box 556, Wellington, KS	316-326-8631
Townley, Jon/61 Sunnyside Lane, Columbus, OH	614-888-1597
Trusilo, Jim/535 N Michigan Ave, Chicago, IL	312-943-1668
Tughan, James/1179-A King St W #310, Toronto, Ont M6K3C5, CN	416-535-9149
TURGEON, JAMES/233 E WACKER DR #1102, CHICAGO, IL (P 262)	**312-861-1039**

VW

Vanderbeek, Don/235 Monteray Ave, Dayton, OH	513-293-5326
VANN, BILL STUDIO/1706 S 8TH ST, ST LOUIS, MO (P 266)	**314-231-2322**
Vuksanovich, Bill/3224 N Nordica, Chicago, IL	312-283-2138
Vuksanovich, Fran/3224 N Nordica, Chicago, IL	312-283-2138
Walsh, Cathy/323 S Franklin, Chicago, IL	312-427-6120
WESTPHAL, KEN/7616 FAIRWAY, PRAIRIE VILLAGE, KS (P 276, 277)	**913-381-8399**
Willson Graphics/100 E Ohio #314, Chicago, IL	312-642-5328
Wimmer, Chuck/5000 Ira Ave, Cleveland, OH	216-651-1724
Wolek, Guy/323 S Franklin, Chicago, IL	312-341-1282
Wolf, Leslie/2350 N Cleveland, Chicago, IL	312-935-1707
The Wozniaks, Elaine & Dorothy/15520 Clifton Blvd, Cleveland, OH	216-226-3565

ILLUSTRATORS CONT'D.

Please send us your additions and updates.

YZ

YOUSSI, JOHN/RT 1, 220 POWERS RD, GILBERTS, IL (P 284)	**312-428-7398**
Zadnik, Pat/14816 Clifton Blvd, Cleveland, OH	216-521-6273
Zaresky, Don/9320 Olde Rt 8, Northfield Center, OH	216-467-5917
Zimnicki Design/798 Oregon Trail, Roselle, IL	312-893-2666

SOUTHWEST

ABC

Andrews, Chris/1515 N Beverly Ave, Tucson, AZ	602-325-5126
Ballenger, Tom/301 E 4th St #354, Austin, TX	512-478-2433
Bates, Al/7714 Rolling Fork Ln, Houston, TX	713-466-4977
Brazeal, Lee Lee/9131 West View, Houston, TX	713-973-0433
Campbell, Carol/1802 W Sixth St, Austin, TX	512-472-9161
Collier, Steve/5512 Chaucer Dr, Houston, TX	713-522-0205
Connally, Connie/3333 Elm, Dallas, TX	214-742-4302
Criswell, Ron/703 McKinney Ave #201, Dallas, TX	214-954-4497
Curry, Tom/1802 W Sixth St, Austin, TX	212-472-9161

DEF

DEAN, MICHAEL/5512 CHAUCER, HOUSTON, TX (P 148)	**713-527-0295**
Dewy, Jennifer/102 W San Francisco #16, Santa Fe, NM	505-988-2924
Durbin, Mike/4034 Woodcraft, Houston, TX	713-667-8129
Eagle, Bruce/1000 W Wilshire #428, Oklahoma City, OK	405-840-3201
Escobedo, Louis/803 Arthur Dr, Arlington, TX	817-261-8197
Falk, Rusty/707 E Alameda Dr, Tempe, AZ	602-966-1626
Forbes, Bart/2706 Fairmount, Dallas, TX	214-748-8436

GH

GARNS, G ALLEN/3314 EAST EL MORO, MESA, AZ (P 162)	**602-830-7224**
Griffin, David/2706 Fairmount, Dallas, TX	214-742-6746
GRIMES, DON/3514 OAK GROVE, DALLAS, TX (P 168)	**214-526-0040**
Grimes, Rick/2416 1/2 McKinney, Dallas, TX	214-760-9833
HALPERN, DAVID/4153 S 87TH EAST AVE, TULSA, OK (P 72)	**918-622-8218**
HIGH, RICHARD/4500 MONTROSE #D, HOUSTON, TX (P 177)	**713-521-2772**
Hill, Chris/2626 Westheimer Rd #200, Houston, TX	713-523-7363
Hodgell, Kristen/1309 Dorchester, Norman, OK	405-360-0983
Hoffmitz, Leah Toby/304 Bayland, Houston, TX	713-868-4614

KLM

Kirkman. Rick/313 E Thomas Rd #205, Phoenix, AZ	602-279-0119
KUPPER, KETTI/6527 LAKEWOOD BLVD, DALLAS, TX (P 200)	**214-824-3435**
LAPSLEY, BOB/3707 NOTTINGHAM, HOUSTON, TX (P 46)	**713-667-4393**
Lewis, Maurice/3704 Harper St, Houston, TX	713-664-1807
Lindlof, Ed/603 Carolyn Ave, Austin, TX	512-472-0195
Lisieski, Peter/418 Mound St, Nacogdoches, TX	617-757-5733
MacPherson, Kevin/313 E Thomas Rd #205, Phoenix, AZ	602-279-0119

NP

Nott, Michael/1802 W Sixth St, Austin, TX	512-451-3986
Payne, Chris F/1800 Lear St, Dallas, TX	214-421-3993
Pendleton, Nancy/313 E Thomas Rd #205, Phoenix, AZ	602-279-0119
Peters, Bob/313 E Thomas Rd #205, Phoenix, AZ	602-279-0119
Poli, Kristina/4211 Pebblegate Ct, Arlington, TX	713-353-6910
Punchatz, Don Ivan/2605 Westgate Dr, Arlington, TX	817-469-8151

RS

Ricks, Thom/6511 Adair Dr, San Antonio, TX	512-680-6540
Roberts, Mark/Art Direction/2127 Banks St, Houston, TX	713-523-2325
Ruland, Mike/8946 Long Point Rd, Houston, TX	713-465-2413
Salem, Kay/13418 Splintered Oak, Houston, TX	713-469-0996
Sketch Pad/2605 Westgate Dr, Arlington, TX	817-469-8151
Skistimas, James/7701 N Stemmons Frwy #854, Dallas, TX	214-630-2574
STEIRNAGLE, MICHAEL/4141 PINNACLE #132, EL PASO, TX (P 86)	**915-533-9295**
Strand, David/603 W Garland Ave #206, Garland, TX	214-494-0095

WZ

Washington, Bill/330 Glenarm, San Antonio, TX	512-734-6216
Watford, Wayne/313 E Thomas Rd #205, Phoenix, AZ	602-279-0119
Wells, Steve/754 International #T-38, Houston, TX	713-629-6330
Zapata, Deborah/5222 E Windsor Ave #8, Phoenix, AZ	602-840-6286

ROCKY MOUNTAIN

AC

Anderson, Jon/1465 Ellendale Ave, Logan, UT	801-752-8936
Christensen, James C/656 West 550 South, Orem, UT	801-224-6237
CUNEO, JOHN/2544 15TH ST, DENVER, CO (P 88)	**303-458-7086**

D

DAZZELAND STUDIOS/209 EDISON, SALT LAKE CITY, UT (P 146,147)	**801-355-8555**
Droy, Brad/1521 S Pearl, Denver, CO	303-871-0707
Duell, Nancy/90 Corona #508, Denver, CO	303-591-9309

EFG

ENRIGHT, CINDY/2544 15TH ST, DENVER, CO (P 89)	**303-458-7086**
FUJISAKI, PAT/5917 S KENTON WAY, ENGLEWOOD, CO (P 63)	**303-698-0073**
General Graphics/880 Folsom, San Francisco, CA	415-777-3333
Graphics Studio/219 E 7th St, Denver, CO	303-830-1110

H

Hardiman, Miles/30 Village Dr, Littleton, CO	303-988-2926
Harris, Ralph/PO Box 1091, Sun Valley, ID	208-726-8077
HEINER, JOE & KATHY/1612 SHERMAN AVE, SALT LAKE CITY, UT (P 173)	**801-581-1612**
Hinds, Joe/7615 Vance Dr, Arvada, CO	303-424-2067

LMN

Lediard, Al/2216 Kensington Ave, Salt Lake City, UT	801-328-0573
Lyman, Kenvin/209 Edison St, Salt Lake City, UT	801-355-8555
Masami/90 Corona #508, Denver, CO	303-778-6016
McGowan, Daniel/90 Corona #508, Denver, CO	303-778-6016
Meents, Len/Estes Industries, Penrose, CO	303-372-3080
Nelson, Will/1307 W Jefferson, Boise, ID	208-342-7507

RST

Released Imagination/132 W Front St, Missoula, MT	406-549-3248
SAUTER, RON/1032 S YORK ST, DENVER, CO (P 63)	**303-698-0073**
Spira, David/90 Corona #508, Denver, CO	303-778-6016
Timmons, Bonnie/90 Corona #508, Denver, CO	303-778-6016

W

WHITESIDES, KIM/PO BOX 2189, PARK CITY, UT (P 280)	**801-649-0490**
WINBORG, LARRY/464 SOUTH, 275 EAST, FARMINGTON, UT (P 46)	**801-451-5310**

WEST

A

ACE STUDIO/PO BOX 332, OREGON HOUSE, CA (P 118)	**916-692-1816**
Ad Illustration/18 Montanas Norte, Irvine, CA	14-851-1939
Aitken, Barbara/6455 La Jolla Blvd, La Jolla, CA	619-459-2045
Akimoto, George/621 Villa Mont Ave, Monterey Park, CA	213-573-3930
Allaire, Michael/405 Union St #2, San Francisco, CA	415-982-5598
Allison, Gene/1808 Stanley Ave, Placentia, CA	714-524-5955
Alsina, Gustav/5103 Pico Blvd, Los Angeles, CA	213-939-1900
Alt, Tim/2800 28th St #152, Santa Monica, CA	213-392-4877
Alvin, John/15942 Londelius, Sepulveda, CA	213-279-1775
Anderson, Kevin/1259 Orkney, Cardiff, CA	619-753-8410
Anderson, Terry/5902 W 85th Pl, Los Angeles, CA	213-645-8469
Andreoli, Rick/5638-1 Etiwanda Ave, Tarzana, CA	714-966-2380
Anka/954 Howard St, San Francisco, CA	415-543-7377
ANSLEY, FRANK/1782 FIFTH ST, BERKELEY, CA (P 122)	**415-644-0585**
Arkle's Art/133 Nearglen Ave #A, Covina, CA	213-967-8009
Arshawsky, David/9401 Alcott St, Los Angeles, CA	213-276-6058
Artists in Print/Fort Mason Bldg D, San Francisco, CA	415-673-6941
Artman Studio IV/4009 Flintlock Way, Anaheim, CA	714-974-7395
Atkins, Bill/PO Box 1091, Laguna Beach, CA	714-499-3857

B

Baine, Vernon/114 Marshall Dr, Walnut Creek, CA	415-933-5973
Baker, Bill/554 Sunset Blvd #803, W Hollywood, CA	213-652-4016
Baker, Darcy/7270 Ponto Rd, Carlsbad, CA	619-438-1841
BANTHIEN, BARBARA/166 SOUTH PARK, SAN FRANCISCO, CA (P 124)	**415-552-4252**
Banuelos, Art/1743 S Douglas Rd, Anaheim, CA	714-771-4335
Banyai, Istvan/1241 9th St #3, Santa Monica, CA	213-394-8035
Barbee, Joel/209 San Pablo, San Clemente, CA	714-498-0067

ILLUSTRATORS CONT'D.

Please send us your additions and updates.

Batcheller, Keith/624 W Cypress Ave, Covina, CA	818-331-0439
Beach, Lou/5312 W 8th St, Los Angeles, CA	213-934-7335
Beersworth, Roger/618 S Western Ave #201, Los Angeles, CA	213-392-4877
Beigle, David/5632 Meinhardt Rd, Westminster, CA	714-893-7749
Bellinger, Cathy/9 Plymouth St, Irvine, CA	714-559-6225
Bennett, Mark/13752 Claremont St, Westminister, CA	714-897-9873
Benzamin, Michele/247 Horizon Ave, Venice, CA	213-396-5054
BERGENDORFF, ROGER/17106 SIMS ST #A, HUNTINGTON BEACH, CA (P 126)	**714-840-7665**
Bernstein, Sol/649 Encino Vista Dr, Thousand Oaks, CA	805-497-7967
Bettoli, Delana/737 Vernon Ave, Venice, CA	213-396-0296
Birmbaum, Dianne/17301 Elsinore Circle, Huntington Beach, CA	714-847-7631
Bjorkman, Steve/1711 Langley, Irvine, CA	714-540-4847
Blair, Barry/25131 Alicia Dr, Dana Point, CA	714-661-3575
Blonder, Ellen/PO Box 5513, Mill Valley, CA	415-388-9158
Bohn, Richard/595 W Wilson St, Costa Mesa, CA	714-548-6669
Boyle, Neil/5455 Wilshire Blvd #1212, Los Angeles, CA	213-937-4472
Bradbury, Jack/3725 Wood Valley Rd, Sonoma, CA	707-938-2975
Bradley, Barbara/750 Wildcat Canyon Rd, Berkeley, CA	415-673-4200
Brady, Elizabeth/510 N Orange Dr, Los Angeles, CA	213-939-1932
Broad, David/100 Golden Hinde Blvd, San Rafael, CA	415-479-5505
Brown, Charley/716 Montgomery St, San Francisco, CA	415-433-1222
Brown, Dennis/PO Box 16931, Irvine, CA	714-832-8090
Brown, Janis/Rt3 Box 456 #A, Escondido, CA	619-743-1795
Broyles, Kathie/1838 El Cerrito Pl #3, Hollywood, CA	213-874-1661
Budley, Don/PO Box 742, Point Reyes Station, CA	415-555-1212
Buerge, Bill/2153 Charlemagne, Long Beach, CA	213-455-3181
Bull, Michael/75 Water St, San Francisco, CA	415-776-7471
Burnside, John E/4204 Los Feliz Blvd, Los Angeles, CA	213-665-8913
C Calsbeek, Craig/704 Angelus, Venice, CA	213-821-8839
Camozzi, Teresa/770 California St, San Francisco, CA	415-392-1202
Campbell, Elisa/37 Rainbow Ridge, Irvine, CA	714-752-2345
Carroll, Justin/1118 Chautauqua, Pacific Palisades, CA	213-450-4197
Catom, Don/638 S Van Ness Ave, Los Angeles, CA	213-382-6281
Chaney, Bud/7732 Belgrave, Garden Grove, CA	714-537-6035
Chang, Warren/1283 Vicente Dr #217, Sunnyvale, CA	415-964-1701
Chewning, Randy/360 1/2 N Mansfield Ave, Los Angeles, CA	213-935-4696
Chiado, Joe/2124 Froude St, San Diego, CA	619-222-2476
Chorney, Steven/10855 Beckford Ave, Northridge, CA	818-985-8181
Clark, Tim/8800 Venice Blvd, Los Angeles, CA	213-202-1044
Clarke, Coralie/PO Box 6057, Bonsall, CA	619-941-1476
Clenney, Linda/610 22nd St #304, San Francisco, CA	415-641-4794
Coconis, Ted/2244 Santa Ana, Palo Alto, CA	415-856-9055
Colby, Janet/3589 First Ave, San Diego, CA	619-298-4037
The Committee/15468 Ventura Blvd, Sherman Oaks, CA	213-986-4420
Coppock, Chuck/638 S Van Ness Ave, Los Angeles, CA	213-382-6281
Costelloe, Richard/14258 Aetna St, Van Nuys, CA	213-901-1077
Cotter, Debbie/248 Alhambra, San Francisco, CA	415-331-9111
Coviello, Ron/4055 Falcon #102, San Diego, CA	619-265-6647
Cressy, Mike/936 S Oxford Ave #8, Los Angeles, CA	213-384-7655
Criss, Keith/4329 Piedmont Ave, Oakland, CA	415-655-2171
Critz, Carl/638 S Van Ness Ave, Los Angeles, CA	213-382-6281
Cummings, B D/3845 E Casselle, Orange, CA	714-633-3322
Curtis, Todd/2046 14th St #10, Santa Monica, CA	213-452-0738
D Daniels, Alan/3443 Wade St, Los Angeles, CA	213-306-6878
Daniels, Beau/10434 Corfu Ln, Los Angeles, CA	213-279-1775
Daniels, Shelley/7247 Margerun Ave, San Diego, CA	619-286-8087
Daniels, Stewart/961 Terrace Dr, Oakdale, CA	209-847-5596
Darrow, David R/7893 Rancho Fanita #D, Santee, CA	619-448-5448
Davidson, Kevin/505 S Grand St, Orange, CA	714-633-9061
Davis, Jack/3785 Mt Everest Blvd, San Diego, CA	619-565-0336
Dean, Bruce/360 1/2 N Mansfield Ave, Los Angeles, CA	213-935-4696
Dean, Donald/2936 Domingo Ave #2, Berkeley, CA	415-644-1139
DeAnda, Ruben/1744 6th Ave, San Diego, CA	619-231-4702
Densham, Robert S/781 1/2 California Blvd, San Luis Obispo, CA	805-541-2920
Dietz, James/2203 13th Ave E, Seattle, WA	206-325-2857
Diffenderfer, Ed/32 Cabernet Ct, Lafayette, CA	415-254-8235
DISMUKES, JOHN TAYLOR/4844 VAN NOORD, SHERMAN OAKS, CA (P 36)	**213-907-9087**
Doe, Bart/3300 Temple St, Los Angeles, CA	213-383-9707
Dohrmann, Marsha J/144 Woodbine Dr, Mill Valley, CA	415-383-0188
Donato, Robert/2330 W 3rd, Los Angeles, CA	808-396-6544
Doody, Jim/6802 Skyview Dr, Huntington Bch, CA	714-498-4128
Drake, Bob/1510 Hi-Point, Los Angeles, CA	213-931-8690
Drayton, Richard/5018 Dumont Pl, Woodland Hills, CA	213-347-2227
Drennon, Tom/916 N Formosa, Hollywood, CA	213-874-1276
Duffus, Bill/1745 Wagner, Pasadena, CA	213-792-7921
DUKE, LAWRENCE W/STAR ROUTE BOX 93, WOODSIDE, CA (P 154)	**415-851-2705**
Dunlap-Freidenrich, Doree/17922 Gillman, Irvine, CA	714-559-4388
Durfee, Tom/25 Hautling Ln, San Francisco, CA	415-781-0527
E Eastman, Bryant/14333 Addison St #201, Sherman Oaks, CA	213-990-6482
EDELSON, WENDY/85 S WASHINGTON, SEATTLE, WA (P 107)	**206-625-0109**
Ellescas, Richard/321 N Martel, Hollywood, CA	213-939-7396
Ellmore, Dennis/3245 Orange Ave, Long Beach, CA	213-424-9379
Elstad, Ron/18253 Solano River Ct, Fountain Valley, CA	714-964-7753
Emerson, Terry/505 Wyoming St, Pasadena, CA	213-791-3819
Endicott, James R/Rte 1 Box 27 B, Newberg, OR	503-538-5466
Ente, Anke/50 Kings Rd, Brisbane, CA	415-957-0325
Ericksen, Mark/1045 Sansome, San Francisco, CA	415-362-1214
Erickson, Kernie/Box 2175, Mission Viejo, CA	714-831-2818
Etow, Carole/221 17th St #B, Manhattan Beach, CA	213-545-0795
Evans, Bill/2030 First Ave #201, Seattle, WA	206-623-9459
Evans, Robert/1045 Sansome, San Francisco, CA	415-397-5322
Evenson, Stan/1830 S Robertson Blvd #203, Los Angeles, CA	213-204-1995
F Feign, Larry/660 S Glassell St #75, Orange, CA	714-633-6722
Ferrero, Felix/215 Liedesdorff, San Francisco, CA	415-981-1162
Fish, Arlene/3487 Clarington Ave #4, Los Angeles, CA	213-839-0225
Foster, Ron/379 La Perle Pl, Costa Mesa, CA	714-631-3019
Fox, Ronald/2274 237th St, Torrance, CA	213-325-4970
Francuch, George/638 S Van Ness Ave, Los Angeles, CA	213-382-6281
Franks, Bill/638 S Van Ness Ave, Los Angeles, CA	213-382-6281
Fraze, Jon/17081 Kenyon Dr #C, Tustin, CA	714-731-8493
French, Lisa/489 Norton St, Long Beach, CA	213-423-8741
Fulp, Jim/834 Duboce Ave, San Francisco, CA	415-621-5462
Funcich, Tina/14461 Wilson St, Westminster, CA	714-897-6874
G Gadbois, Brett/854 1/2 Mariposa, Los Angeles, CA	213-383-5511
Gaines, David/2337 Duane St, Los Angeles, CA	213-663-8763
Gallon, Dale B/251 Shipyd Way Bth A #9, Newport Beach, CA	714-673-4971
Galloway, Nixon/5455 Wilshire Blvd #1212, Los Angeles, CA	213-937-4472
GARCIA, MANUEL/1352 HORNBLENDE ST, SAN DIEGO, CA (P 101)	**619-272-8147**
Garland, Gil/1115 5th St #202, Santa Monica, CA	213-394-6502
Garnett, Joe/638 S Van Ness Ave, Los Angeles, CA	213-382-6281
Garo, Harry/7738 E Allen Grove, Downey, CA	213-928-2768
Geary, Rick/2124 Froude St, San Diego, CA	619-222-2476
Gellos, Nancy/20 Armour St, Seattle, WA	206-285-5838
George, Jeff/2204 Matthews Ave #D, Redondo Beach, CA	213-370-1417
Germain, Frank/5455 Wilshire Blvd #1212, Los Angeles, CA	213-937-4472
Gerrie, Dean/222 W Main St #101, Tuscan, CA	714-838-0234
Gerry Hampton Inc/PO Box 16304, Irvine, CA	213-431-6979
GIRVIN, TIM DESIGN/911 WESTERN AVE #408, SEATTLE, WA (P 114)	**206-623-7918**
Gisko, Max/248 Alhambra, San Francisco, CA	415-331-9111
Glad, Deanna/PO Box 3261, Santa Monica, CA	213-393-7464
Glassford, Carl/25361 Posada Ln, Mission Viejo, CA	714-895-5623
Gleason, Bob/618 S Western Ave #206, Los Angeles, CA	213-384-3898
Gleis, Linda/12080 Browns Canyon Rd, Chatsworth, CA	213-851-8013
Goddard, John/2774 Los Alisos Dr, Fallbrook, CA	619-728-5473
Gohata, Mark/1492 W 153 St, Gardena, CA	213-327-6595
Goldstein, Howard/7031 Aldea Ave, Van Nuys, CA	213-987-2837
Gomez, Ignacio/812 Kenneth Rd, Glendale, CA	213-243-2838
Gordon, Duane/638 S Van Ness Ave, Los Angeles, CA	213-382-6281
Gordon, Roger/3111 4th St #202, Santa Monica, CA	213-396-2365

Please send us your additions and updates.

ILLUSTRATORS

Gould, Ron/8039 Paso Robles Ave, Van Nuys, CA	818-345-1436
Graphicswork/1325 Rincon Rd, Escondido, CA	619-743-8736
Greco, Peter/7250 Beverly Blvd #101, Los Angeles, CA	213-620-0967
Green, Peter/4433 Forman Ave, Toluca Lake, CA	213-760-1011
Gribbitt Ltd/5419 Sunset Blvd, Los Angeles, CA	213-462-7362
Griffith, Linda/13972 Hilo Ln, Santa Ana, CA	714-770-9738
Grim, Elgas/638 S Van Ness Ave, Los Angeles, CA	213-382-6281
Grossman, Myron/8800 Venice Blvd, Los Angeles, CA	213-559-9344
Grove, David/382 Union St, San Francisco, CA	415-433-2100
Guidice, Rick/9 Park Ave, Los Gatos, CA	408-354-7787
Gurvin, Abe/845 Mason Rd, Vista, CA	619-941-1838
Haight, Sandy/2214 Via Aprilia, Del Mar, CA	619-481-2312
Hall, Patricia/6601 Convoy Ct, San Diego, CA	619-268-0176
HAMAGAMI, JOHN/7822 CROYDON AVE,	
LOS ANGELES, CA (P 172)	**213-641-1522**
Hamilton, Jack/1040 E Van Bibber Ave, Orange, CA	714-771-5017
Hamilton, Pamela/2956 S Robertson Blvd #9, Los Angeles, CA	213-838-7888
Hammond, Roger/5455 Wilshire Blvd #1212, Los Angeles, CA	213-937-4472
Hanes, Marsha/7455 Collet Ave, Van Nuys, CA	213-994-2926
Hasenbeck, George/3600 15th Ave W #201 A, Seattle, WA	206-283-0980
Hasselle, Bruce/2620 Segerstrom #A, Santa Ana, CA	714-662-5731
Hatzer, Fred/5455 Wilshire Blvd #1212, Los Angeles, CA	213-937-4472
Havey, Paula/5727 Canoga Ave, Woodland Hills, CA	818-888-2445
Haydock, Robert/49 Shelley Dr, Mill Valley, CA	415-383-6986
Hays, Jim/3809 Sunnyside Blvd, Marysville, WA	206-334-7596
Heidrich, Tim/14824 Ibex Ave, Norwalk, CA	213-828-9653
Heimann, Jim/618 S Western Ave, Los Angeles, CA	213-387-9688
Hendricks, Steve/1050 Elsiemae Dr, Boulder Creek, CA	408-338-6639
Herrero, Lowell/870 Harrison St, San Francisco, CA	415-543-6400
Hicks, Brad/2161 W 25th St, San Pedro, CA	213-519-9321
Hill, Glenn/28026 Fox Run Circle, Lake Castaic, CA	805-257-4909
HILLIARD, FRED/5425 CRYSTAL SPRINGS DR NE,	
BAINBRIDGE ISLAND, WA (P 178)	**206-842-6003**
Hinton, Hank/6118 W 6th St, Los Angeles, CA	213-938-9893
Hoburg, Maryanne Regal/1695 8th Ave, San Francisco, CA	415-731-1870
Hodges, Ken/12401 Bellwood, Los Alamitos, CA	213-431-4343
Holt, Katheryn/116 Smith St, Seattle, WA	206-281-9876
Honea, Richard/11 Rocky Knoll, Irvine, CA	714-851-0592
HOPKINS, CHRISTOPHER/228 MAIN ST #R,	
VENICE, CA (P 179)	**213-392-9695**
Hopkins/ Sisson Inc/12077 Wilshire Blvd #638,	
W Los Angeles, CA	213-392-9695
Hord, Bob/1760 Monrovia #B-10, Costa Mesa, CA	714-631-3890
Hoyos, Andy/360 1/2 N Mansfield Ave, Los Angeles, CA	213-935-4696
Hubbard, Roger/7461 Beverly Blvd #405, Los Angeles, CA	213-938-5177
Hughes, James/12021 Wilshire Blvd, Los Angeles, CA	213-820-7075
Huhn, Tim/4718 Kester Ave #208, Sherman Oaks, CA	213-986-2352
Hull, Richard/776 W 3500 South, Bountiful, UT	801-298-1632
HULSEY, KEVIN/14755 MAGNOLIA BLVD,	
SHERMAN OAKS, CA (P 180)	**818-501-7105**
Hunt, Robert/4376 21st St, San Francisco, CA	415-824-1824
Hunter, Llyn/1200 Riverside Dr #323, Burbank, CA	213-842-5492
Hwang, Francis/999 Town & Country Rd, Orange, CA	714-567-2557
Ikkanda, Richard/2800 28th St #152, Santa Monica, CA	213-450-4881
Irvin, Fred/1702 Hillcrest Rd, Santa Barbara, CA	805-965-2309
Irvine, Rex John/6026 Dovetail Dr, Agoura, CA	213-991-2522
Jacobi, Kathryn/17830 Osborne St, Northridge, CA	213-886-4482
JENKS, ALETA/409 BRYANT ST,	
SAN FRANCISCO, CA (P 36)	**415-495-4278**
Jenott, John/234 Miller Ave #A, Mill Valley, CA	415-383-2330
Johnson, Dori/529 Sturgeon Dr, Coast Mesa, CA	714-754-7172
Johnson, Karen/1600 Beach St #301, San Francisco, CA	415-567-3089
Jones, Steve/1081 Nowita Pl, Venice, CA	213-396-9111
Joy, Pat/247 Alestar #3, Vista, CA	619-762-2781
Judd, Jeff/827 1/2 N McCadden Pl, Los Angeles, CA	213-469-0333
Kamifuji, Tom/409 Bryant St, San Francisco, CA	415-495-4278
Kanegawa, Doug/506 W 157th St, Gardena, CA	213-321-3891
Katayama, Mits/515 Lake Washington Blvd, Seattle, WA	206-324-1199
Kaufman, Van/10290 Seabury Ln, Bel Air, CA	213-279-1924
Keefer, Mel/847 5th St #108, Santa Monica, CA	213-395-1147
KEELING, GREGG BERNARD/659 BOULEVARD WAY,	
OAKLAND, CA (P 196)	**415-444-8688**
Kelez, Steven/414 W Stevens Ave #A, Santa Ana, CA	714-751-9935
Kelley, Barbara/2022 Jones St, San Francisco, CA	415-928-0457
Kenyon, Chris/1537 Franklin St #102, San Francisco, CA	415-775-7276
Kiesow, Paul Studio/459 1/2 N Fairfax Ave, Los Angeles, CA	213-655-1897
Kimble, David/711 S Flower, Burbank, CA	213-849-1576
King, Heather/2029 Pierce St #3, San Francisco, CA	415-563-1613
Kitchell, Joyce/PO Box 33363, San Diego, CA	619-272-8147
KITCHNELL, JOYCE/1352 HORNBLEND ST,	
SAN DIEGO, CA (P 101)	**619-272-8147**
Kriss, Ron/6671 W Sunset #1519, Los Angeles, CA	213-462-5731
Krogle, Bob/11607 Clover Ave, Los Angeles, CA	213-828-9653
Labadie, Ed/1012 San Rafael Ave, Glendale, CA	213-240-0802
Lake, Larry/360 1/2 N Mansfield Ave, Los Angeles, CA	213-935-4696
Lamb, Dana/PO Box 1091, Yorba Linda, CA	714-996-3449
Larson, Ron/940 N Highland Ave, Los Angeles, CA	213-465-8451
Lee, Warren/88 Meadow Valley Rd, Corte Madera, CA	415-924-0261
Leech, Richard & Associates/725 Filbert St, San Francisco, CA	415-981-4840
Leedy, Jeff/209 North St, Sausalito, CA	415-332-9100
Levine, Bette/149 N Hamilton Dr #A, Beverly Hills, CA	213-653-9765
Lewis, Dennis/6671 Sunset #1519, Los Angeles, CA	213-462-5731
Lewis, Louise/2030 First Ave #201, Seattle, WA	206-623-9459
Lieppman, Jeff/526 Lakeside Ave S #2, Seattle, WA	206-323-1799
Lillard, Jill/2930 Lombardy Rd, Pasadena, CA	213-792-5921
Lindsay, Martin/4469 41st St, San Diego, CA	619-281-8851
Litz, B/20 N Raymond #5, Pasadena, CA	213-796-3247
Livingston, Francis/1537 Franklin St #105, San Francisco, CA	415-776-1531
Lloyd of Laguna/264 Myrtle St, Laguna Beach, CA	714-494-8376
Lloyd, Gregory/5534 Red River Dr, San Diego, CA	619-582-3487
Locke, Charles/PO Box 61986, Sunnyvale, CA	408-734-5298
Locke, Margo/619 Benvenue Ave, Los Altos, CA	415-948-3434
Lohstoeter, Lori/278 Glen Arm, Pasadena, CA	818-441-0601
Losch, Diana/Pier 33 N Embarcadero, San Francisco, CA	415-956-5648
Lozano, Henry Jr/3205 Belle River Dr, Hacienda, CA	818-330-2095
Lund, Gary/360 1/2 N Mansfield Ave, Los Angeles, CA	213-935-4696
Lytle, John/PO Box 5155, Sonora, CA	209-532-1115
MacDonald, Richard/1299 Ferrelo Rd, Santa Barbara, CA	805-966-3101
Maltese, Cristy/PO Box 1347, Ramona, CA	619-789-0309
Manoogian, Michael/7457 Beck Ave, N Hollywood, CA	213-764-6114
Manzelman, Judy/9 1/2 Murray Ln, Larkspur, CA	415-461-9685
Marcotte Studios/441 Pennsylvania Ave, San Diego, CA	619-296-3197
Marsh, Cynthia/4434 Matilija Ave, Sherman Oaks, CA	213-789-5232
Marshall, Craig/28 Abbey St, San Francisco, CA	415-621-3644
Marshall, Patricia/816 NW 177th Pl, Seattle, WA	206-542-3370
Mattos, John/1546 Grant Ave, San Francisco, CA	415-397-2138
Maughan, William/3182 Penview Dr, Vista, CA	619-724-3340
Mayeda, Kaz/3847 Bentley Ave #2, Culver City, CA	213-559-6839
McCandlish, Mark Edward/1334 W Foothill Blvd #8H,	
Upland, CA	714-982-1428
McCargar, Lucy/563 Pilgrim Dr #A, Foster City, CA	415-363-2130
McConnell, Jim/7789 Greenly Dr, Oakland, CA	415-569-0852
McCullough, Lendy/5511 Seashore Dr, Newport Beach, CA	714-642-2244
McDougall, Scott/712 N 62nd St, Seattle, WA	206-783-1403
McDraw, Brooker/2030 First Ave #201, Seattle, WA	206-623-9459
McElroy, Darlene/720 Iris #B, Corona Del Mar, CA	714-631-7700
McKee, Ron/5455 Wilshire Blvd #1212, Los Angeles, CA	213-937-4472
McKiernan, James E/346 Park Ave, Long Beach, CA	213-438-0846
McMahon, Bob/6820 Independence Ave #31, Canoga Park, CA	213-999-4127
Mediate, Frank/2975 Wilshire Blvd #210, Los Angeles, CA	213-381-3977
Megowan, John/3114 1/2 Sherwood Ave, Alhambra, CA	213-289-5826
Merritt, Norman/5455 Wilshire Blvd #1212, Los Angeles, CA	213-937-4472
Metz Air Art/2817 E Lincoln Ave, Anaheim, CA	714-630-3071
MEYER, GARY/227 W CHANNEL RD,	
SANTA MONICA, CA (P 222)	**213-454-2174**
Mikkelson, Linda S/1624 Vista Del Mar, Hollywood, CA	213-463-3116
Miller, Chris/2124 Froude St, San Diego, CA	619-222-2476
Miller, Steve/5929 Irvine Ave, N Hollywood, CA	213-985-5610
Millsap, Darrel/1744 6th Ave, San Diego, CA	619-232-4519

Please send us your additions and updates.

Mitchell, Kathy/828 21st St #6, Santa Monica, CA	213-828-6331
Mitoma, Tim/1200 Dale Ave #97, Mountain View, CA	415-965-9734
Monahan, Leo/1624 Vista Del Mar, Los Angeles, CA	213-463-3116
Montoya, Ricardo/1025 E Lincoln Ave #D, Anaheim, CA	714-533-0507
Moreau, Alain/1461 1/2 S Beverly Dr, Los Angeles, CA	213-553-8529
Morgan, Kari/3516 Sawtelle Blvd #226, Los Angeles, CA	231-390-1343
Mouri, Gary/22435 Caminito Pacifico, Laguna Hills, CA	714-951-8136
MUKAI, DENNIS/831 PACIFIC ST #5,	
SANTA MONICA, CA (P 115)	**213-452-9060**
Murphy, James/1824 4th St, Berkeley, CA	415-276-2734

NO

Nakamura, Tak/411 Benton Way, Los Angeles, CA	213-383-6991
Nasser, Christine/PO Box 3881, Manhattan Beach, CA	213-318-1066
Neila, Anthony/270 Sutter St 3rd Fl, San Francisco, CA	415-956-6344
Nelson, Craig/6010 Graciosa Dr, Los Angeles, CA	213-466-6483
Nelson, Mike/1836 Woodsdale Ct, Concord, CA	707-746-0800
Nelson, Susan/2363 N Fitch Mtn Rd, Healdsburg, CA	707-431-7166
Nesbitt, John/307 1/2 Ruby Ave, Newport Beach, CA	714-673-0785
Nethery, Susan/618 S Western Ave #201, Los Angeles, CA	213-383-5646
Nichols, Mike/11602 S Lisburn Pl, La Miranda, CA	714-929-8992
Nicholson, Norman/410 Pacific Ave, San Francisco, CA	415-421-2555
NIKOSEY, TOM/7417 MELROSE AVE,	
LOS ANGELES, CA (P 87)	**213-655-2184**
Nishiyama, Curtis/2719 Fourth St #C, Santa Monica, CA	213-396-8626
Nitch, J L/23001 Redhill #220, Costa Mesa, CA	714-751-3578
Noble, Larry/10434 Corfu Ln, Los Angeles, CA	213-279-1775
Nordell, Dale/515 Lake Washington Blvd, Seattle, WA	206-324-1199
Nordell, Marilyn/515 Lake Washington Blvd, Seattle, WA	206-324-1199
Norman, Gary/11607 Clover Ave, Los Angeles, CA	213-828-9653
Oden, Richard/631 Cliff Dr, Laguna Blvd, CA	714-760-7001
Odgers, Jayme/703 S Union, Los Angeles, CA	213-484-9965
Ohanian, Nancy/22234 Victory Blvd #6303, Woodland Hills, CA	213-247-0135
O'Mary, Tom/8418 Menkar Rd, San Diego, CA	619-578-5361
O'Neil, Sharon/409 Alberto Way #6, Los Gatos, CA	408-354-3816

PQ

Pace, Julie/1115 5th St #202, Santa Monica, CA	213-394-6502
Page, Frank/10434 Corfu Ln, Los Angeles, CA	213-279-1775
Palombi, Peter/19811 Quiet Surf Cir, Huntington Beach, CA	714-536-5850
Pansini, Tom/16222 Howland Ln, Huntington Bch, CA	714-847-9329
PARKINSON, JIM/6170 BROADWAY TERRACE,	
OAKLAND, CA (P 230)	**415-547-3100**
Passey, Kim/3443 Wade St, Los Angeles, CA	213-306-6878
Peck's Builders Art/17865 Skypark Cir #K, Irvine, CA	714-261-6233
PECK, EVERETT/1352 HORNBLEND ST,	
SAN DIEGO, CA (P 101)	**619-272-8147**
Pederson, Sharleen/7742 Redland St #H3036,	
Plaza Del Ray, CA	213-306-7847
PERINGER, STEPHEN/6046 LAKESHORE DR SO,	
SEATTLE, WA (P 107)	**206-725-7779**
Peterson, Barbara/2629 W Northwood, Santa Ana, CA	714-546-2786
Peterson, Eric/270 Termino Avenue, Long Beach, CA	213-438-2785
Peterson, Julie/1717 Union, San Francisco, CA	415-221-0238
Phillips, Barry/1318 1/2 S Beverly Glen, Los Angeles, CA	213-275-6524
Phister, Suzanne/248 Alhambra, San Francisco, CA	415-922-4304
Platz, Henry III/15922 118th Pl NE, Bothell, WA	206-488-9171
Platz, Rusty/515 Lake Washington Blvd, Seattle, WA	206-324-1199
Pluym, Todd Vander/425 Via Anita, Redondo Beach, CA	213-378-5559
Podevin, J F/223 South Kenmore #4, Los Angeles, CA	213-739-5083
Pound, John/2124 Froude St, San Diego, CA	619-222-2476
Powell, Doug/4518 Rueda Dr, San Diego, CA	619-571-7185
Precision Illustration/10434 Corfu Ln, Los Angeles, CA	213-279-1775
Prochnow, Bill/1717 Union, San Francisco, CA	415-673-0825
PUTNAM, DENISE/7059-83 PARK MESA WAY,	
SAN DIEGO, CA (P 101)	**619-565-7568**
Putnam, Jamie/10th and Parker, Berkeley, CA	415-549-2500
Pyle, Chuck/146 10th Ave, San Francisco, CA	415-751-8087
Quarnstrom, Doris/19681 Lancewood Plaza, Yorba Linda, CA	714-970-2271
Quon, Milton/3900 Somerset Dr, Los Angeles, CA	213-293-0706

R

Rand, Ted/515 Lake Washington Blvd, Seattle, WA	206-324-1199
Ray, Christian/2022 Jones St, San Francisco, CA	415-928-0457
Ray, Greg/824 Providencia Ave E, Burbank, CA	213-845-2375

Raymond, T/1010 Urania Ave, Leucadia, CA	619-753-3341
Redmond, Russell/1744 Sixth Ave, San Diego, CA	619-232-7093
Ren, Chuck/842 Alta Vista Dr, Vista, CA	714-758-7386
Richardson, Rich/9225 Chesapeake Dr #K, San Diego, CA	619-268-0033
Rieser, Bill/419 Via Linda Vista, Redondo Beach, CA	213-373-4762
Rinaldi, Linda/23462 Gilmore St, Canoga Park, CA	818-887-3017
Robbins, George/2700 Neilson Way #1423, Santa Monica, CA	213-392-4439
Robles, Bill/5455 Wilshire Blvd #1212, Los Angeles, CA	213-937-4472
Rodriguez, Bob/618 S Western Ave, Los Angeles, CA	213-384-4413
Roman, Thom/PO Box 584, Cypress, CA	714-522-5614
Ronn's Studio/4020 N Palm #207, Fullerton, CA	714-773-9131
Rosenthal, Martin/PO Box 3452, Culver City, CA	213-397-6805
Rossi, Tom/120 S Roosevelt St #2, Pasadena, CA	213-356-0122
ROTHER, SUE/1537 FRANKLIN ST #103,	
SAN FRANCISCO, CA (P 46)	**415-441-8893**
Rowe, Ken C./36325 Panorama Dr, Yucaipa, CA	714-797-7030
Ruben, Deanda/1744 6th Ave, San Diego, CA	619-231-4702
Rutherford, John/55 Alvarado Ave, Mill Valley, CA	415-383-1788

S

Sakahara, Dick/28826 Cedar Bluff Dr,	
Rncho Palos Verdes, CA	213-541-8187
Salk, Larry/7461 Beverly Blvd #405, Los Angeles, CA	213-938-5177
Sanford, James/1153 Oleander Rd, Lafayette, CA	415-284-9015
Sano, Kazu/105 Stadium Ave, Mill Valley, CA	415-381-6377
Scanlon, Dave/2523 Valley Dr, Manhattan Beach, CA	213-545-0773
Schaar, Bob/23282 Morobe Cr, Laguna Niguel, CA	714-831-9845
Schaefer, Ed/14421 Redhill Ave #25, Tustin, CA	714-731-6891
Schields, Gretchen/708 Montgomery St, San Francisco, CA	415-558-8851
Schilens, Tim/1372 Winston Ct, Upland, CA	714-623-4999
Schumacher, Michael/2030 First Ave #201, Seattle, WA	206-623-9459
Scribner, Joanne L/N 3314 Lee, Spokane, WA	509-484-3208
Shannon, Tom/17291 Marken Ln, Huntington Bch, CA	714-842-1602
Shehorn, Gene/1672 Lynwood Dr, Concord, CA	415-687-4516
Shepherd, Roni/1 San Antonio Pl, San Francisco, CA	415-421-9764
Shields, Bill/2231 Pine St, San Francisco, CA	415-346-0376
Shimokochi, Momoru/2260 Lakeshore Ave, Los Angeles, CA	213-660-4217
Shumacker, Ward/3443 Wade St, Los Angeles, CA	213-306-6878
Sigwart, Forrest/1033 S Orlando Ave, Los Angeles, CA	213-655-7734
Siminger, Suzanne/3542 Broderick, San Francisco, CA	415-346-7314
Simmons, Russ/1555 S Brockton Ave #5, Los Angeles, CA	213-820-7477
Sky Pie Graphics/240 S Helix, Solana Beach, CA	714-755-8692
Smith, Douglas R/3667 Irlanda Way, San Jose, CA	408-265-4811
Smith, J Peter/PO Box 69559, Los Angeles, CA	213-464-1163
Smith, John C/2030 First Ave #201, Seattle, WA	206-623-9459
Smith, Kenneth/3545 El Caminito St, La Crescenta, CA	213-248-2531
Sneaky Duck Studio/1079 Golden Rd, Encinitas, CA	619-436-6965
Snyder, Teresa/4291 Suzanne Dr, Pittsburg, CA	415-436-5661
Snyder, Wayne/4291 Suzanne Dr, Pittsburg, CA	415-439-5661
Sobel, June/706 Marine St, Santa Monica, CA	213-392-2842
Solvang-Angell, Diane/515 Lake Washington Blvd, Seattle, WA	206-324-1199
Somersett, Nyease/PO Box 340, Dobbins, CA	926-692-2242
SPEAR, JEFFREY A/540 SAN VINCENTE BLVD #8,	
SANTA MONICA, CA (P 254)	**213-395-3939**
Spear, Randy/4325 W 182nd St, Torrance, CA	213-370-6071
Specht/Watson Studio/1252 S LaCienega Blvd,	
Los Angeles, CA	213-652-2682
Spencer, Joe/11201 Valley Spring Ln, Studio City, CA	213-760-0216
Spohn, Cliff/3216 Bruce Dr, Fremont, CA	415-651-4597
Sprattler, Rob/1947 El Arbolita Dr, Glendale, CA	213-935-4696
Starkweather, Teri/4633 Galendo St, Woodland Hills, CA	213-992-5938
Steele, Robert/1537 Franklin #104, San Francisco, CA	415-885-2611
Stehrenberger, Mark/10434 Corfu Ln, Los Angeles, CA	213-279-1775
Stein, Mike/4340 Arizona, San Diego, CA	619-295-2455
Stepp, Don/275 Marguerita Ln, Pasadena, CA	213-799-0263
Stermer, Dugald/515 Lake Washington Blvd, Seattle, WA	206-324-1199
Stevenson, Kay/410 S Griffith Park Dr, Burbank, CA	213-845-4069
Stewart, Barbara/PO Box 345, San Luis Rey, CA	619-439-9023
Stewart, Walt/PO Box 621, Sausalito, CA	415-868-0481
Stout, William G/812 S LaBrea, Hollywood, CA	213-936-6342
Strange, Jedd/1951 Abbott St, San Diego, CA	619-224-7730
Studio/922 Grand Ave, San Diego, CA	619-272-4801
Suvityasiri, Sarn/1811 Leavenworth St, San Francisco, CA	415-928-1602

Please send us your additions and updates.

TV

Tanenbaum, Robert/5505 Corbin Ave, Tarzana, CA	818-345-6741
Taylor, C Winston/17008 Lisette St, Granada Hills, CA	213-363-5761
Terry, Emerson/505 Wyoming St, Pasadena, CA	213-791-3819
Thomas, Debra/6307 Lake Shore Dr, San Diego, CA	619-698-5135
Thon, Bud/2027 Powell, San Francisco, CA	415-397-5080
Tilley, Debbie/944 Virginia Ln, Escondido, CA	619-746-1739
Tompkins, Tish/1660 Redcliff St, Los Angeles, CA	213-662-1660
Triffet, Kurt/80 Grace Terrace #5, Pasadena, CA	818-799-2208
Truesdale Art & Design/5482 Complex St #112, San Diego, CA	619-268-1026
Tsuchiya, Julie/409 Bryant St, San Francisco, CA	415-495-4278
Turner, Charles/3880 Begonia St, San Diego, CA	619-453-6710
Vance, Jay/676 Lafayette Park Place, Los Angeles, CA	213-387-1171
Vandervoort, Gene/3201 S Ramona Dr, Santa Ana, CA	714-549-3194
Vanle, Jay/638 S Van Ness Ave, Los Angeles, CA	213-382-6281
Vargas, Kathy/5082 Tasman Dr, Huntington Beach, CA	213-721-5960
Varon, Russell/18371 Warren Ave, Tustin, CA	714-832-6595
Vigon, Jay/708 S Orange Grove Ave, Los Angeles, CA	213-937-0355
Vinson, W T/4118 Vernon, Glen Avon, CA	714-685-7697
Vogelman, Jack H/1314 Dartmouth Dr, Glendale, CA	213-243-3204
Voss, Tom/525 West B St #G, San Diego, CA	619-238-1673

W

Wack, Jeff/3614 Berry Dr, Studio City, CA	213-508-0348
Walden, Craig/515 Lake Washington Blvd, Seattle, WA	206-324-1199
Wastead, Curt/1115 5th St #202, Santa Monica, CA	213-394-6502
Waters Art Studio/1820 E Garry St #207, Santa Ana, CA	714-546-1039
WATSON, RICHARD JESSE/PO BOX 1470, MURPHYS, CA (P 275)	**209-728-2701**
Watts, Stan/3896 San Marcus Ct, Newbury Park, CA	805-499-4747
Weller, Don/2427 Park Oak Dr, Los Angeles, CA	213-467-4576
Westlund Design Assoc/5410 Wilshire Blvd #503, Los Angeles CA	213-938-5218

Weston, Will/135 S LaBrea, Los Angeles, CA	213-390-9595
WEXLER, ED/11668 KIOWA AVE #208, LOS ANGELES, CA (P 278)	**213-826-1968**
Whidden Studios/11760 Sorrento Vlly Rd #H, San Diego, CA	619-455-1776
Wicks, Ren/5455 Wilshire Blvd #1212, Los Angeles, CA	213-937-4472
WILLARDSON + ASSOC/8383 GRAND VIEW DR, LOS ANGELES, CA (P 82)	**213-656-9461**
Williams, John A/1091 N Pershing #2, San Bernadino, CA	714-885-7175
Wilson, Dick/11607 Clover Ave, Los Angeles, CA	213-828-9653
Wilson, Rowland/33871 Calle Acordarse, San Juan Capistrano, CA	714-240-8081
Wilson, Terry/2110 Orange, Costa Mesa, CA	714-646-6788
WOLFE, BRUCE/206 EL CERRITO AVE, PIEDMONT, CA (P 110,111)	**415-655-7871**
Wolfe, Corey/15716 Menlo, Gardena, CA	213-325-4138
Wolin, Ron/3977 Oeste Ave, North Hollywood, CA	213-984-0733
Woodward, Teresa/544 Paseo Miramar, Pacific Palisades, CA	213-459-2317
Wright, Jonathan/1838 El Cerrito Pl #3, Hollywood, CA	213-874-1661

YZ

Yamada, Jane/1243 Westerly Terr, Los Angeles, CA	213-663-6264
Yamada, Tony/1243 Westerly Terr, Los Angeles, CA	213-663-6264
Yenne, Bill/576 Sacramento, San Francisco, CA	415-989-2450
Yeomans, Jeff/820 Deal Ct #C, San Diego, CA	619-488-2502
Yousling, Jim/208 S Witmer St, Los Angeles, CA	213-977-0454
Zaslavsky, Morris/228 Main St Studio 6, Venice, CA	213-399-3666
Zebot, George/PO Box 4295, Laguna Beach, CA	714-499-5027
ZICK, BRIAN/3251 PRIMERA AVE, LOS ANGELES, CA (P 75)	**213-855-8855**
Zingarelli, Mark/4630 Rolando Blvd, San Diego, CA	619-287-4974
Zippel, Arthur/2110 E McFadden #D, Santa Ana, CA	714-835-8400
Zito, Andy/135 S La Brea Ave, Los Angeles, CA	213-931-1181
Zitting, Joel/2404 Ocean Pk Blvd Ste A, Santa Monica, CA	213-452-7009

GRAPHIC DESIGNERS

NEW YORK CITY

A
AKM Associates	212-687-7636
Abramson, Michael R Studio	212-683-1271
Adams, Gaylord Design	212-684-4625
Album Graphics Inc	212-489-0793
Allied Graphic Arts	212-730-1414
American Express Publishing Co	212-382-5600
Anagraphics Inc	212-279-2370
Ancona Design Atelier	212-947-8287
Anspach Grossman Portugal	212-692-9000
Antler & Baldwin Graphics	212-751-2031
Antupit and Others Inc	212-686-2552
Appelbaum Company	212-752-0679
Appletree Ad Agencey	212-697-8746
Apteryx Ltd	212-972-1396
Art Department	212-391-1826
The Art Farm Inc	212-688-4555
Art Plus Studio	212-564-8258
Associated Industrial Design Inc	212-624-0034

B
BN Associates	212-682-3096
Bain, S Milo	914-946-0144
Balasas, Cora	212-633-7753
Balin & Veres Inc	212-684-7450
Bantam Books Inc	212-765-6500
Barmache, Leon Design Assoc Inc	212-752-6780
Barnett Design Group	212-677-8830
Barry, Jim	212-873-6787
Becker Hockfield Design Assoc	212-505-7050
Bell, James Graphic Design Inc	212-929-8855
Bellows, Amelia	212-777-7012
Berger, Barry David	212-734-4137
Besalel, Ely	212-759-7820
Bessen & Tully, Inc	212-838-6406
Binns, Betty Graphic Design	212-679-9200
Biondo, Charles Design Assoc	212-867-0760
Birch, Colin Assoc Inc	212-223-0499
Bloch, Graulich & Whelan, Inc	212-687-8375
Boker Group	212-686-1132
Bonnell Design Associates Inc	212-921-5390
Bordnick & Assoc	212-563-1544
Botero, Samuel Assoc	212-935-5155
Bradbury Heston Ward Inc	212-308-4800
Bradford, Peter	212-982-2090
Branin, Max	212-254-9608
Braswell, Lynn	212-222-8761
Breth, Jill Marie	212-781-8370
Brochure People	212-696-9185
Brodsky Graphics	212-684-2600
Brown, Alastair Assoc	212-221-3166
Brown, Kim	212-567-5671
Buckley Designs Inc.	212-861-0626
Burdick, Joshua Assoc Inc	212-696-4440
Burns, Tom Assoc Inc	212-594-9883
By Design	212-684-0388
The Byrne Group	212-354-3996

C
CCI Art Inc	212-687-1552
Cain, David	212-691-5783
Cannan, Bill & Co Inc	212-563-1004
Caravello Studios	212-620-0620
Carnase, Inc	212-679-9880
Cetta, Al	212-989-9696
Chajet Design Group Inc	212-684-3669
Chang, Ivan	212-777-6102
Chapman, Sandra S	718-855-7396
Charles, Irene Assoc	212-765-8000
Chermayeff & Geismar Assoc.	212-532-4499
Chu, H L & Co Ltd	212-889-4818
Church, Wallace Assoc	212-755-2903

Cohen, Norman Design	212-679-3906
Composto, Mario Assoc	212-689-3657
Condon, J & M Assoc	212-242-7811
Corchia Woliner Assoc	212-977-9778
Corpographics, Inc.	212-483-9065
Corporate Annual Reports Inc.	212-889-2450
Corporate Graphics Inc	212-599-1820
Cosgrove Assoc Inc	212-889-7202
Cotler, Sheldon Inc	212-719-9590
Cousins, Morison S & Assoc	212-751-3390
Crane, Eileen	212-644-3850
Crane, Susan Inc	212-260-0580
Csoka/Benato/Fleurant Inc	212-242-6777
Cuevas, Robert	212-661-7149
Curtis Design Inc.	212-685-0670

D
DMCD	212-682-9044
Daniel Design	212-889-0071
Danne & Blackburn Inc.	212-371-3250
Davis-Delaney-Arrow Inc	212-686-2500
DeCamps, Craig	212-564-2691
DeHarak, Rudolph	212-929-5445
Delgado, Lisa	212-685-5925
Delphan Company	212-371-6700
DeMartin-Marona-Cranstoun-Downes	212-682-9044
Design Alliance	212-799-0095
Design Derivatives Inc	212-751-7650
Design Influence Inc	212-840-2155
Designframe	212-924-2426
The Designing Women	212-864-0909
Diamond Art Studio	212-685-6622
Diane Adzema	212-982-5657
DiComo, Charles & Assoc	212-689-8670
Dinand, Pierre Design	212-751-3086
DiSpigna, Tony	212-674-2674
Displaycraft	718-784-8186
Domino, Bob	212-935-0139
Donovan & Green Inc	212-755-0477
DORET, MICHAEL (P 152)	**212-929-1688**
Douglas, Barry Designs Ltd	212-734-4137
Dratedesign	212-620-4672
Dreyfuss, Henry Assoc	212-957-8600
Dubins, Milt Designer Inc	212-691-0232
Dubrow, Oscar Assoc	212-688-0698
Duffy, William R	212-682-6755
Dwyer, Tom	212-986-7108

E
Edelman Studios Inc	212-505-9020
Edge, Dennis Design	212-679-0927
Eichinger, Inc	212-421-0544
Eisenman and Enock	212-431-1000
Ellies, Dave Industrial Design Inc	212-679-9305
Emerson, Wajdowicz	212-807-8144
Environetics Inc	212-759-3830
Environment Planning Inc	212-661-3744
Erikson Assoc.	212-688-0048
Etc Graphics, Inc	212-889-8777
Etheridge, Palombo, Sedewitz	212-944-2530
Eucalyptus Tree Studio	212-226-0331

F
FDC Planning & Design Corp	212-355-7200
Failing, Kendrick G Design	212-677-5764
Falkins, Richard Design	212-840-3045
Farmlett Barsanti Inc	212-691-9398
Farrell, Bill	212-562-8931
Feucht, Fred Design Group Inc	212-682-0040
Filicori, Mauro Visual Communications	212-677-0065
Fineberg Associates	212-734-1220
Florville, Patrick Design Research	718-475-2278
Flying Eye Graphics	212-725-0658
Forman, Yale Designs Inc	212-799-1665
Freeman, Irving	212-674-6705

GRAPHIC DESIGNERS

Friday Saturday Sunday Inc	212-260-8479
Friedlander, Ira	212-580-9800
Frye Assoc	212-986-5454
Fulgoni, Louis	212-243-2959
Fulton & Partners	212-695-1625

G

GL & C Advertising Design Inc.	212-683-5811
Gale, Cynthia	212-860-5429
Gale, Robert A Inc	212-535-4791
Gardner, Beau Assoc Inc	212-832-2426
Gatter Inc	212-687-4821
Gentile Studio	212-986-7743
George, Hershell	212-925-2505
Gerstman & Meyers Inc.	212-586-2535
Gianninoto Assoc, Inc.	212-759-5757
Giber, Lauren	212-473-2062
Giovanni Design Assoc.	212-725-8536
Gips & Balkind & Assoc	212-421-5940
Gladstein, Renee	212-873-0257
Gladych, Marianne	212-925-9712
Glaser, Milton	212-889-3161
Glusker Group	212-757-4438
Goetz Graphics	212-679-4250
Goldman, Neal Assoc	212-687-5058
Gorbaty, Norman Design	212-684-1665
Gorman, W Chris Assoc	212-696-9377
Graphic Art Resource Assoc	212-929-0017
The Graphic Expression Inc.	212-759-7788
Graphics 60 Inc.	212-687-1292
Graphics Institute	212-887-8670
Graphics by Nostradamus	212-581-1362
Graphics for Industry	212-889-6202
Graphics to Go	212-889-9337
Gray, George	212-873-3607
Griffler Designs	212-794-2625
Grossberg, Manuel	212-620-0444
Gruber, Philip	212-243-6154
Grunfeld Graphics Ltd	212-431-8700
Gucciardo & Shapokas	212-683-9378

H

H.G. Assoc, Inc.	212-221-3070
HBO Studio Productions Inc	212-477-8600
Haas, Arie	212-382-1677
Halversen, Everett	718-438-4200
Hamid, Helen	212-752-2546
Handler Group Inc	212-391-0951
Harris-Gorbaty Assoc Inc	212-684-1665
Haydee Design Studio	212-242-3110
Hecker, Mark Studio	212-620-9050
Heimall, Bob Inc	212-245-4525
Heiney, John & Assoc	212-686-1121
HERBICK, DAVID (P 175)	**718-852-6450**
Holland, DK	212-789-3112
Holzsager, Mel Assoc Inc	212-741-7373
Hooper, Ray Design	212-924-5480
Hopkins, Will	212-580-9800
Horvath & Assoc Studios Ltd	212-741-0300
Hub Graphics	212-421-5807
HUERTA, GERARD (P 263)	**212-753-2895**
Human Factors/Industrial Design Inc	212-730-8010

I

IGC Graphics	212-689-5148
ISD Incorporated	212-751-0800
Image Communications Inc	212-807-9677
Infield & D'Astolfo	212-924-9206
Inner Thoughts	212-674-1277
Intersight Design Inc	212-696-0700

J

Jaffe Communications, Inc	212-697-4310
Johnson, Dwight	718-834-8529
Johnston, Shaun & Susan	212-663-4686
Jonson Pedersen Hinrichs & Shakery	212-889-9611

K

KLN Publishing Services Inc	212-686-8200
Kacik Design	212-753-0031
Kaeser & Wilson Design	212-563-2400
Kahn, Al Group	212-580-3517
Kahn, Donald	212-889-8898
Kallir Phillips Ross Inc.	212-878-3700
Kass Communications	212-868-3133
Kass, Milton Assoc Inc	212-874-0418
Kaye Graphics	212-889-8240
Keithley & Assoc	212-807-8388
Kleb Associates	212-246-2847
Ko Noda and Assoc International	212-759-4044
Kollberg-Johnson Assoc Inc	212-686-3648
Koons, Irv Assoc	212-752-4130
Kozlowski, Edward C Design Inc	212-988-9761

L

LCL Design Assoc Inc	212-758-2604
Lacy, N Lee	212-532-6200
Lake, John	212-644-3850
The Lamplight Group	212-682-6270
Landi-Rosiak Inc	212-661-3630
LEBBAD, JAMES A (P 202)	**212-679-2234**
Lee & Young Communications	212-689-4000
Lefkowith Inc.	212-758-8550
Leo Art Studio	212-736-8785
Lesley-Hille Inc	212-677-7570
Lester & Butler	212-889-0578
Levine, Gerald	212-986-1068
Levine, William V & Assoc	212-683-7177
Lichtenberg, Al Graphic Art	212-865-4312
LIEBERMAN, RON (P 208)	**212-947-0653**
Liebert Studios Inc	212-686-4520
Lika Association	212-490-3660
Lind Brothers Inc.	212-924-9280
Lippincott & Margulies Inc	212-832-3000
LITTLE APPLE ART (P 209)	**718-499-7045**
Lopez, Dick Inc	212-599-2327
Loukin, Serge Inc	212-255-5651
Lubliner/Saltz	212-679-9810
Luckett Slover & Partners	212-620-9770
Lukasiewicz Design Inc	212-581-3344
Luth & Katz Inc	212-644-5777

M

M & Co Design Group	212-243-0082
Maddalone, John	212-807-6087
Maggio, Ben Assoc Inc	212-697-8600
Maggio, J P Design Assoc Inc	212-725-9660
Maleter, Mari	718-726-7124
Mantel Koppel & Scher Inc	212-683-0870
Marchese, Frank	212-988-6267
Marciuliano Inc.	212-697-0740
Marckrey Design Group Inc	212-475-2822
Marcus, Eric	212-789-1799
Marino, Guy Graphic Design	212-935-1141
Mauro, C L & Assoc Inc	212-868-3940
Mauro, Frank Assoc Inc	212-719-5570
Mayo-Infurna Design	212-888-7883
McDonald, B & Assoc	212-869-9717
McGhie Assoc. Inc.	212-661-2990
McGovern & Pivoda	212-840-2912
Meier Adv	212-355-6460
Mentkin, Robert	212-534-5101
Merrill, Abby Studio Inc	212-753-7565
Messling, Jack A	212-724-6445
The Midnight Oil	212-582-9071
Millenium Design	212-986-4540
The Miller Organization Inc	212-685-7700
Miller, Irving D Inc	212-755-4040
Mirenburg, Barry	718-885-0835
Mitchell, E M Inc	212-986-5595
Mizerek Design	212-986-5702

Please send us your additions and updates.

Modular Marketing Inc.	212-581-4690
Mont, Howard Assoc Inc	212-683-4360
Montoya, Juan Design Corp	212-242-3622
Morris, Dean	212-420-0673
Moshier, Harry & Assoc	212-873-6130
Moskof & Assoc.	212-333-2015
Mossberg, Stuart Design Assoc	212-873-6130
Muir, Cornelius, Moore	212-687-4055
Murro, A & Assoc Inc	212-691-4220
Murtha Desola Finsilver Fiore	212-832-4770

N

N B Assoc Inc	212-684-8074
Nelson, George & Assoc Inc	212-777-4300
Nemser & Howard, Inc	212-832-9595
New American Graphics	212-532-3551
Newman, Harvey Assoc	212-391-8060
Nicholson Design	212-206-1530
Nightingale, Gordon	212-685-9263
NITZBURG, ANDREW (P 61)	**212-686-3514**
Nobart NY Inc	212-475-5522
Noneman & Noneman Design	212-473-4090
North, Charles W Studio	212-242-6300
Notovitz & Perrault Design Inc	212-686-3300
Novus Visual Communications Inc	212-689-2424

O

Oak Tree Graphics Inc	212-398-9355
Offenhartz, Harvey Inc	212-751-3241
Ohlsson, Eskil Assoc Inc	212-758-4412
Ong & Assoc	212-355-4343
O'Reilly, Robert Graphic Studio	212-832-8992
Orlov, Christian	212-873-2381
Oz Communications Inc	212-686-8200

P Q

Page, Arbitrio, Resen Ltd.	212-421-8190
Palladino, Tony	212-751-0068
Parshall, C A Inc	212-947-5971
Parsons School of Design	212-741-8900
Patel, Harish Design Assoc	212-686-7425
Pellegrini & Assoc	212-686-4481
Pencils Portfolio Inc	212-355-2468
Penpoint Studio Inc.	212-243-5435
Penraat Jaap Assoc	212-873-4541
Performing Dogs	212-260-1880
Perlman, Richard Design	212-599-2380
Peters, Stan Assoc Inc	212-684-0315
Peterson Blythe & Cato	212-557-5566
Pettis, Valerie	212-683-7382
Plumb Design Group Inc	212-673-3490
Podob, Al	212-697-6643
Prendergast, J W & Assoc Inc	212-687-8805
Primary Design Group	212-219-1000
Profile Press Inc	212-736-2044
Projection Systems International	212-682-0995
Push Pin Lubalin Pecolick	212-674-8080
QUON, MIKE DESIGN OFFICE (P 236)	**212-226-6024**

R

RC Graphics	212-755-1383
RD Graphics	212-889-5612
Rafkin Rubin Inc	212-869-2540
Rapecis Assoc. Inc.	212-972-1775
Ratzkin, Lawrence	212-279-1314
Regn-Califano Inc	212-239-0380
Rogers, Richard Inc	212-685-3666
Rosenthal, Herb & Assoc Inc	212-685-1814
Ross Design Assoc	212-206-0044
Ross/Pento Inc.	212-757-5604
Royce Graphics	212-239-1990
Russell, Anthony Inc	212-255-0650

S

SCR Design Organization	212-752-8496
Saiki Design	212-679-3523
Sakin, Sy	212-688-3141

Saks, Arnold	212-861-4300
Salisbury & Salisbury Inc.	212-575-0770
Salpeter, Paganucci, Inc	212-683-3310
Saltzman, Mike Group	212-929-4655
Sandgren Associates Inc	212-679-4650
Saxton Communications Group	212-953-1300
Say It In Neon	212-691-7977
Schaefer-Cassety Inc	212-840-0175
SchaefferBoehm, Ltd	212-947-4345
Schechter Group Inc.	212-752-4400
Schecterson, Jack Assoc Inc	212-889-3950
Schumach, Michael P	718-445-1587
Schwartz, Robert & Assoc	212-689-6482
Scott, Louis Assoc	212-674-0215
Serge Loukin Inc.	212-255-5651
Shapiro, Ellen Graphic Design	212-221-2625
Shareholder Graphics	212-661-1070
Shareholders Reports	212-686-9099
Sherin & Matejka Inc	212-686-8410
Shreeve, Draper Design	212-675-7534
Siegel & Gale Inc.	212-730-0101
Silberlicht, Ira	212-595-6252
Silverman, Bob Design	212-371-6472
Singer, Paul Design	718-449-8172
SLOAN, WILLIAM (P 250)	**212-988-6267**
SMITH, LAURA (P 153)	**212-206-9162**
Sochynsky, Ilona	212-686-1275
Solay/Hunt	212-840-3313
Sorvino, Skip	212-580-9638
St Vincent Milone & McConnells	212-921-1414
Stuart, Gunn & Furuta	212-689-0077
Studio 42	212-354-7298
The Sukon Group, Inc	212-986-2290
Swatek and Romanoff Design Inc	212-807-0236
Systems Collaborative Inc	212-608-0584

T

Tapa Graphics	212-243-0176
Tauss, Jack George	212-279-1658
Taylor & Ives	212-244-0750
Taylor, Stan	212-685-4741
Teague, Walter Dorwin Assoc	212-557-0920
Tercovich, Douglas Assoc Inc	212-838-4800
Theoharides Inc.	212-838-7760
Thompson Communications	212-685-4400
Three	212-988-6267
Tobias, William	212-741-1712
Tower Graphics Arts Corp	212-421-0850
Tribich, Jay Design Assoc	212-679-6016
Tscherny, George Design	212-734-3277
Tunstull Studio	718-875-9356
Turner/Miller	212-371-3035
Type Trends	212-986-1783

U V

Ultra Arts Inc	212-679-7493
VECCHIO, CARMINE (P 268)	**212-683-2679**
Viewpoint Graphics	212-685-0560
Vignelli Assoc.	212-593-1416
Visible Studio Inc	212-683-8530
Visual Accents Corp	212-777-7766
Visual Development Corp	212-532-3202

W

Wajdowicz, Jurek	212-807-8144
Waldman, Veronica	212-260-3552
Waters, John Assoc Inc	212-807-0717
Waters, Pamela Studio Inc	212-620-8100
Webster, Robert Inc	212-677-2966
Weed, Eunice Assoc Inc	212-725-4933
Weeks & Toomey	212-564-8260
Whelan Design Office	212-691-4404
The Whole Works	212-575-0765
Wijtvliet, Ine	212-684-4575
Wilke, Jerry	212-689-2424

Please send us your additions and updates.

GRAPHIC DESIGNERS

Wilke/Davis Assoc Inc	212-532-5500
Withers, Bruce Graphic Design	212-599-2388
Wizard Graphics Inc	212-686-8200
Wolf, Henry Production Inc	212-472-2500
Wolff, Rudi Inc	212-873-5800
Wood, Alan	212-889-5195
Works	212-696-1666

YZ

Yoshimura-Fisher Graphic Design	212-431-4776
Young Goldman Young Inc	212-697-7820
Zeitsoff, Elaine	212-580-1282
Zimmerman & Foyster	212-674-0259

NORTHEAST

A

Action Incentive/Rochester, NY	716-427-2410
Adam Filippo & Moran/Pittsburgh, PA	412-261-3720
Advertising Design Assoc Inc/Baltimore, MD	301-752-2181
Alber Associates/Philadelphia, PA	215-969-4293
Another Color Inc/Washington, DC	202-328-1414
Aries Graphics/Manchester, NH	603-668-0811
Art Service Assoc Inc/Pittsburgh, PA	412-391-0902
Art Services Inc/Washington, DC	202-526-5607
The Artery/Baltimore, MD	301-752-2979
Arts and Words/Washington, DC	202-463-4880
Artwork Unlimited Inc/Washington, DC	202-638-6996
Autograph/Annapolis, MD	301-268-3300
The Avit Corp/Fort Lee, NJ	201-886-1100

B

Bally Design Inc/Carnegie, PA	412-276-5454
Banks & Co/Boston, MA	617-262-0020
Barancik, Bob/Philadelphia, PA	215-893-9149
Barton-Gillet/Baltimore, MD	301-685-3626
Bedford Photo-Graphic Studio/Bedford, NY	914-234-3123
Belser, Burkey/Washington, DC	202-462-1482
Bennardo, Churik Design Inc/Pittsburgh, PA	412-963-0133
Berns & Kay Ltd/Washington DC,	202-387-7032
Beveridge and Associates, Inc/Washington, DC	202-337-0400
Blum, William Assoc/Boston, MA	617-232-1166
Bogus, Sidney A & Assoc/Melrose, MA	617-662-6660
Bookmakers/Westport, CT	203-226-4293
Boscobel Advertising, Inc/Laurel, MD	301-953-2600
Boulanger Associates Inc/Armonk, NY	914-273-5571
Bradick Design & Methods Inc/Guys Mills, PA	814-967-2332
Brady, John Design Consultants/Pittsburgh, PA.	412-227-9300
Bressler, Peter Design Assoc/Philadelphia, PA	215-925-7100
Bridy, Dan/Pittsburgh, PA	412-288-9362
Brown and Craig Inc/Baltimore, MD	301-837-2727
Brown, Michael David Inc/Rockville, MD	301-762-4474
Buckett, Bill Assoc/Rochester, NY	716-546-6580
Burke & Michael Inc/Pittsburgh, PA	412-321-2301
Byrne, Ford/Philadelphia, PA	215-564-0500

C

Cabot, Harold & Co Inc/Boston, MA	617-426-7600
Cameron Inc/Boston, MA	617-267-2667
Captain Graphics/Boston, MA	617-367-1008
Carmel, Abraham/Peekskill, NY	914-737-1439
Case/Washington, DC	202-328-5900
Casey Mease Inc/Wilmington, DE	302-655-2100
Chaparos Productions Limited/Washington, DC	202-289-4838
Charysyn & Charysyn/Westkill, NY	518-989-6720
Chase, David O Design Inc/Skaneateles, NY	315-685-5715
Colopy Dale Inc/Pittsburgh, PA	412-332-6706
Concept Packaging Inc/Ft Lee, NJ	201-224-5762
Consolidated Visual Center Inc/Tuxedo, MD	301-772-7300
Cook & Shanosky Assoc/Princeton, NJ	609-921-0200
Creative Communications Center/Pennsauken, NJ	609-665-2058
The Creative Dept/Philadelphia, PA	215-988-0390
Creative Presentations Inc/Washington, DC	202-737-7152
Curran & Connors Inc/Jericho, NY	516-433-6600

D

D J C Design Assoc/Washington, DC	202-965-6040
Dakota Design/King of Prussia, PA	215-265-1255
Daroff Design Inc/Philadelphia, PA	215-636-9900
D'Art Studio Inc/Boston, MA	617-482-4442
Dawson Designers Associates/Assonet, MA	617-644-2940
DeCesare, John/Darien, CT	203-655-6057
DeMartin-Marona-Cranstoun-Downes/Wilmington, DE	302-654-5277
Design Associates/Arlington, VA	703-243-7717
Design Center Inc/Boston, MA	617-542-1254
Design Communication Collaboration/Washington, DC	202-833-9087
Design Group of Boston/Boston, MA	617-437-1084
Design Technology Corp/Billerica, MA	617-272-8890
Design Trends/Valhalla, NY	914-948-0902
Design for Medicine Inc/Philadelphia, PA	215-925-7100
Designworks Inc/Watertown, MA	617-926-6286
DiFiore Associates/Pittsburgh, PA	412-471-0608
Dimensional Design & Fabrication/Rochester, NY	716-473-1704
Dohanos, Steven/Westport, CT	203-227-3541
Downing, Allan/Needham, MA	617-449-4784
Drafting and Design Studio/Columbia, MD	301-730-5596
Duffy, Bill & Assoc/Washington, DC	202-965-2216

E

Edigraph Inc/Katonah, NY	914-232-3725
Educational Media/Graphics Division/Washington, DC	202-625-2211
Egress Concepts/Katonah, NY	914-232-8433
Environetics DC Inc/Washington, DC	202-466-7110
Eucalyptus Tree Studio/Baltimore, MD	301-243-0211
Evans Garber & Paige/Utica, NY	315-733-2313
Evans, Timothy Graphics/Washington, DC	202-293-0266

F

Fader Jones & Zarkades/Boston, MA	617-267-7779
Falcone & Assoc/Chatham, NJ	201-635-2900
Fall, Dorothy Graphic Design/Washington, DC	202-338-2022
Fannell Studio/Boston, MA	617-267-0895
Fitzpatrick & Associates/Silver Springs, MD	301-946-4677
Forum Inc/Fairfield, CT	203-259-5686
Fossella, Gregory Assoc/Boston, MA	617-267-4940
Fraser, Robert & Assoc Inc/Baltimore, MD	301-685-3700
Fresh Produce/Lutherville, MD	301-821-1815
Friday Design Group Inc/Washington, DC	202-965-9600
Froelich Advertising Service/Mahwah, NJ	201-529-1737

G

Galasso, Gene Assoc Inc/Silver Spring, MD	202-439-1282
Gasser, Gene/Chatham, NJ	201-635-6020
Gateway Studios/Pittsburgh, PA	412-471-7224
Geyer, Jackie/Pittsburgh, PA	412-261-1111
Glickman, Frank Inc/Boston, MA	617-524-2200
Glidden, Thea & Assoc/Baltimore, MD	301-523-5903
Good, Peter Graphic Design/Chester, CT	203-526-9597
Graham Associates Inc/Washington, DC	202-833-9657
Grant Marketing Assoc./Conshohocken, PA	215-834-0550
The Graphic Suite/Pittsburgh, PA	412-661-6699
Graphic Workshop/Emerson, NJ	201-967-8500
Graphics By Gallo/Washington, DC	202-234-7700
Graphics Plus Corp/St Malden, MA	617-321-7500
Graphicus Corp/Baltimore, MD	301-727-5553
Grear, Malcolm Designers Inc/Providence, RI	401-331-5656
Gregory & Clyburne/New Canaan, CT	203-966-8343
Groff-Long Associates/Bethesda, MD	301-654-0279
Group Four Inc/Avon, CT	203-678-1570
Gunn Associates/Boston, MA	617-267-0618

H

Hain, Robert Assoc/Scotch Plains, NJ	201-322-1717
Hammond Design Assoc/Milford, NH	603-673-5253
Harrington-Jackson/Boston, MA	617-536-6164
Hegemann Associates/Nyack, NY	914-358-7348
Herbick & Held/Pittsburgh, PA	412-321-7400
Herbst Lazar Rogers & Bell Inc/Lancaster, PA	717-291-9042
Herman & Lees/Cambridge, MA	617-876-6463
Hiestand Design Associates/Watertown, MA	617-923-8800

Please send us your additions and updates.

Hillmuth, James/Washington, DC	202-244-0465
Hough, Jack Inc/Norwalk, CT	203-846-2666
The Hoyt Group/Waldwick, NJ	201-652-6300
Hrivnak, James/Silver Spring, MD	301-681-9090

IJ Image Consultants/Burlington, MA

Image Consultants/Burlington, MA	617-273-1010
Innovations & Development Inc/Ft Lee, NJ	201-944-9317
Jaeger Design Studio/Washington, DC	202-785-8434
Jarrin Design Inc/Pound Ridge, NY	914-764-4625
Jensen, R S/Baltimore, MD	301-727-3411
Johnson & Simpson Graphic Design/Newark, NJ	201-624-7788
Johnson Design Assoc/Acton, MA	617-263-5345
Jones, Tom & Jane Kearns/Washington, DC	202-232-1921

K KBH Graphics/Baltimore, MD

KBH Graphics/Baltimore, MD	301-539-7916
Kahana Associates/Jenkintown, PA	215-887-0422
Katz-Wheeler Design/Philadelphia, PA	215-567-5668
Kaufman, Henry J & Assoc Inc/Washington, DC	202-333-0700
Keaton Design/Washington, DC	202-547-4422
Kell & Chaddick/Silver Spring, MD	202-585-4000
Ketchum International/Pittsburgh, PA	412-456-3693
King-Casey Inc/New Canaan, CT	203-966-3581
Klim, Matt & Assoc/Avon, CT	203-678-1222
Knox, Harry & Assoc/Washington, DC	202-833-2305
Kostanecki, Andrew Inc/New Canaan, CT	203-966-1681
Kovanen, Erik/Wilton, CT	203-762-8961
Kramer/Miller/Lomden/Glossman/Philadelphia, PA	215-545-7077
Krone Graphic Design/Lemoyne, PA	717-774-7431

L LAM Design Inc/White Plains, NY

LAM Design Inc/White Plains, NY	914-948-4777
LaGrone, Roy/Somerset, NJ	201-463-4515
LANGDON, JOHN/WENONAH, NJ (P 201)	**609-468-7868**
Lange, Erwin G/Wenonah, NJ	609-468-7868
Lapham/Miller Assoc/Andora, MA	617-367-0110
Latham Brefka Associates/Boston, MA	617-536-8787
Lausch, David Graphics/Baltimore, MD	301-235-7453
Lebowitz, Mo/N Bellemore, NY	516-826-3397
Leeds, Judith K Studio/West Caldwell, NJ	201-226-3552
Leotta Designers Inc/Conshohocken, PA	215-828-8820
Lester Associates Inc/West Nyack, NY	914-358-6100
Levinson Zaprauskis Assoc/Philadelphia, PA	215-248-5242
Lewis, Hal Design/Philadelphia, PA	215-563-4461
Lion Hill Studio/Baltimore, MD	301-837-6218
Lizak, Matt/N Smithfield, RI	401-766-8885

M M&M Graphics/Baltimore, MD

M&M Graphics/Baltimore, MD	301-747-4555
MacIntosh, Rob Communication/Boston, MA	617-267-4912
Macey-Noyes/Ossining, NY	914-941-7120
Mahoney, Ron/Pittsburgh, PA	412-261-3824
Major Assoc/Baltimore, MD	301-752-6174
Mandala/Philadelphia, PA	215-923-6020
Mansfield, Malcolm R Graphics/Boston, NY	615-437-1922
Marcus, Sarna/Amazing Graphic Design/Washington, DC	202-234-4592
Mariuzza, Pete/Briarcliff Manor, NY	914-769-3310
Martucci Studio/Boston, MA	617-266-6960
Media Concepts/Boston, MA	617-437-1382
Media Graphics/Washington, DC	202-265-9259
Media Loft/Minneapolis, MN	612-831-0226
Melanson, Donya Assoc/Boston, MA	617-482-0421
Micolucci, Nicholas Assoc/King of Prussia, PA	215-265-3320
Miho, J Inc/Redding, CT	203-938-3214
Milcraft/Annandale, NJ	201-735-8632
Miller, Ronald R & Co/Rockaway, NJ	201-625-9280
Mitchell & Company/Washington, DC	202-342-6025
Mitchell & Webb Inc/Boston, MA	617-262-6980
Morlock Graphics/Tuson, MD	301-825-5080
Moss, John C/Chevy Chase, MD	301-320-3912
Mossman Art Studio/Baltimore, MD	301-243-1963
Mueller & Wister/Philadelphia, PA	215-568-7260
Muller-Munk, Peter Assoc/Pittsburgh, PA	412-261-5161
Myers, Gene Assoc/Pittsburgh, PA	412-661-6314
Myers, Patricia Inc/Chevy Chase, MD	202-363-8363

NO Nason Design Assoc/Boston, MA

Nason Design Assoc/Boston, MA	617-266-7286
National Photo Service/Fort Lee, NJ	212-860-2324
Navratil Art Studio/Pittsburgh, PA	412-471-4322
Nimeck, Fran/South Brunswick, NJ	201-821-8741
Nolan & Assoc/Washington, DC	202-363-6553
North Charles Street Design Org./Baltimore, MD	301-539-4040
Odyssey Design Group, Inc/Washington, DC	202-783-6240
Ollio Studio/Pittsburgh, PA	412-281-4483
Omnigraphics/Cambridge, MA	617-354-7444
On Target/Riverside, CT	203-637-8300
One Harvard Sq Design Assoc/Cambridge, MA	617-876-9673

P Paganucci, Bob/Montvale, NJ

Paganucci, Bob/Montvale, NJ	201-391-1752
Paine/ Bluett/ Paine Inc/Bethesda, MD	301-493-8445
Paragraphics Inc./White Plains, NY	914-948-4777
Parks, Franz & Cox, Inc/Washington, DC	202-797-7568
Parry, Ivor A/Eastchester, NY	914-961-7338
Pasinski, Irene Assoc/Pittsburgh, PA	412-683-0585
Patazian Design Inc/Boston, MA	617-262-7848
Pesanelli, David Assoc/Washington, DC	202-363-4760
Phillips Design Assoc/Boston, MA	617-787-5757
Planert, Paul Design Assoc/Pittsburgh, PA	412-621-1275
Plataz, George/Pittsburgh, PA	412-322-3177
Porter, Al/Graphics Inc/Washington, DC	202-244-0403
Presentation Associates/Washington, DC	202-333-0080
Prestige Marking & Coating Co/Stamford, CT	203-329-0384
Production Studio/Port Washington, NY	516-944-6688
Publication Services Inc./Stamford, CT	203-348-7351

R RSV/Boston, MA

RSV/Boston, MA	617-262-9450
RZA Inc/Westwood, NJ	201-664-4543
Ralcon Inc/West Chester, PA	215-692-2840
Rand, Paul Inc/Weston, CT	203-227-5375
Redtree Associates/Washington, DC	202-628-2900
Research Planning Assoc/Philadelphia, PA	215-561-9700
Rieb, Robert/Westport, CT	203-227-0061
Ringel, Leonard Lee Graphic Design/Kendall Park, NJ	201-297-9084
Rinnisana Communications/Silver Spring, MD	301-587-1505
Ritter, Richard Design Inc/Berwyn, PA	215-296-0400
Romax Studio/Stamford, CT	203-324-4260
Rosborg Inc/Newton, CT	203-426-3171
Roth, J H Inc/Peekskill, NY	914-737-6784
Rubin, Marc Design Assoc/Breesport, NY	607-739-0871

S Sanchez/Philadelphia, PA

Sanchez/Philadelphia, PA	215-564-2223
Schneider Design/Baltimore, MD	301-467-2611
Schoenfeld, Cal/Fairfield, NJ	201-575-7335
Schwartz, Adler Graphics Inc/Baltimore, MD	301-433-4400
Selame Design Associates/Newton Lower Falls, MA	617-969-6690
Shapiro, Deborah/Jersey City, NJ	201-432-5198
Simpson Booth Designers/Cambridge, MA	617-661-2630
Smith, Doug/Larchmont, NY	914-834-3997
Smith, Gail Hunter III/Barnegat Light, NJ	609-494-9136
Smith, Tyler Art Direction/Providence, RI	401-751-1220
Snowden Associates Inc/Washington, DC	202-362-8944
Sparkman & Bartholomew/Washington, DC	202-785-2414
Star Design Inc/Moorestown, NJ	609-235-8150
Steel Art Co Inc/Allston, MA	617-566-4079
Stettler, Wayne Design/Philadelphia, PA	215-235-1230
Stockman & Andrews Inc/E Providence, RI	401-438-0694
Stolt, Jill Design/Rochester, NY	716-461-2594
Stuart, Neil/Mahopac, NY	914-618-1662
Studio Six Design/Springfield, NJ	201-379-5820
Studio Three/Philadelphia, PA	215-665-0141

T Takajian, Asdur/N Tarrytown, NY

Takajian, Asdur/N Tarrytown, NY	914-631-5553
Telesis/Baltimore, MD	301-235-2000
Tetrad Inc/Annapolis, MD	301-268-8680
Thompson, Bradbury/Riverside, CT	203-637-3614
Thompson, George L/Reading, MA	617-944-6256
TOELKE, CATHLEEN/BOSTON, MA (P 52,53)	**617-266-8790**

Torode, Barbara/Philadelphia, PA	215-732-6792
Town Studios Inc/Pittsburgh, PA	412-471-5353
Troller, Fred Assoc Inc/Rye, NY	914-698-1405

V
Van Der Sluys Graphics Inc/Washington, DC	202-265-3443
VanDine, Horton, McNamara, Manges Inc/Pittsburgh, PA	412-261-4280
Vance Wright Adams & Assoc/Pittsburgh, PA	412-322-1800
Vinick, Bernard Assoc Inc/Hartford, CT	203-525-4293
Viscom Inc/Baltimore, MD	301-764-0005
Visual Research & Design Corp/Boston, MA	617-536-2111
The Visualizers/Pittsburgh, PA	412-488-0944

W
Warkulwiz Design/Philadelphia, PA	215-546-0880
Wasserman's, Myron Graphic Design Group/Philadelphia, PA	215-922-4545
Weadock, Rutka/Baltimore, MD	301-358-3588
Weitzman & Assoc/Bethesda, MD	301-652-7035
Weymouth Design/Boston, MA	617-542-2647
White, E James Co/Alexandria, VA	703-750-3680
Wickham & Assoc Inc/Washington, DC	202-296-4860
Wilke, Jerry Design/Croton-On-Hudson, NY	914-271-6766
Willard, Janet Design Assoc/Allison Park, PA	412-486-8100
Williams Associates/Lynnfield, MA	617-599-1818
Wright, Kent M Assoc Inc/Sudbury, MA	617-443-9909

YZ
Young & Thomas Design/Weston, CT	203-227-5672
Yurdin, Carl Industrial Design Inc/Port Washington, NY	516-944-7811
Zeb Graphics/Washington, DC	202-293-1687
Zmiejko & Assoc Design Agcy/Freeland, PA	717-636-2304

SOUTHEAST

A
Ace Art/New Orleans, LA	504-861-2222
The Alderman Co/High Point, NC	919-889-6121
Alphabet Group/Atlanta, GA	404-892-6500
Anderson & Santa Inc/Ft Lauderdale, FL	305-561-0551
Art Services/Atlanta, GA	404-892-2105
Arts & Graphics/Annandale, VA	703-941-2560
Arunski, Joe & Assoc/Miami, FL	305-387-2130
Aurelio & Friends Inc/Miami, FL	305-385-0723

B
Baskin & Assoc/Alexandria, VA	703-836-3316
Blair, Inc/Baileys Cross Roads, VA	703-820-9011
Bodenhamer, William S Inc/Miami, FL	305-253-9284
Bonner Advertising Art/New Orleans, LA	504-895-7938
Brimm, Edward & Assoc/Palm Beach, FL	305-655-1059
Brothers Bogusky/Miami, FL	305-891-3642
Bugdal Group/Miami, FL	305-264-1860
Burch, Dan Associates/Louisville, KY	502-895-4881

C
Carlson Design/Gainesville, FL	904-373-3153
Chartmasters Inc/Atlanta, GA	404-262-7610
Communications Graphics Inc/Atlanta, GA	404-231-9039
Creative Design Assoc/Lake Park, FL	305-845-6126
Creative Services Inc/New Orleans, LA	504-943-0842
Creative Services Unlimited/Naples, FL	813-262-0201

DEF
Design Workshop Inc/Miami, FL	305-884-6300
Emig, Paul E/Arlington, VA	703-522-5926
First Impressions/Tampa, FL	813-224-0454
Foster, Kim A/Miami, FL	305-642-1801
From Us Advertising & Design/Atlanta, GA	404-373-0373

G
Garrett Lewis Johnson/Atlanta, GA	404-221-0700
Garrett, Kenneth/Atlanta, GA	404-221-0700
Gerbino Advertising Inc/Ft Lauderdale, FL	305-776-5050
Gestalt Associates, Inc/Alexandria, VA	703-683-1126
Get Graphic Inc/Vienna, VA	202-938-1822
Graphics 4/Ft Lauderdale, FL	305-764-1470
Graphics Associates/Atlanta, GA	404-873-5858
Graphics Group/Atlanta, GA	404-261-5146
Graphicstudio/N Miami, FL	305-893-1015

Great Incorporated/Alexandria, VA	703-836-6020
Gregg, Bill Advertising Design/Miami, FL	305-854-7657
Group 2 Atlanta/Atlanta, GA	404-355-3194

H
Hall Graphics/Coral Gables, FL	305-443-8346
Hall, Stephen Design Office/Louisville, KY	502-584-5030
Hannau, Michael Ent. Inc/Hialeah, FL	305-887-1536
Hauser, Sydney/Sarasota, FL	813-388-3021
Helms, John Graphic Design/Memphis, TN	901-363-6589

IJK
Identitia Incorporated/Tampa, Fl	813-221-3326
Jensen, Rupert & Assoc Inc/Atlanta, GA	404-892-6658
Johnson Design Group Inc/Arlington, VA	703-525-0808
Jordan Barrett & Assoc/Miami, FL	305-667-7051
Kelly & Co Graphic Design Inc/St Petersburg, FL	813-327-1009
Kjeldsen, Howard Assoc Inc/Atlanta, GA	404-266-1897

LM
Lowell, Shelley Design/Atlanta, GA	404-636-9149
Mabrey Design/Sarasota, FL	813-957-1063
MARKS, DAVID/ATLANTA, GA (P 216)	**404-872-1824**
Maxine, J & Martin Advertising/McLean, VA	703-356-5222
McGurren Weber Ink/Alexandria, VA	703-548-0003
Michael, Richard S/Knoxville, TN	615-584-3319
Miller, Hugh K/Orlando, FL	305-293-8220
Morgan-Burchette Assoc/Alexandria, VA	703-549-2393
Morris, Robert Assoc Inc/Ft Lauderdale, FL	305-973-4380
Muhlhausen, John Design Inc/Atlanta, GA	404-393-0743

P
PL&P Advertising Studio/Ft Lauderdale, FL	305-776-6505
PRB Design Studio/Winter Park, FL	305-671-7992
Parallel Group Inc/Atlanta, GA	404-261-0988
Pertuit, Jim & Assoc Inc/New Orleans, LA	504-568-0808
Platt, Don Advertising Art/Hialeah, FL	305-888-3296
Point 6/Ft Lauderdale, FL	305-563-6939
Polizos, Arthur Assoc/Norfolk, VA	804-622-7033
Positively Main St Graphics/Sarasota, FL	813-366-4959
Price Weber Market Comm Inc/Louisville, KY	502-499-9220
Promotion Graphics Inc/N Miami, FL	305-891-3941

RS
Rasor & Rasor/Cary, NC	919-467-3353
Rebeiz, Kathryn Dereki/Vienna, VA	703-560-7784
Reinsch, Michael/Hilton Head Island, SC	803-842-3298
Revelations Studios, Inc./Orlando, Fl	305-896-4240
Rodriguez, Emilio Jr/Miami, FL	305-235-4700
Sager Assoc Inc/Sarasota, FL	813-366-4192
Salmon, Paul/Burke, VA	703-250-4943
Schulwolf, Frank/Coral Gables, FL	305-665-2129
Seay, Jack Design Group/Norcross, GA	404-447-4840
Showcraft Designworks/Clearwater, FL	813-586-0061
Sirrine, J E/Greenville, SC	803-298-6000
Supertype/Hialeah, FL	305-885-6241

TVW
Thayer Dana Industrial Design/Monroe, VA	804-929-6359
Thomas, Steve Design/Charlotte, NC	704-332-4624
Turpin Design Assoc./Atlanta, GA	404-320-6963
Varisco, Tom Graphic Design Inc/New Orleans, LA	504-949-2888
Visualgraphics Design/Tampa, FL	813-877-3804
Wells Squire Assoc Inc/Ft Lauderdale, FL	305-763-8063
Whitver, Harry K Graphic Design/Nashville, TN	615-320-1795
Wilsonwork Graphic Design/Washington, DC	202-332-9016
Winner, Stewart Inc/Louisville, KY	502-583-5502
Wood, Tom/Atlanta, GA	404-262-7424
The Workshop Inc/Atlanta, GA	404-875-0141

MIDWEST

A
Aarons, Allan Design/Northbrook, IL	312-291-9800
Ades, Leonards Graphic Design/Northbrook, IL	312-564-8863
Advertising Art Studios Inc/Milwaukee, WI	414-276-6306
Album Graphics/Melrose Park, IL	312-344-9100
Allied Design Group/Chicago, IL	312-743-3330

GRAPHIC DESIGNERS

GRAPHIC DESIGNERS CONT'D.

Please send us your additions and updates.

Anderson Studios/Chicago, IL	312-922-3039
Anderson, I K Studios/Chicago, IL	312-664-4536
Architectural Signing/Chicago, IL	312-871-0100
Art Forms Inc/Cleveland, OH	216-361-3855
Arvind Khatkate Design/Chicago, IL	312-337-1478

B
Babcock & Schmid Assoc/Bath, OH	216-666-8826
Bal Graphics Inc/Chicago, IL	312-337-0325
Bali Design Ltd/Chicago, IL	312-642-6134
Banka Mango Design Inc/Chicago, IL	312-467-0059
Benjamin, Burton E Assoc/Highland Park, IL	312-432-8089
Berg, Don/Milwaukee, WI	414-276-7828
Bieger, Walter Assoc/Arden Hills, MN	612-636-8500
Blake, Hayward & Co/Evanston, IL	312-864-9800
Blau-Bishop & Assoc/Chicago, IL	312-321-1420
Boelter Industries Inc/Minneapolis, MN	612-831-5338
Boller-Coates-Spadero/Chicago, IL	312-787-2798
Bowlby, Joseph A/Chicago, IL	312-922-0890
Bradford-Cout Graphic Design/Skokie, IL	312-539-5557
Brooks Stevens Assoc Inc/Mequon, WI	414-241-3800
Busch, Lonnie/Fenton, MO	314-343-1330

C
CMO Graphics/Chicago, IL	312-527-0900
Campbell Art Studio/Cincinnati, OH	513-221-3600
Campbell Creative Group Inc/Milwaukee, WI	414-351-4150
Carter, Don W/ Industrial Design/Kansas City, MO	816-356-1874
Centaur Studios Inc/St Louis, MO	314-421-6485
Chartmaster Inc/Chicago, IL	312-787-9040
Chestnut House/Chicago, IL	312-822-9090
Claudia Janah Designs Inc/Chicago, IL	312-726-4560
Combined Services Inc/Minneapolis, MN	612-339-7770
Container Corp of America/Chicago, IL	312-580-5500
Contours Consulting Design Group/Bartlett, IL	312-837-4100
Coons/Beirise Design Associate/Cincinnati, OH	513-751-7459

D
Day, David Design & Assoc/Cincinnati, OH	513-621-4060
DeBrey Design/Minneapolis, MN	612-935-2292
DeGoede & Others/Chicago, IL	312-951-6066
Dektas Eger Inc/Cincinnati, OH	513-621-7070
Design Alliance Inc/Cincinnati, OH	513-621-9373
Design Consultants/Chicago, IL	312-642-4670
Design Dynamics Inc/Union, IL	815-923-2221
Design Factory/Overland Park, KS	913-383-3085
The Design Group/Madison, WI	608-274-5393
Design Group Three/Chicago, IL	312-337-1775
Design Mark Inc/Indianapolis, IN	317-872-3000
Design Marks Corp/Chicago, IL	312-327-3669
Design North Inc/Racine, WI	414-639-2080
The Design Partnership/Minneapolis, MN	612-338-8889
Design Planning Group/Chicago, IL	312-943-8400
Design Train/Cincinnati, OH	513-761-7099
Design Two Ltd/Chicago, IL	312-642-9888
Dezign House III/Cleveland, OH	216-621-7777
Di Cristo & Slagle Design/Milwaukee, WI	414-273-0980
Dickens Design Group/Chicago, IL	312-222-1850
Dimensional Designs Inc/Indianapolis, IN	317-637-1353
Doty, David Design/Chicago, IL	312-348-1200
Dresser, John Design/Libertyville, IL	312-362-4222
Dynamic Graphics Inc/Peoria, IL	309-688-9800

E
Eaton and Associates/Minneapolis, MN	612-871-1028
Ellies, Dave IndustrialDesign Inc/Columbus, OH	614-488-7995
Elyria Graphics/Elyria, OH	216-365-9384
Engelhardt Design/Minneapolis, MN	612-377-3389
Environmental Graphics Inc/Indianapolis, IN	317-634-1458
Epstein & Assoc/Cleveland, OH	216-421-1600
Evans, Cecil Jr Interiors/Chicago, IL	312-943-8974

F
Falk, Robert Design Group/St Louis, MO	314-531-1410
Feldkamp-Malloy/Chicago, IL	312-263-0633
Ficho & Corley Inc/Chicago, IL	312-787-1011
Final Draft Graphic Art/Cleveland, OH	216-861-3735

Fleishman-Hillard, Inc/St Louis, MO	314-982-1700
Fleming Design Office/Minneapolis, MN	612-830-0099
Flexo Design/Chicago, IL	312-321-1368
Ford & Earl Assoc Inc/Warren, MI	313-536-1999
Forsythe-French Inc/Kansas City, MO	816-561-6678
Frederiksen Design/Villa Park, IL	312-343-5882
Frink, Chin, Casey Inc/Minneapolis, MN	612-333-6539

G
Gellman, Stan Graphic Design Studio/St Louis, MO	314-361-7676
Gerhardt and Clements/Chicago, IL	312-337-3443
Glenbard Graphics Inc/Carol Stream, IL	312-653-4550
Goldsholl Assoc/Northfield, IL	312-446-8300
Goldsmith Yamasaki Specht Inc/Chicago, IL	312-266-8404
Goose Graphics/Minneapolis, MN	612-333-3502
Gournoe, M Inc/Chicago, IL	312-787-5157
Graphic Corp/Des Moines, IA	515-247-8500
Graphic House Inc/Detroit, MI	313-259-7790
Graphic Productions/Chicago, IL	312-236-2833
Graphic Specialties Inc/Minneapolis, MN	612-722-6601
Graphica Corp/Troy, MI	313-649-5050
Graphics Group/Chicago, IL	312-782-7421
Graphics-Cor Associates/Chicago, IL	312-332-3379
Greenberg, Jon Assoc Inc/Berkley, MI	313-548-8080
Greenlee-Hess Ind Design/Mayfield Village, OH	216-461-2112
Greiner, John & Assoc/Chicago, IL	312-644-2973
Grusin, Gerald Design/Chicago, IL	312-944-4945

H
Handelan-Pedersen/Chicago, IL	312-782-6833
Hans Design/Northbrook, IL	312-272-7980
Harley, Don E Associates/West St Paul, MN	612-455-1631
Herbst Lazar Rogers & Bell Inc/Chicago, IL	312-822-9660
Higgins Hegner Genovese, Inc/Chicago, IL	312-644-1882
Hirsch, David Design Group Inc/Chicago, IL	312-329-1500
Hirsh Co/Skokie, IL	312-267-6777
Hoekstra, Grant Graphics/Chicago, IL	312-641-6940
Hoffman-York Inc/Minneapolis, MN	612-835-5313
Horvath, Steve Design/Milwaukee, WI	414-271-3992

I
IGS Design Div of Smith Hinchman & Grylls/Detroit, MI	313-964-3000
ISD Incorporated/Chicago, IL	312-467-1515
Idenity Center/Schaumburg, IL	312-843-2378
Indiana Design Consortium/Lafayette, IN	317-423-5469
Industrial Technological Assoc/Cleveland, OH	216-349-2900
Ing, Victor Design/Morton Grove, IL	312-965-3459
Intelplex/Maryland Hts, MO	314-739-9996

J
J M H Corp/Indianapolis, IN	317-639-2535
James, Frank Direct Marketing/Clayton, MO	314-726-4600
Jansen, Ute/Chicago, IL	312-922-5048
Johnson, Stan Design Inc/Brookfield, WI	414-783-6510
Johnson, Stewart Design Studio/Milwaukee, WI	414-265-3377
Jones, Richmond Designer/Chicago, IL	312-935-6500
Joss Design Group/Chicago, IL	312-828-0055

K
KDA Industrial Design Consultants Inc/Addison, IL	312-495-9466
Kaulfuss Design/Chicago, IL	312-943-2161
Kearns, Marilyn/Chicago, IL	312-645-1888
Kovach, Ronald Design/Chicago, IL	312-461-9888
Krupp, Merlin Studios/Minneapolis, MN	612-871-6611

L
LVK Associates Inc/St Louis, MO	314-534-2104
Lange, Jim Design/Chicago, IL	312-228-2089
Larson Design/Minneapolis, MN	612-835-2271
Lehrfeld, Gerald/Chicago, IL	312-944-0651
Lerdon, Wes Assoc/Columbus, OH	614-486-8188
Lesniewicz/Navarre/Toledo, OH	419-243-7131
Lipson Associates Inc/Northbrook, IL	312-291-0500
Lipson Associates Inc/Cincinnati, OH	513-961-6225
Liska & Assoc/Chicago, IL	312-943-5910
Loew, Dick & Assoc/Chicago, IL	312-787-9032
Lubell, Robert/Toledo, OH	419-531-2267

Please send us your additions and updates.

M

Maddox, Eva Assoc Inc/Chicago, IL	312-670-0092
Manning Studios Inc/Cincinnati, OH	513-621-6959
Market Design/Cleveland, OH	216-771-0300
Marsh, Richard Assoc Inc/Chicago, IL	312-236-1331
McCoy, Steven/Omaha, NB	402-554-1416
McDermott, Bill Graphic Design/St Louis, MO	314-962-6286
McGuire, Robert L Design/Kansas City, MO	816-523-9164
McMurray Design Inc./Chicago, IL	312-527-1555
Media Corporation/Columbus, OH	614-488-7767
Minnick, James Design/Chicago, IL	312-527-1864
Moonink Inc/Chicago, IL	312-565-0040
Murrie White Drummond Leinhart/Chicago, IL	312-943-5995

NO

Naughton, Carol & Assoc/Chicago, IL	312-454-1888
Nobart Inc/Chicago, IL	312-427-9800
Nottingham-Spirk Design Inc/Cleveland, OH	216-231-7830
Oak Brook Graphics, Inc/Elmhurst, IL	312-832-3200
Osborne-Tuttle/Chicago, IL	312-565-1910
Oskar Designs/Evanston, IL	312-328-1734
Our Gang Studios/Omaha, NB	402-341-4965
Overlock Howe Consulting Group/St Louis, MO	314-533-4484

P

Pace Studios/Lincolnwood, IL	312-676-9770
Painter/Cesaroni Design, Inc/Glenview, IL	312-724-8840
Palmer Design Assoc/Wilmette, IL	312-256-7448
Paramount Technical Service Inc/Cleveland, OH	216-585-2550
Patterson Graphics/Dayton, OH	513-275-0080
Percept/Chicago, IL	312-664-4774
Perman, Norman/Chicago, IL	312-642-1348
Phares Associates Inc/Birmingham, MI	313-645-9194
Pinzke, Herbert Design/Chicago, IL	312-528-2277
Pitt Studios/Cleveland, OH	216-241-6720
Polivka-Logan Design/Minnetonka, MN	612-474-1124
Porter-Matjasich/Chicago, IL	312-670-4355
Powell/Kleinschmidt Inc/Chicago, IL	312-726-2208
Pride and Perfomance/St Paul, MN	612-646-4800
Prodesign Inc/Plymouth, MI	612-476-1200
Purviance, George Marketing Comm/Clayton, MO	314-721-2765
Pycha and Associates/Chicago, IL	312-944-3679

QR

Quality Graphics/Akron, OH	216-375-5282
Qually & Co Inc/Chicago, IL	312-944-0237
Redmond, Patrick Design/St Paul, MN	612-292-9851
Reed Design Assoc Inc/Madison, WI	608-238-1900
Richardson/Smith Inc/Worthington, OH	614-885-3453
Robertz, Webb and Co./Chicago, IL	312-861-0060
Robinson, Thompson & Wise/Overland Park, KS	913-451-9473
Ross & Harvey Inc./Chicago, IL	312-467-1290
Roth, Randall/Chicago, IL	312-467-0140
Rotheiser, Jordan I/Highland Park, IL	312-433-4288

S

Samata Design Group Ltd/West Dundee, IL	312-428-8600
Sargent, Ann Design/Minneapolis, MN	612-870-9995
Savlin/ Williams Assoc/Evanston, IL	312-328-3366
Schlatter Group Inc/Battle Creek, MI	616-964-0898
Schmidt, Wm M Assoc/Harper Woods, MI	313-881-8075
Schultz, Ron Design/Chicago, IL	312-528-1853
Seltzer, Meyer Design & Illustration/Chicago, IL	312-348-2885
Sherman, Roger Assoc Inc/Dearborn, MI	313-582-8844
Simanis, Vito/St Charles, IL	312-584-1683
Simons, I W Industrial Design/Columbus, OH	614-451-3796
Skolnick, Jerome/Chicago, IL	312-944-4568
Slavin Assoc Inc/Chicago, IL	312-944-2920
Smith, Glen The Co/Minneapolis, MN	612-871-1616
Source Inc/Chicago, IL	312-236-7620
Space Design International Inc/Cincinnati, OH	513-241-3000
Spatial Graphics Inc/Milwaukee, WI	414-545-4444
Stepan Design/Mt. Prospect, IL	312-364-4121
Strizek, Jan/Chicago, IL	312-664-4772
Stromberg, Gordon H Visual Design/Chicago, IL	312-275-9449
Studio One Graphics/Livonia, MI	313-522-7505

Studio One Inc/Minneapolis, MN	612-831-6313
Swoger Grafik/Chicago, IL	312-943-2491
Synthesis Concepts/Chicago, IL	312-787-1201

TU

T & Company/Chicago, IL	312-463-1336
Tassian, George Org/Cincinnati, OH	513-721-5566
Tepe Hensler & Westerkamp/Cincinnati, OH	513-241-0100
Thorbeck & Lambert Inc/Minneapolis, MN	612-871-7979
TURGEON, JAMES/CHICAGO, IL (P 262)	**312-861-1039**
Underwood, Muriel/Chicago, IL	312-236-8472
Unicom/Milwaukee, WI	414-354-5440
Unimark International Corp/Schaumberg, IL	312-843-3394

V

Vallarta, Frederick Assoc Inc/Chicago, IL	312-944-7300
Vanides-Mlodock/Chicago, IL	312-663-0595
Vann, Bill Studio/St Louis, MO	314-231-2322
Vista Three Design/Minneapolis, MN	612-920-5311
Visual Image Studio/St Paul, MN	612-644-7314

WXZ

Wallner Harbauer Bruce & Assoc/Chicago, IL	312-787-6787
Weber Conn & Riley/Chicago, IL	312-527-4260
Weiss, Jack Assoc/Evanston, IL	312-866-7480
Widmer, Stanley Assoc Inc/Staples, MN	218-894-3466
Winbush Design/Chicago, IL	312-527-4478
Worrel, W Robert Design/Minneapolis, MN	612-340-1300
Xeno/Chicago, IL	312-327-1989
Zender and Associates/Cincinnati, OH	513-561-8496

SOUTHWEST

A

3D/International/Houston, TX	713-871-7000
A Worthwhile Place Comm/Dallas, TX	214-946-1348
A&M Associates Inc/Phoenix, AZ	602-263-6504
Ackerman & McQueen/Oklahoma City, OK	405-843-9451
The Ad Department/Ft Worth, TX	817-335-4012
Ad-Art Studios/Ft Worth, TX	817-335-9603
Advertising Inc/Tulsa, OK	918-747-8871
Arnold Harwell McClain & Assoc/Dallas, TX	214-521-6400
Art Associates/Irving, TX	214-258-6001

BC

Beals Advertising Agency/Oklahoma City, OK	405-848-8513
The Belcher Group Inc/Houston, TX	713-271-2727
Brooks & Pollard Co/Little Rock, AR	501-375-5561
Cathey Graphics Group/Dallas, TX	214-638-0731
Central Advertising Agency/Fort Worth, TX	817-390-3011
Chandler, Jeff/Dallas, TX	214-946-1348
Chesterfield Interiors Inc/Dallas, TX	214-747-2211
Clark, Betty & Assoc/Dallas, TX	214-980-1685
Coffee Design Inc/Houston, TX	713-780-0571
Cranford/ Johnson & Assoc/Little Rock, AR	501-376-6251

DEF

Design Bank/Austin, TX	512-445-7584
Design Enterprises, Inc/El Paso, TX	915-594-7100
Designmark/Houston, TX	713-626-0953
Ellies, Dave Industrial Design Inc/Dallas, TX	214-742-8654
Fedele Creative Consulting/Dallas, TX	214-528-3501
First Marketing Group/Houston, TX	713-626-2500
Friesenhahn, Michelle/San Antonio, TX	512-822-3325

G

GKD/Oklahoma City, OK	405-943-2333
The Goodwin Co/El Paso, TX	915-584-1176
Gore, Fred M & Assoc/Dallas, TX	214-521-5844
Graphic Designers Group Inc/Houston, TX	713-622-8680
Graphics Hardware Co/Phoenix, AZ	602-242-4687
Graphics Intrnl Adv & Dsgn/Fort Worth, TX	817-731-9941
GRIMES, DON/DALLAS, TX (P 168)	**214-526-0040**
Grimm, Tom/Dallas, TX	214-526-0040

HIK

Harrison Allen Design/Houston, TX	713-771-9274
Hood Hope & Assoc/Tulsa, OK	918-250-9511
ISD Incorporated/Houston, TX	713-236-8232

GRAPHIC DESIGNERS CONT'D.

Please send us your additions and updates.

Konig Design Group/San Antonio, TX	512-824-7387

LMNO
Lowe Runkle Co/Oklahoma City, OK	405-848-6800
Mantz & Associates/Dallas, TX	214-521-7432
McGrath, Michael Design/Richardson, TX	214-644-4358
Morales, Frank Design/Dallas, TX	214-827-2101
Neumann, Steve & Friends/Houston, TX	713-629-7501
Owens & Assoc Advertising Inc/Phoenix, AZ	602-264-5691

PRS
Pen'N'Inc Studio/Ft Worth, TX	817-332-7687
Pirtle Design/Dallas, TX	214-522-7520
Reed Melnichek Gentry/Dallas, TX	214-634-7337
The Richards Group/Dallas, TX	214-987-2700
Strickland, Michael & Co/Houston, TX	713-961-1323
Sullivan, Jack Design Group/Phoenix, AZ	602-271-0117
Suntar Designs/Prescott, AZ	602-778-2714

TVW
Total Designers/Houston, TX	713-688-7766
Varner, Charles/Dallas, TX	214-744-0148
WW3 Papagalos/Phoenix, AZ	602-279-2933
Weekley & Penny Inc/Houston, TX	713-529-4861
Winius Brandon/Bellaire, TX	713-666-1765
Witherspoon/Fort Worth, TX	817-335-1373

ROCKY MOUNTAIN

Ad-Venture/Denver, CO	303-771-6520
American Now Inc/Denver, CO	303-573-1663
Ampersand Studios/Denver, CO	303-388-1211
Arnold Design Inc/Denver, CO	303-832-7156
The Art Directors Club of Denver/Denver, CO	303-831-9251
Barnstorm Studios/Colorado Springs, CO	303-630-7200
Blanchard, D W & Assoc/Salt Lake City, UT	801-484-6344
Consortium West/Concept Design/Salt Lake City, UT	801-278-4441
Cuerden Advertising Design/Denver, CO	303-321-4163
Design Center/Salt Lake City, UT	801-532-6122
Entercom/Denver, CO	303-393-0405
General Graphics/Denver, CO	303-832-5258
Gibby, John Design/Layton, UT	801-544-0736
Graphic Concepts Inc/Salt Lake City, UT	801-359-2191
Markowitz & Long/Boulder, CO	303-449-7394
Okland Design Assoc/Salt Lake City, UT	801-484-7861
Radetsky Design Associates/Denver, CO	303-629-7375
Three B Studio & Assoc/Denver, CO	303-777-6359
Visual Communications/Littleton, CO	303-773-0128
Visual Images Inc/Denver, CO	303-388-5366
Walker Design Associates/Denver, CO	303-773-0426
Wilson, Cheryl/Boulder, CO	303-444-0979
Woodard Racing Graphics Ltd/Boulder, CO	303-443-1986
Worthington, Carl A Partnership/Boulder, CO	303-443-7271

WEST

A
A & H Graphic Design/Rancho Bernardo, CA	619-486-0777
ADI/Los Angeles, CA	213-254-7131
AGI/Los Angeles, CA	213-462-0821
Ace Design/Sausalito, CA	415-332-9390
Adfiliation/Eugene, OR	503-687-8262
Advertising Design & Production Service/San Diego, CA	619-483-1393
Advertising/Design Assoc/Walnut Creek, CA	415-421-7000
Albertazzi, Mark/San Diego, CA	619-452-9845
Allied Artists/San Francisco, CA	415-421-1919
Antisdel Image Group/Santa Clara, CA	408-988-1010
Art Zone/Honolulu, HI	808-537-6647
Artists In Print/San Francisco, CA	415-673-6941
Artmaster Studios/San Fernando, CA	213-365-7188
Artworks/Los Angeles, CA	213-380-2187
Asbury Tucker & Assoc/Long Beach, CA	213-595-6481
Aurora Borealis/San Francisco, CA	415-392-2971

B
Bailey, Robert Design Group/Portland, OR	503-228-1381

Banuelos Design/Orange, CA	714-771-4335
Barile & Garnas Design/Oakland, CA	415-339-8360
Barnes, Herb Graphics/S Pasadena, CA	213-682-2420
Basic Designs Inc/Sausalito, CA	415-388-5141
Bass, Yager and Assoc/Hollywood, CA	213-466-9701
Bean, Carolyn Associates Inc/San Francisco, CA	415-957-9573
Beggs Langley Design/Palo Alto, CA	415-327-5275
Belew, Tandy/San Francisco, CA	415-543-7377
Bennett, Douglas Design/Seattle, WA	206-324-9966
Bennett, Ralph Assoc/Van Nuys, CA	213-782-3224
Bhang, Samuel Design Assoc/Los Angeles, CA	213-382-1126
Blazej, Rosalie Graphics/San Francisco, CA	415-586-3325
Blik, Ty/San Diego, CA	619-299-4227
Bloch & Associates/Santa Monica, CA	213-450-8863
Boelter, Herbert A/Burbank, CA	213-845-5055
Boyd, Douglas Design/Los Angeles, CA	213-655-9642
Bright & Associates, Inc/Los Angeles, CA	213-658-8844
Briteday Inc/Mountain View, CA	415-968-5668
Brookins, Ed/Studio City, CA	213-766-7336
Brosio Design/San Diego, CA	619-226-4322
Brown, Bill & Assoc/Los Angeles, CA	213-386-2455
Brown, Steve/Northridge, CA	213-349-0785
Burns & Associates Inc/San Francisco, CA	415-567-4404
Burridge Design/Santa Barbara, CA	805-965-8023
Burridge, Robert/Santa Barbara, CA	805-964-2087
Business Graphics/Los Angeles, CA	213-467-0292
Busse and Cummins/San Francisco, CA	415-957-0300

C
CAG Graphics/Van Nuys, CA	213-901-1077
Carlson, Keith Advertising Art/San Francisco, CA	415-397-5130
Carre Design/Santa Monica, CA	213-395-1033
Cassidy Photographic Design/Santa Clara, CA	408-735-8443
Catalog Design & Production Inc/San Francisco, CA	415-468-5500
Chan Design/Santa Monica, CA	213-393-3735
Chandler Media Productions/Irvine, CA	714-261-6183
Chapman Productions/Los Angeles, CA	213-460-4302
Chartmasters Inc/San Francisco, CA	415-421-6591
Churchill, Steven/San Diego, CA	619-560-1225
Clark, Tim/Los Angeles, CA	213-202-1044
Coak, Steve/Altadena, CA	818-797-5477
The Coakley Heagerty Co/Santa Clara, CA	408-249-6242
Coates Advertising/Portland, OR	503-241-1124
Cognata Associates Inc/San Francisco, CA	415-931-3800
CommuniCreations/Denver, CO	303-759-1155
Communication Design/San Diego, CA	619-455-5500
Conber Creations/Portland, OR	503-288-2938
Conversano, Henry & Assoc/Oakland, CA	415-547-6890
Corporate Comms Group/Marina Del Rey, Ca	213-821-9086
Corporate Graphics/San Francisco, CA	415-474-2888
Crawshaw, Todd Design/San Francisco, CA	415-956-3169
Creative Consultant/Venice, CA	213-399-3875
Cronan, Michael Patrick/San Francisco, CA	415-543-6745
Crop Mark/Los Angeles, CA	213-388-3142
Cross, James/Los Angeles, CA	213-474-1484
Crouch, Jim & Assoc/Delmar, CA	619-450-9200

D
Dahm & Assoc Inc/Torrance, CA	213-320-0460
Dancer Fitzgerald & Sample/San Francisco, CA	415-981-6250
Danziger, Louis/Los Angeles, CA	213-935-1251
Davis, Pat/Sacramento, CA	916-442-9025
Dawson, Chris/Los Angeles, CA	213-937-5867
Dayne, Jeff The Studio/Portland, OR	503-222-7144
Daystar Design/La Mesa, CA	619-463-5014
Dellaporta Adv & Graphic/Santa Monica, CA	213-394-0023
DeMaio Graphics & Advertising/Reseda, CA	213-785-6551
Design & Direction/Torrance, CA	213-320-0822
Design Corps/Los Angeles, CA	213-651-1422
Design Direction Group/Pasadena, CA	213-792-4765
Design Element/Los Angeles, CA	213-656-3293
Design Graphics/Los Angeles, CA	213-749-7347
Design Office/San Francisco, CA	415-543-4760
Design Projects Inc/Encino, CA	213-995-0303

Please send us your additions and updates.

Design Vectors/San Francisco, CA	415-391-0399
The Design Works/Los Angeles, CA	213-477-3577
Design/Graphics/Portland, OR	503-227-7247
Designamite/Santa Ana, CA	714-549-8210
The Designory Inc/Long Beach, CA	213-432-5707
Detanna Advertising Design/Beverly Hills, CA	213-852-0808
Dimensional Design/N Hollywood, CA	213-769-5694
Diniz, Carlos/Los Angeles, CA	213-387-1171
Doane, Dave Studio/Orange, CA	714-548-7285
Doerfler Design/La Jolla, CA	619-455-0506
Dupre Design/Coronado, CA	619-435-8369
Dyer-Cahn/Los Angeles, CA	213-937-4100
Dyna-Pac/San Diego, CA	619-560-0117

EF
Earnett McFall & Assoc/Seattle, WA	206-364-4956
Ehrig & Assoc/Seattle, WA	206-623-6666
Engle, Ray/Los Angeles, CA	213-381-5001
Exhibit Design Inc/San Mateo, CA	415-342-3060
Farber, Melvyn Design Group/Santa Monica, CA	213-829-2668
Farber, Rose Graphic Design/Venice, CA	213-392-3049
Finger, Julie Design Inc/Los Angeles, CA	213-653-0541
Five Penguins Design/Burbank, CA	213-841-5576
Floyd Design & Assoc/Lafayette, CA	415-563-0500
Flying Colors/San Francisco, CA	415-563-0500
Follis Design/Los Angeles, CA	213-735-1283
Fox, BD & Friends Advertising Inc/Hollywood, CA	213-464-0131
Frey, Karin/San Francisco, CA	415-552-7172
Furniss, Stephanie Design/San Rafael, CA	415-488-4692

G
Garner, Glenn Graphic Design/Seattle, WA	206-323-7788
Garnett, Joe Design/Illus/Los Angeles, CA	213-279-1539
Georgopoulos/Imada Design/Los Angeles, CA	213-933-6425
Gerber Advertising Agency/Portland, OR	503-221-0100
Gillian Assoc/San Francisco, CA	415-346-4845
GIRVIN, TIM DESIGN/SEATTLE, WA (P 114)	**206-623-7918**
Glickman, Abe Design/Van Nuys, CA	213-989-3223
The Gnu Group/Sausalito, CA	415-332-8010
Gohata, Mark/Gardena, CA	213-327-6595
Gotschalk's Graphics/San Diego, CA	619-578-5094
Gould & Assoc/W Los Angeles, CA	213-208-5577
Graformation/N Hollywood, CA	213-985-1224
Graphic Data/Pacific Beach, CA	714-274-4511
Graphic Designers, Inc/Los Angeles, CA	213-381-3977
Graphic Designs by Joy/Newport Beach, CA	714-642-0271
Graphic Ideas/San Diego, CA	619-299-3433
Greiman, April/Los Angeles, CA	213-462-1771
Guido, Jeff/Los Angeles, CA	213-858-5906

H
Hale, Dan Ad Design Co/Woodland Hills, CA	213-347-4021
Hall Kelley Org/Palo Alto, CA	415-327-8210
Hardbarger, Dave Design/Oakland, CA	415-655-4928
Harper and Assoc/Bellevue, WA	206-462-6486
Harrington and Associates/Los Angeles, CA	213-876-5272
Harte-Yamashita & Forest/Los Angeles, CA	213-884-1727
Hauser, S G Assoc Inc/Woodland Hills, CA	213-884-1727
Helgesson, Ulf Ind Dsgn/Woodland Hills, CA	213-883-3772
Hornall Anderson Design Works/Seattle, WA	206-467-5800
Hosick, Frank Design/Seattle, WA	206-789-5535
Hubert, Laurent/Menlo Park, CA	415-321-5182
Humangraphic/San Diego, CA	619-299-0431
Hyde, Bill/Foster City, CA	415-345-6955

IJ
Imag'Inez/San Francisco, CA	415-398-3203
Image Stream/Los Angeles, CA	213-933-9196
ImageMakers/Santa Barbara, CA	805-965-8546
Imagination Creative Services/Santa Clara, CA	408-988-8696
J J & A/Burbank, CA	213-849-1444
Jaciow Design Inc/Mountain View, CA	415-962-8860
Jerde Partnership/Los Angeles, CA	213-413-0130
Johnson Rodger Design/Rolling Hills, CA	213-377-8860
Johnson, Paige Graphic Design/Palo Alto, CA	415-327-0488
Joly Major Product Design Group/San Francisco, CA	415-641-1933

Jones, Steve/Venice, CA	213-396-9111
Jonson Pedersen Hinrichs & Shakery/San Francisco, CA	415-981-6612
Juett Dennis & Assoc/Los Angeles, CA	213-385-4373

K
K S Wilshire Inc/Los Angeles, CA	213-879-9595
KLAC Metro Media/Los Angeles, CA	213-462-5522
Kageyama, David Designer/Seattle, WA	206-622-7281
Kate Keating Associates/San Francisco, CA	415-398-6611
Keser, Dennis/San Francisco, CA	415-387-6448
Kessler, David Photographics/Hollywood, CA	213-462-6043
Klein/Los Angeles, CA	213-278-5600
Klein, Larry Designer/San Carlos, CA	415-595-1332
Kleiner, John A Graphic Design/Santa Monica, CA	213-747-0604
Kuey, Patty/Yorba Linda, CA	714-970-5286
Kuwahara, Sachi/Los Angeles, CA	213-937-8360

L
Lacy, N Lee Assoc Ltd/Los Angeles, CA	213-852-1414
LaFleur Design/Sausalito, CA	415-332-3725
Landes & Assoc/Torrance, CA	213-540-0907
Landor Associates/San Francisco, CA	415-955-1200
Larson, Ron/Los Angeles, CA	213-465-8451
Laurence-Deutsch Design/Los Angeles, CA	213-937-3521
Leipzig, Dale/Huntington Beach, CA	714-847-1240
Leong, Russel Design Group/Palo Alto, CA	415-321-2443
Lesser, Joan/Etcetera/Los Angeles, CA	213-450-3977
Levine & Company, Steve Levine/Venice, CA	213-399-9336
Littles, Dolores/Los Angeles, CA	213-937-6639
Logan Carey & Rehag/San Francisco, CA	415-543-7080
Loveless, J R Design/Santa Ana, CA	714-754-0886
Lum, Darell/Monterey Park, CA	213-613-2538
Lumel-Whiteman Assoc/North Hollywood, CA	213-769-5332
Lumel-Whiteman Assoc/Monterey Park, CA	213-613-2538

M
Maddu, Patrick & Co/San Diego, CA	619-238-1340
Malmberg & Assoc/Aurora, CO	303-699-9364
Manhattan Graphics/Manhattan Beach, CA	213-376-2778
Manwaring, Michael Office/San Francisco, CA	415-421-3595
Mar, Vic Designs/North Shore, CA	619-393-3968
Marketing Tools/Encinitas, CA	619-942-6042
Marra, Ann Graphic Design/Portland, OR	503-227-5207
Martino Design/Portland, OR	503-227-7247
Matrix Design Consultants/Los Angeles, CA	213-487-6300
Matrix International Inc/Denver, CO	303-388-9353
McKee, Dennis/San Francisco, CA	415-673-0852
Media Services Corp/San Francisco, CA	415-928-3033
Mediate, Frank/Los Angeles, CA	213-381-3977
Mikkelson, Linda S/Hollywood, CA	213-463-3116
Miura Design/Torrance, CA	213-320-1957
Mize, Charles Advertising Art/San Francisco, CA	415-421-1548
Mizrahi, Robert/Buena Park, CA	714-527-6182
Mobius Design Assoc/Los Angeles, CA	213-937-0331
Molly Designs Inc/Irvine, CA	714-768-7155
Monahan, Leo/Los Angeles, CA	213-463-3116
Mortensen, Gordon/Santa Barbara, CA	805-962-5315
Multimedia/Denver, CO	303-777-5480
Murphy, Harry & Friends/Mill Valley, CA	415-383-8586
Murray/Bradley Inc/Seattle, WA	206-622-7082

N
N Graphic/San Francisco, CA	415-863-3392
Naganuma, Tony K Design/San Francisco, CA	415-433-4484
Nagel, William Design Group/Palo Alto, CA	415-328-0251
New Breath Productions/Los Angeles, CA	213-876-3491
New Concepts Industrial Design Corp/Seattle, WA	206-633-3111
Nicholson Design/San Diego, CA	619-235-9000
Nicolini Associates/Oakland, CA	415-531-5569
Niehaus, Don/Los Angeles, CA	213-279-1559
Nine West/Pasadena, CA	213-799-2727
Nordenhook Design/Newport Beach, CA	714-752-8631

O
Odgers, Jayme/Los Angeles, CA	213-484-9965
Olson & Assoc/San Diego, CA	619-235-9993
Orr, R & Associates Inc/El Toro, CA	714-770-1277

Please send us your additions and updates.

Osborn, Michael Design/San Francisco, CA	415-495-4292
Osborn, Stephen/San Francisco, CA	415-495-4292
Oshima, Carol/Covina, CA	213-966-0796

PQ
Pacific Rim Design/Vancouver V5V2K9, BC	604-879-6689
Package Deal/Tustin, CA	714-731-2301
Pease, Robert & Co/Alamo, CA	415-820-0404
Peddicord & Assoc/Santa Clara, CA	408-727-7800
Persechini & Co/Beverly Hills, CA	213-657-6175
Petzold & Assoc/Portland, OR	503-221-1800
Pihas Schmidt Westerdahl Co/Portland, WA	503-228-4000
Ponce de Leon Design/Costa Mesa, CA	714-957-8920
Popovich, Mike c/o Pacific Graphic Assoc/City of Industry, CA	213-336-6958
Powers Design International/Newport Beach, CA	714-645-2265
Primo Angeli Graphics/San Francisco, CA	415-974-6100
The Quorum/Clinton, WA	206-522-6872

R
RJL Design Graphics/Fremont, CA	415-657-2038
Regis McKenna Inc/Palo Alto, CA	415-494-2030
Reid, Scott/Santa Barbara, CA	805-963-8926
Reineck & Reineck/San Francisco, CA	415-566-3614
Reineman, Richard Industrial Design/Newport Beach, CA	714-673-2485
Reis, Gerald & Co/San Francisco, CA	415-543-1344
Rickabaugh Design/Portland, OR	503-223-2191
Ritola, Roy Inc/San Francisco, CA	415-788-7010
Roberts, Eileen Design/Carlsbad, CA	619-439-7800
Robinson, David & Assoc/San Diego, CA	714-298-2021
Rogow & Bernstein Interpretive Design & Fabricate/Los Angeles, Ca	213-936-9916
Rolandesign/Woodland Hills, CA	213-346-9752
Ross, Deborah Design/Studio City, CA	818-985-5205
Runyan, Richard Design/West Los Angeles, CA	213-477-8878
Runyan, Robert Miles & Assoc/Playa Del Rey, CA	213-823-0975
Rupert, Paul Designer/San Francisco, CA	415-391-2966

S
Sackheim, Morton Enterprises/Beverly Hills, CA	213-652-0220
San Diego Art Prdctns/San Diego, CA	619-239-5523
Sanchez, Michael Assoc/Pasadena, CA	213-793-4017
Sandvick, John Studios/Los Angeles, CA	213-685-7148
Sant'Andrea, Jim West Inc/Compton, CA	213-979-9100
Schaefer, Robert Television Art/Hollywood, CA	213-462-7877
Schorer, R Thomas/Palos Verdes, CA	213-377-0207
Schwab, Michael Design/San Francisco, CA	415-546-7559
Schwartz, Clem & Bonnie Graphic Design/San Diego, CA	619-291-8878
Scroggin & Fischer Advertising/San Francisco, CA	415-391-2694
See Design & Production Inc/Salem, OR	503-393-1733
Seigle Rolfs & Wood Inc/Honolulu, HI	808-524-5080
Seiniger & Assoc/Los Angeles, CA	213-653-8665
Sellers, Michael Advertising/San Francisco, CA	415-781-7200
Shaw, Michael Design/Manhattan Beach, CA	213-545-0516
Shenon, Mike/Palo Alto, CA	415-326-4608
Shoji Graphics/Los Angeles, CA	213-384-3091
Shuman, Sharon Designer/Los Angeles, CA	213-837-6998
Sidjakov, Nicholas/San Francisco, CA	415-931-7500
Siege, Gretchen/Seattle, WA	206-623-9459
Signworks Inc/Seattle, WA	206-525-2718
Smidt, Sam/Palo Alto, CA	415-327-0707
The Smith Group/Portland, OR	503-224-1905
Sorensen, Hugh Industrial Design/Brea, CA	714-529-8493
Soyster & Ohrenschall Inc/San Francisco, CA	415-956-7575
Spangler Leonhardt/Seattle, WA	206-624-0551
Spear Design Associates/Santa Monica, CA	213-395-3939
SPEAR, JEFFREY A/SANTA MONICA, CA (P 254)	**213-395-3939**
Spivey, William Design Inc/Newport Beach, CA	714-752-1203
The Stansbury Company/Beverly Hills, CA	213-273-1138
Steinberg, Bruce/San Francisco, CA	415-864-0739
Stephenz, The Group/Campbell, CA	408-379-4883
Stockton, James & Assoc/San Francisco, CA	415-929-7900
Strong, David Design Group/Seattle, WA	206-447-9160
The Studio/San Francisco, CA	415-928-4400
Sugi, Richard Design & Assoc/Los Angeles, CA	213-385-4169
Sullivan & Assoc/Los Angeles, CA	213-384-3331

Superior Graphic Systems/Long Beach, CA	213-433-7421
Sussman & Prejza/Santa Monica, CA	213-829-3337

T
Tamburello, Michael Communications/Littleton, CO	303-733-0128
Tandem Design Group Inc/Denver, CO	303-831-9251
Tartak Libera Design/Los Angeles, CA	213-477-3571
Taylor, Robert W Design Inc/Boulder, CO	303-443-1975
Teitelbaum, William/Los Angeles, CA	213-277-0597
Thomas & Assoc/Santa Monica, CA	213-451-8502
Thomas, Greg/Los Angeles, CA	213-479-8477
Thomas, Keith M Inc/Santa Ana, CA	714-979-3051
Thompson, Larry Design/San Bernadino, CA	714-885-4976
Tops Talent Agency/Honolulu, HI	808-537-6647
Trade Marx/Seattle, WA	206-623-7676
Tribotti Design/Sherman Oaks, CA	213-784-6101
Trygg Stefanic Advertising/Los Altos, CA	415-948-3493
Tycer Fultz Bellack/Palo Alto, CA	415-856-1600

UV
Unigraphics/San Francisco, CA	415-398-8232
Valentino Graphic Design/Thousand Oaks, CA	805-495-9933
Van Hamersveld Design/Los Angeles, CA	213-656-3815
Van Noy & Co Inc/Los Angeles, CA	213-386-7312
Vanderbyl Design/San Francisco, CA	415-543-8447
Vanderwielen Designs/Irvine, CA	714-851-8078
Vantage Advertising & Marketing Assoc/San Leandro, CA	415-352-3640
Vicom Associates/San Francisco, CA	415-391-8700
Village Design/Irvine, CA	714-857-9048
Visual Resources Inc/Los Angeles, CA	213-851-6688
Voltec Associates/Los Angeles, CA	213-467-2106

W
Warner Design/Berkeley, CA	415-658-0733
Watson, Gary/Corona Del Mar, CA	714-644-6174
Webster, Ken/Orinda, CA	415-254-1098
Weideman and Associates/North Hollywood, CA	213-769-8488
Weller Institute/Los Angeles, CA	213-467-4576
West End Studios/San Francisco, CA	415-434-0380
West, Suzanne Design/Palo Alto, CA	415-324-8068
White, Ken Design/Los Angeles, CA	213-467-4681
Whitely, Mitchell Assoc/San Francisco, CA	415-398-2920
Wilkerson, Haines/Manhattan Beach, CA	213-372-3325
Wilkins & Peterson Graphic Design/Seattle, WA	206-624-1695
Willardson + Assoc/Los Angeles, CA	213-656-9461
Williams & Ziller Design/San Francisco, CA	415-621-0330
Williams, Leslie/Norwalk, CA	213-864-4135
Williamson & Assoc Inc/Los Angeles, CA	213-836-0143
Winters, Clyde Design/San Francisco, CA	415-391-5643
Woodward Design Assoc/Hollywood, CA	213-461-4141
Woodward, Teresa/Pacific Palisades, CA	213-459-2317
Workshop West/Beverly Hills, CA	213-278-1370

YZ
Yamaguma & Assoc/San Jose, CA	408-279-0500
Yanez, Maurice & Assoc/Los Angeles, CA	213-462-1309
Young & Roehr Adv/Portland, OR	503-297-4501
Yuguchi Krogstad/Los Angeles, CA	213-383-6915
Zamparelli Design/Pasadena, CA	213-799-4370
Zolotow, Milton/Westwood, CA	213-453-4885

NOTES:

NOTES:

NOTES:

NOTES:

INDEX

continued

INDEX

continued

INDEX